1984

THE BRADFORD BOOK OF COLLECTOR'S PLATES

CHARLES WINTHROPE & SONS

New York   Chicago   Paris   London   Sydney   Toronto   Frankfurt

1984

THE BRADFORD BOOK OF

COLLECTOR'S PLATES

THE OFFICIAL GUIDE TO ALL EDITIONS
TRADED ON THE WORLD'S LARGEST EXCHANGE

THE BRADFORD EXCHANGE, LTD.
NILES CHICAGO, ILLINOIS 60648

EDITED BY

Harriet Dalaskey   Susanne Southwood
Gerald Eckert   Paul Traiber
Livingston Platt   Rita Vander Meulen
Susan Polodna   Peggy Williams

Photography by Gerald Hoos
Art Direction by Sylvia Koenig

CHARLES WINTHROPE & SONS
New York   Chicago   Paris   London   Sydney   Toronto   Frankfurt

The editors acknowledge with gratitude the invaluable supplementary information supplied by:

Anna-Perenna, Inc.
Klaus D. Vogt
Arabia of Finland
Dennis Vizenor
Armstrong's
Dave Armstrong
Artists of the World
James LaFond
Belleek Pottery Ltd.
Charles Thompson
Bing & Grøndahl Copenhagen Porcelain, Inc.
Jean Gwardyak
Canadian Collector Plates Limited
Robert Henderson
Christian Bell Porcelain Ltd.
Horst Müller
Creative World, Ltd.
Richard Gabbe
Crown Parian, Ltd.
Jim Carter
D'Arceau-Limoges
Gerard Boyer
Ernst Enterprises
Ray Ernst
Fairmont China
Thomas W. Hogan
Goebel of North America
Dieter Schneider

Gorham Division of Textron, Inc.
David Wrenn
Hackett American Collectors Co.
James Hackett
The Hamilton Mint
Melanie Hart
Haviland & Co., Inc.
Frederick Haviland
Hibel Studio
William Hibel
Hutschenreuther
Stephen S. Barnet
Incolay Studios Inc.
Elvin M. Bright, Sr.
Kaiser Porcelain Co.
Hubert E. W. Kaiser
Kern Collectibles
Matthew P. Brummer
Kosta Boda U.S.A. Ltd.
Raymond W. Zrike
Lenox China Co.
Karen Cohen
Modern Masters, Ltd.
Richard Sitarski
Pemberton & Oakes
John Hugunin
Pickard China Co.
Henry Pickard
Porcelaine Georges Boyer
Gerard Boyer

Rasmussen Import Co.
R. D. Rasmussen
Reco International Corp.
Heio Reich
Reed & Barton Silversmiths
Patrice Johnson
River Shore, Ltd.
Arch Patterson
Rosenthal U.S.A. Limited
Ellen S. Miller
Royal Copenhagen Porcelain Corp.
Ivar Ipsen
Royal Doulton
Paul Warner
Royal Worcester Spode Inc.
Joyce Hendlewich
Schmid
Dennis Hurst
Vague Shadows
Richard Habeeb
Viking Import House, Inc.
Pat Owen
Villeroy & Boch
Marcia Richards
Wara Intercontinental Co.
Walter A. Rautenberg
Wedgwood, Inc.
Jim Fulks

Library of Congress Catalog Card No. 77-77526

ISBN 0-9611012-1-0

CONTENTS

INTRODUCTION

BRADEX-LISTED PLATES

APPENDIXES

INDEXES

Chart of the U.S. yearly Market Bradex since its inception in 1974.

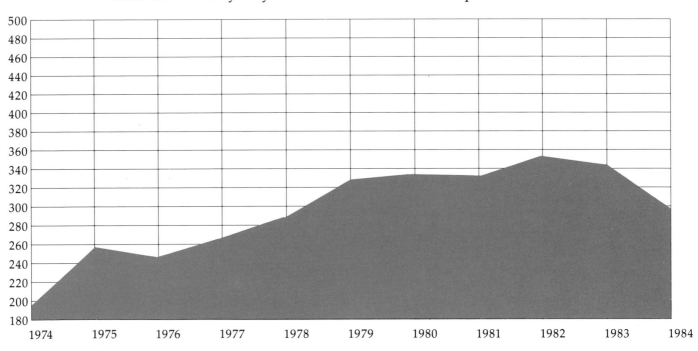

THE WORLD'S MOST TRADED ART

by **J. Roderick MacArthur**
Director of the Board of Governors
of The Bradford Exchange

When people ask me to define a collector's plate, I like to quote a simple definition from some years back: "A collector's plate is a decorative plate produced in a limited edition for the purpose of being collected."

A collector's plate *is* an object created for an aesthetic purpose; it is intended to be art. It is also a tangible possession that can have potential for dramatic secondary-market price appreciation. This stems from the one characteristic common to all collector's plates: although they come in many sizes, illustrate many themes, are made in various materials and shapes, they are *always* produced in limited editions.

Once the edition limit is reached, the edition is closed, never to reopen again, and the subsequent market price of plates from the edition is determined only by how much collectors are willing to pay. The fact that collector's plates are affordable art which can rise spectacularly in price has led to the phenomenal growth of the plate market in recent years.

THE UNEXPLAINED PHENOMENON

By the early 1970s, collector's plates were gaining recognition as the "world's most traded art." Skeptics argued this point—citing other collectible businesses or even the antique trade as generators of considerable buy and sell activity.

But a close look confirms that collector's plates occupy a unique position in the vast world of art. No other art form—regardless of style, medium, or popularity—is traded on a reasonably uniform market with the same frequency and volume. There are 13,598 primary and secondary transactions *everyday* on the U.S. Bradford Exchange alone.

J. Roderick MacArthur

Paintings, lithographs, prints, and sculptures are extensively collected, yet trading in the sense of uniform buy/sell transactions on an organized exchange simply does not exist. In the organized auctions in which these things are traded, many of them are one-of-a-kind or produced in such very small numbers that uniform trading is impossible and the frequency with which a given piece of art reaches the market is very low.

MORE THAN A "PICTURE BOOK"

Today's thriving marketplace for collector's plates is unique and the 1984 *Bradford Book of Collector's Plates* is *the* comprehensive source guide to this world's most traded art. Since the first edition appeared in 1976, the *Bradford Book* has been the most widely used guide in the modern plate market. Revised and updated each

year, it is the only plate collectors' reference work that illustrates, documents, and reports yearly market activity on the more than 1,250 "Bradex-listed" (actively traded) plates on the U.S. market.

At first glance, the *Bradford Book* looks like a "picture book" of plates—and certainly illustrates in detail the scope and variety of the plate market. But far more than a mere visual reference, it is a complete guide to the substance of one of the most interesting and fastest-growing markets in the world today. For every photograph there is the information invaluable to new and experienced collectors alike. It explains the plates, their origins and development, and their unique position as commodities, *not* securities—and art commodities at that—which are traded in a uniform, stable marketplace.

The book is organized the same as the Bradford Exchange *Current Quotations*, or "Bradex." The plates are said to be "Bradex-listed," i.e., listed on the Bradford Exchange.

The *Current Quotations* are the basis for the yearly summaries of 1983 market performance under each plate pictured. And just as the plates are arranged on the *Current Quotations* by country of origin, maker, series name, year of issue, and plate title, so they are presented in this book. Also included is the name of the artist, the edition limit, and the issue price.

All plates listed are indexed by a plate code number called the Bradex number which identifies the country of origin, maker, series, and position within the series, and permits precise identification of every plate.

For example, **84-R70-3.1** is the Bradex number for the first plate in the Rockwell Society *Heritage* series, the 1977 "Toy Maker." The number *84* identifies the country

of origin (United States); the alpha-numeric code *R70* identifies the *maker* (Rockwell Society of America); the number *3* indicates that this is their *third series*, and the number after the decimal point, *1*, identifies that this is the *first plate* in that series. (For more complete information on the Bradex numbering system, see page 47.

The Bradford Exchange North American Headquarters

1983 MARKET PERFORMANCE AT A GLANCE

At a glance you can also compare a plate's original issue price with its 1983 high and low, and the final 1983 closing price quotation. (This, of course, can be long out of date by the time you get this book. For accurate current prices on this fast-paced market, refer to the bimonthly *Bradford Exchange Current Quotations*, or phone our new "Instaquote"™ trading system for up-to-the-minute market prices.)

Also included in this year's book is a listing of more than 4,800 plates which are traded "over-the-counter." These over-the-counter issues (identified as OTC) are also true limited-edition plates; most are also available on the exchange, but they are not traded in sufficient volume to be listed on the U.S. exchange (even though a very few may be Bradex-listed on the German, English, Danish, or Canadian exchanges). Most have little interest for the mainstream of collectors, and some are "coterie" plates—plates made in such small editions that in today's vast market they remain unknown except to a very small number, or "coterie," of collectors.

A type of plate which you will never find in the *Bradford Book* is the supermarket plate. As the name implies, these plates are sold in supermarkets or are given away as premiums by merchants or banks. They are frequently poorly made, have little artistic value, and their edition limits are often unreliable. Nor will you find one of the many single-issue plates which have been made to commemorate the anniversary of your town, your school, or your state.

GUIDE TO THE HEART OF THE MARKET

What you *will* find in the *Bradford Book* are more than 1,250 plates which make up the heart of the U.S. market—plates varied in artistry, theme, and material to suit the tastes of almost any collector—plates from 12 countries, by 61 makers, and in 151 series.

(84-R70-3.1) "The Toy Maker"
1977 Rockwell Society *Heritage*

A REMARKABLY VARIED ART FORM

Collector's plates may feature two-dimensional pictures or three-dimensional sculptures, may be made in any one of a dozen countries, and come in a variety of sizes, but they are mainly only one shape—round. A few square plate series have been introduced, but so far only three—the Rörstrand *Christmas* (**76-R54-1**), the Royal Doulton *Beswick Christmas* (**26-R62-1**) and Arabia's *Kalevala* (**16-A69-1**) are listed on the exchange.

The plates can be wafer-thin china (Belleek, Great Britain [**26-B18-0**]), or heavily sculptured stone (Studio Dante di Volteradici, Italy [**38-V90-0**] and Incolay Studios, U.S.A. [**84-I31-0**]). They can be metal such as silver, silverplate, copper or pewter; crystal (Lalique, France [**18-L3-0**], and Morgantown Crystal, U.S.A. [**84-M58-0**]); even wood (Anri, Italy [**38-A54-0**]). But most are some form of ceramic, from simple terra-cotta to true hard-fire porcelain.

(16-A69-1.1) "Vainamoinen's Sowing"
1976 Arabia *Kalevala*

(26-B18-1.1) "Castle Caldwell"
1970 Belleek *Christmas*

(84-I31-1.1) "She Walks in Beauty"
1977 Incolay *Romantic Poets*

(38-A54-1.3) "Alpine Horn"
1973 Anri *Christmas*

(18-L3-1.1) "Deux Oiseaux"
1965 Lalique *Annual*

(14-B36-3.1) "Dog and Puppies"
1969 Bing & Grøndahl *Mother's Day*

(84-K41-5.1) "Annie and Sandy"
1983 Knowles *Annie*

THE BREAK WITH TRADITION

For more than half a century, the collector's plate market was dominated by Danish makers whose Christmas series, picturing winter and religious scenes on cobalt-blue-and-white porcelain, were collected around the world. But in 1965, a plate entitled "Deux Oiseaux" (18-L3-1.1), from the famous French cristallerie, Lalique, broke that tradition; it was not porcelain, not blue-and-white, not Danish, not even a Christmas plate. An Art Nouveau-style interpretation of two entwined birds, it was simply designed as the first in an annual series not tied to a specific season (the Lalique *Annual* series continued for twelve years, to 1976). The plate almost immediately sold out, and its subsequent spectacular appreciation on the secondary market established limited-edition plates as true "collector's items."

Not surprisingly, Lalique's success spurred other makers to experiment with new themes. Bing & Grøndahl, makers of the very first collector's plate in 1895, introduced a *Mother's Day* series (14-B36-3) in 1969, and it too sold out and shot up in price. The idea was quickly adopted by rival makers, Royal Copenhagen (14-R59-2) and Porsgrund (54-P62-2) among others. The U.S. Bicentennial provided the theme for several series in the early 1970s. In the latter half of the decade the field expanded dramatically to include series with themes from literature, cinema, history, the great masters, and even the whimsy of cartoons.

THE SCOPE OF PLATE COLLECTING

Arabia's *Kalevala* series (16-A69-1) recreates scenes from Finland's national epic poem, the *Kalevala*. Incolay Studios pays tribute to the great poets in its *Romantic Poets* collection (84-I31-1). Three series by Edwin M. Knowles China Company are inspired by popular films: *The Wizard of Oz* (84-K41-1), *Gone With the Wind* (84-K41-3), and *Annie* (84-K41-5). D'Arceau-Limoges produced a distinctive historical series with its *Women of the Century* collection (18-D15-3), a graphic chronology of women's social role reflected in Paris fashion. Works by Renoir, Raphael, and Leonardo da Vinci have all been reproduced on plates (84-P29-4; 18-H8-2.1 and 2.3; 38-V22-6). And Schmid's *Peanuts Christmas* (42-S12-1) and *Disney Christmas* (42-S12-3) series illustrate that there is even a place for the comics in the eclectic world of collector's plates.

Plate themes can be unconventional as in Fairmont's *Classical American Beauties* (84-F4-8), or endearingly familiar as in Gorham's *Rockwell Four Seasons* (84-G58-1) and Knowles' *Csatari Grandparent Plate* series (84-K41-4). There are series set in locales all around the world: Hong Kong (Artists of the World's *Children of Aberdeen* [84-A72-1]); Russia (Heinrich's *Russian Fairy Tales* [22-H18-1]); the American West (Fairmont's *DeGrazia Children* [84-F4-4]); and Germany (Bareuther's *Father's Day* [22-B7-2]); and the Orient (Rosenthal's *Oriental Gold* [22-R55-8]). There are series with religious themes (Königszelt Bayern's *Hedi Keller Christmas* [22-K46-1]); patriotic

(84-P29-4.1) "A Girl with a Watering Can"
1978 Pickard *Children of Renoir*

(84-F4-4.6) "Wondering"
1983 Fairmont *DeGrazia Children*

(84-K41-4.3) "The Cookie Tasting"
1982 Knowles *Csatari Grandparent*

(22-R55-8.1) "Yasuko"
1976 Rosenthal *Oriental Gold*

(22-H18-1.10) "Maria Morevna and Tsarevich Ivan"
1983 Heinrich/Villeroy & Boch *Russian Fairy Tales*

(22-K46-1.1) "The Adoration"
1979 Königszelt Bayern *Hedi Keller Christmas*

(18-H8-4.4) "Touch"
1980 Haviland & Parlon *The Lady and the Unicorn*

THE BACKSTAMP

With the emphasis on craftsmanship, it's no wonder that makers are proud to fire their names into their plates, usually as part of markings on the reverse side—known as "the backstamp."

Rosenthal of Germany was the first prominent manufacturer to use its name in bold type as its trademark and to include title, artist, and production information on the backs of plates. Their 1910 Christmas issue **(22-R55-1.1)** included the word "handgemalt" (handpainted), and the 1912 issue identified both the title ("Sternschnuppen," Shooting Stars) and artist (Paul Rieth).

The earliest Bing & Grøndahl plates carried only the famous maker's hallmark and the phrase "Made in Denmark"; it wasn't until 1944 that the plate title was included.

Similarly, Royal Copenhagen didn't identify plate titles on the backstamp until their 1954 Christmas plate, or credit the artist until a year later.

Today, although their hallmark is still the single most common mark found on backstamps, many makers now add a great deal more information. This information is significant to collectors. Backstamps vary from series to series—even within series—and reflect the individuality of each edition. For example, the Gorham *Rockwell Four Seasons* plates **(84-G58-1)** contain a brief statement about Norman Rockwell's impact on American art. Mary Vickers, *Blossoming of Suzanne* series **(26-W90-4)** includes

themes (D'Arceau-Limoges' *Lafayette Legacy* **[18-D15-1]**); medieval themes (Haviland & Parlon's *The Lady and the Unicorn* **[18-H8-4]**); and the nature themes (Pickard's *Lockhart Wildlife* **[84-P29-1]**).

The great potential of the collector's plate medium is one reason so many artists have been attracted to it. Such now-familiar artists as Joseph Csatari, Ted De-Grazia, Edna Hibel, G. A. Hoover, Hedi Keller, Raymond Kursár, John McClelland, Francisco Masseria, Irene Spencer, Mary Vickers, Bjørn Wiinblad, and Donald Zolan have each created works for the plate medium and become better known for this than for all their previous work. The range of styles is wide: from photographic realism to surrealism, from impressionism to primitivism, from classical sculpture to Tyrolean wood crafting.

BOTH ART AND CRAFT

Collector's plates are a fusion of art and craft. Both the design on the plate and the technique used to render it are part of the art. The quality of the material itself—be it true hard-fire porcelain or full 24% lead crystal, for example—is of importance.

Serious collectors know, for instance, that D'Arceau-Limoges plates must adhere to the two-century-old Grellet Standard by which the quality of a plate is assessed in seven critical areas: whiteness, thickness, translucence, strength of body, unity of glaze, hardness of glaze, and color.

The craftsmanship of many plate series—di Voltera-dici's work in ivory alabaster, the glass-work of Lalique, Orrefors, and Morgantown Crystal, the Damascene silver craft of Reed & Barton, the woodwork of Anri—all are disciplined skills to be admired as plate artistry.

(84-R18-2.1) "A Partridge in a Pear Tree"
1970 Reed & Barton *Christmas*

(22-R55-1.1) "Winter Peace"
1910 Rosenthal *Traditional Christmas* (Backstamp)

(14-R59-1.10) "Fano Girl"
1955 Royal Copenhagen *Christmas* (Backstamp)

(26-W90-4.1) "Innocence"
1977 Wedgwood *Blossoming of Suzanne* (Backstamp)

quotations from the artist. And both Anri's *Christmas* **(38-A54-1)** and Limoges-Turgot's *Durand's Children* **(18-L52-1)** have short descriptions of the plates' themes.

The usual backstamps are omitted from crystal plates because markings on the reverse would show through the front design. The crystal Lalique *Annual* plates **(18-L3-1)** carry only the phrase "Lalique, France" etched as inconspicuously as possible on the border of the plate bases; Orrefors' *Annual Cathedral* plates **(76-O74-1)** identify only the maker, the year, the country and the fact that the plate is a limited-edition—all etched in small letters on the foot rim of the crystal plate body. The crystal *Yates' Country Ladies* **(84-M58-1)** plates from Morgantown Crystal incorporate the backstamp information into the plate design, using thirty-one words to create a thin etched band around the circumference of the plate base.

EDITION LIMITS AND MARKET VALUE

The backstamp can also reveal the way a plate edition is limited. Some manufacturers such as Anna-Perenna or the Hibel Studio announce the actual number in the edition. Some, like Bing & Grøndahl, cloak their edition sizes in utmost secrecy—saying nothing on the plate but announcing elsewhere that an edition's production is cut off at the end of the year of issue. Still others limit the edition by the total number of firing days.

But however it is determined (and whether or not the plates are numbered), the edition limit is strictly observed; otherwise the plates are simply not true collector's plates. This fact of a finite number of plates within any edition can spark heated trading and unbridled speculation on the market if too many buyers go after too few plates in a "hot" new edition. With one exception*, *no plate in the Bradford Book or listed on the Bradford Exchange has ever been reissued once the edition closed.*†

Edition sizes can be large or small. Announced edition limits listed in the *Bradford Book* range from 500 plates for the 1971 Veneto Flair *Bellini* **(38-V22-1.1)** to 30,000 for the Haviland *Christmas* **(18-H6-1)**. But the undisclosed edition sizes are by far the most frequent, ranging from less than one thousand for the earliest plates into the hundreds of thousands for later ones.

When the plate market was young, plates issued in small editions of 2,000 or less could command a strong following and trade up to incredible prices on the secondary market. Now, with the market expanding around

---

*The one exception is the Rosenthal *Traditional Christmas* series **(22-R55-1)**. Editions from 1910 to 1957 in this series were reopened briefly between 1969 and 1971, with all reissues identified by backstamps containing the reissue dates of manufacture. These plates are now included in the *Bradford Book* on the firm assurance by the maker that the practice ceased forever in 1971.

†In the very rare instance when a manufacturer has issued a plate with artwork that had previously appeared on another maker's plate, this "second-time" plate is *not* a collector's plate by definition.

(18-D15-4.1) "Summer Girl"
1978 D'Arceau-Limoges *Girls of the Seasons*

(18-D15-4.2) "Winter Girl"
1979 D'Arceau-Limoges *Girls of the Seasons*

(18-D15-4.3) "Spring Girl"
1980 D'Arceau-Limoges *Girls of the Seasons*

(18-D15-4.4) "Autumn Girl"
1981 D'Arceau-Limoges *Girls of the Seasons*

the world and including several million collectors, such tiny editions generate comparatively little trading volume. In fact, today any edition under 10,000 would tend to be a "coterie plate," the one prominent exception being the Pickard *Children of Renoir* series **(84-P29-4)**.

But don't let this discourage you from buying an issue from a small edition. Just remember that there is no assurance that the plate will appreciate in value simply

because the edition is small. A market winner is made when demand outstrips supply—and a very small plate edition does not automatically guarantee heightened demand; in fact, it often discourages demand because of its relative obscurity.

Plate series are either "closed-end" with a predetermined number of editions or "open-end," to continue indefinitely. For example, the D'Arceau-Limoges *Girls of*

the Seasons series **(18-D15-4)** is a closed-end series of four annual plates; Bing & Grøndahl's *Christmas* series **(14-B36-1)** is open-end, with a new plate issued each year indefinitely.

As a general rule, the first plate in a series is most in demand. (Some mistakenly call these plates "first editions." However, every limited-edition plate is a first edition since, by definition, there can be no "second edition." The first plate in a series is more properly called a "first issue.")

EXPLOSIVE GROWTH

Whatever the edition size, it is only collector demand in proportion to this size which determines the success or failure of a plate in the market. The Lalique *Annual* **(18-L3-1.1)** which issued in 1965 at $25.00; the Goebel *Hummel Annual* **(22-G54-1.1)** produced in 1971 at $25.00; the Rockwell Society *Heritage* **(84-R70-3.1)** issued in 1977 at $14.50—have appreciated 15 to 59 times in market price as the result of collector demand.

And overall collector demand continues to grow at an explosive rate. In just the ten years from 1971 to 1981, the estimated number of collectors across the globe rose from 1.2 million to 6.8 million, with an additional 539,900 added in the past year alone, bringing the worldwide total to more than 8.1 million. During the same period the estimated average number of daily transactions among the world's distributors, dealers, and individual collectors jumped from 2,900 to 24,802. From an obscure hobby in the early 1960s, plate collecting has become a boom.

(14-B36-1.89) "Christmas in the Old Town"
1983 Bing & Grøndahl *Christmas*

THE ORDERLY MARKET

Until about a dozen years ago, a collector searching for a rare plate, or wishing to sell one from his collection often was frustrated by the few ways to reach prospective traders. Dealers were willing, of course, to help locate a plate, and there were a few periodicals where an advertisement would be seen by other plate collectors. There were even occasional "finds" at auctions or in antique shops or through personal contacts and collec-

The Bradford Exchange Trading Floor

**Trading Floor brokers review hundreds
of trades each business day**

tor's clubs. But for the most part, transactions among collectors were random and infrequent.

By the late 1960s, the vastly increased number of plate collectors demanded an organized market. With plate prices rising and falling dramatically according to the whims of collectors and dealers and with more and more manufacturers entering the field, collectors needed a central and an organized marketplace in which to buy or sell any of the hundreds of issues on the market.

The staff of the Bradford Exchange had monitored daily transactions for some time, and in September, 1973, with the publication of the first bi-monthly *Bradford Exchange Current Quotations*—the "Bradex"—current quote prices on the most actively-traded issues became available to collectors across the United States on a routine basis.

A plate is listed on the Bradex because of the volume of continued trading—either past or expected—not because of its potential to increase in market price. A new plate that continues a series already traded is listed before trading begins; a new series from a maker or artist whose other series are widely traded may be listed if demand is expected to carry over to the new series.

The market performance of twelve key indicator series selected from among the Bradex-listed series serves as a market barometer to both collectors and the industry at large. This "Market Bradex"—a sort of Dow Jones Index of plate market trends—is based on the quote price/

issue price ratio of these key series. When the index goes down, it suggests a broad decline in market prices. When it rises, the market is in good health. At the close of trading in 1983 the Market Bradex stood at 299—a year-to-date decline of forty-four points since the close of 1982.

THE STANDARD YARDSTICK—THE EIGHT-POINT CHECKLIST

At about the same time the first Bradex appeared, the exchange first published its now-famous Eight-point Checklist to assist collectors in appraising plates on the market. No one, of course, can predict how a plate will perform, but the checklist has been helpful in determining a plate's market strengths and has become something of a standard yardstick since it first appeared in 1972.

1. *Maker:* Is the maker known for its insistence on fine workmanship and continuity of its other plate series?
2. *Artistry:* Is it original art created especially for this plate by an artist of note? Is the subject one of broad, but not trite, appeal?
3. *Edition Size:* Is the edition clearly limited but not too limited to create a market? If the edition is closed, are collectors or dealers bidding for it in the secondary market?
4. *Collectibility:* Is it one, preferably the first, of a collectible periodic series or merely a single issue?
5. *Time of Acquisition:* Can you get it at the right time—at issue or while the price is still rising?
6. *Sponsorship:* Is it issued in association with a government or a prestigious institution?
7. *Commemorative Importance:* Does it commemorate a seasonal event or a historic event? If so, does it bring new insight to the event? Or is it an event in the history of the artist or maker?
8. *Material:* If made of ceramic, is it true hard-paste ("hard-fire") porcelain, bone china or fine china? If made of metal, is it pure or plated? If made of glass, is it full 24% lead?

These eight points are listed in order of importance, but I would emphasize that for purposes of investment, Point Five—Time of Acquisition—is crucial. If you pay too much for a plate, it may take years to break even. Yet even well above its issue price, a plate can be a bargain if its market appreciation is expected to continue.

ANNUAL UPDATE

Since its first edition nine years ago, the Bradford Exchange analysts and staff researchers have continued to revise, update, and expand the *Bradford Book* annually in order to make it the most up-to-date and comprehensive guide to the modern plate market available anywhere. I hope that this 1984 edition gives you both the basic knowledge and the new insights into collector's plates that serious collectors have over the years come to expect from the *Bradford Book*.

Bing & Grøndahl's 1895 "Behind the Frozen
Window"—the first true collector's plate

A HISTORY OF COLLECTOR'S PLATES

by John G. McKinven
Vice President, Maker Relations
The Bradford Exchange

On a cold December morning in 1895, we are told, Mr. Harald Bing, director of the Danish porcelain house of Bing & Grøndahl, ordered his astonished workers to destroy the mold for the small blue-and-white plate the company had produced to commemorate the Christmas holiday.

The plate was "Behind the Frozen Window." With Bing's command, it became the first known limited-edition collector's plate and the cornerstone of what is now the world's most actively traded form of art.

By thus limiting the plate's supply, Mr. Bing established the essential condition for the extraordinary collector's plate market we know today.

Limited-edition plates are now bought and sold all over the world by millions of collectors who are seeking not only rare old plates like "Behind the Frozen Window" but also current issues from many makers in many countries. In addition to the thrill of market speculation, these collectors take a special pleasure in owning these scarce objects in the tradition of the connoisseurs who collected art in the medium of plates in earlier times.

This history begins with the hand-painted terra-cotta plates of the ancient Egyptians and proceeds through the Chinese import porcelain first collected in the 14th century to the lead-and tin-glazed plates and soft-paste porcelains of the Renaissance and later. In the 1700s, earthenware, china, and porcelain commemorative plates honoring generals, coronations, and battles were issued by Meissen, Konigliche Porzellan-Manufaktur Berlin (KPM), and the French Royal factory at Sèvres—the first European makers of porcelain.

Harald Bing

By the latter half of the nineteenth century, plate sets (as distinct from collector's plate series as we now know them) were popular in Italy. Decorated with thematically related scenes such as the months, signs of the Zodiac, seasons and biblical events, they foreshadowed the collector's plate series to come.

But they did not fit the definition used today—they were *not* produced in limited-editions. Makers would gladly produce an additional quantity of an issue if demand warranted it. An example was Villeroy & Boch's "Snow White and the Seven Dwarfs" by Heinrich Schlitt produced from 1890 to 1905 to meet continuing demand.

It remained for one maker, Bing & Grøndahl, to create a limited-edition plate which would be the first in a continuing series of the same theme and would never be re-issued, no matter what the demand. When Harald Bing ordered his workers to break the mold for "Behind the Frozen Window" (which now has the Bradex number of **14-B36-1.1**), he changed the course of collecting history.

(14-B36-1.1) "Behind the Frozen Window"
1895 Bing & Grøndahl *Christmas*

(14-R59-1.1) "Madonna and Child"
1908 Royal Copenhagen *Christmas*

(22-R55-1.1) "Winter Peace"
1910 Rosenthal *Traditional Christmas*

THE COLLECTOR'S PLATE IS BORN

Designed by Frans August Hallin, "Behind the Frozen Window" was hand-decorated in the cobalt blue underglaze technique introduced by Arnold Krog at Royal Copenhagen seven years earlier and known as "Copenhagen blue." More importantly, it was the first commemorative plate in which key information—date and occasion of issuance—was permanently fired into the porcelain itself.

Issued in a small edition (knowledgeable estimates put the size at about 500 plates), "Behind the Frozen Window" was the first known true collector's plate. When it was followed the next year by a new plate dated simply "Jule Aften 1896," the collector's plate tradition of the continuing series was born.

Harald Bing could not have known that his "Behind the Frozen Window" plate—which originally sold for two Kroner (then about 50¢)—would one day trade on the U.S. plate market at $4,000.00. Yet other Scandinavian manufacturers did have some inkling of the popularity of Bing's idea, because within a few years they had begun to produce collector's plate series of their own.

Aluminia, a majolica factory in Copenhagen (previously acquired by Royal Copenhagen), introduced its *Children's Day Christmas* plate series in 1904 and produced an annual issue until the outbreak of the Second World War in 1939. Rörstrand of Sweden (Bradex number **76-R54-0**) also began a series in 1904 which survived until 1926. The Norwegian house of Porsgrund **(54-P62-0)** offered a Christmas plate in 1909 but failed to follow it up as a series. (Neither maker re-entered the modern collector's plate market until 1968 after the new American enthusiasm had developed.)

In 1908, Royal Copenhagen began its own famous *Christmas* series **(14-R59-1)** which has continued every year to this day, despite wars and economic crises—making it the second oldest continuing series after that of Bing & Grøndahl.

The German manufacturer Rosenthal joined with a Danish department store, Buck & Nissen, to produce a *Christmas* series for the Danish market as early as 1905. As the number of German collectors grew, Rosenthal began to promote the series in Germany under its own hallmark. This dual edition of identical artwork continued for three years, from 1907 through 1909. In 1910, Rosenthal severed its relationship with Buck & Nissen and issued its first proprietary plate, "Winter Peace" **(22-R55-1.1)**, the first issue in its *Traditional Classic Rose Christmas* series, which has continued for 75 years.

Two other German makers began series of Christmas plates prior to World War I. The Hutschenreuther *Christmas* series began in 1910 and ended in 1935, and the

Konigliche Porzellan-Manufaktur Berlin (KPM) series began in 1914 but managed to survive only until the mid-1920s.

Throughout the 1920s and 1930s, many considered the plates little more than curios. During the Second World War, the few existing series of collector's plates became even scarcer as edition sizes were reduced.

Although the early Christmas plates are true collector's plates, they were not actively collected or traded at their time of issue as new issues are today. Families—especially in Denmark and Germany—bought them in observance of the holiday, never suspecting that one edition might be more valuable than another, and little effort was given to searching out previous editions to complete collections.

DANISH IMMIGRANTS BRING PLATES TO AMERICA

Although Danes emigrating to the United States often brought their plate collections with them, until the late 1940s few other Americans had ever seen a collector's plate unless they chanced upon one in an antique store in a Scandinavian neighborhood or in the home of a Scandinavian friend.

But shortly after World War II, the first American dealers entered what we now know as the collector's plate market.

"If you had told me in 1947 that some day there would be millions of plate collectors, I just wouldn't have believed you," says one of those pioneers, Chicago antique dealer William Freudenberg, Jr. Yet that year he became the first to recognize the potential of Danish plates when he began reselling them to other antique dealers.

"I simply found them (the Danish plates) at an auction house and took a few to see what I could do," he says. Freudenberg's asking price for Bing & Grøndahl's "Behind the Frozen Window," the oldest collector's plate of all, was then a mere $4.50, no different than the others.

Two years later, in 1949, Pat Owen of Viking Import House in Fort Lauderdale, Florida, became the first American dealer to sell collector's plates to gift shops and department stores. She obtained her plates in a roundabout business arrangement. A Danish company wanted to buy American cash registers for resale in Denmark but couldn't pay for them in Kroner because of the ban on the export of Danish currency. To get around this, the firm bought collector's plates from young Danes who had lost interest in their families' collections, and then resold them to Mrs. Owen in the U.S. for dollars.

Also in 1949, the Reverend Elias Rasmussen, a Norwegian-born minister from Minneapolis, was traveling

William Freudenberg, Jr.

Pat Owen

Jon Nielsen

Svend Jensen

in Denmark when he met an elderly lady who was trying—in vain—to sell her plates. As an act of kindness, Reverend Rasmussen brought them back to America to see if he could sell them for her. Within a few years, he was reselling plates by the thousands. A year later, Jon Nielsen of Denmark emigrated to Michigan and began importing plates along with antiques from the old country.

THE MODERN MARKET BEGINS

But the event that really moved collector's plates out of the realm of antiques and giftware took place in 1951. Svend Jensen, a Danish immigrant settled in New York, who had begun importing plates the year before, printed and circulated the first back-issue price list. The different prices were based on Svend Jensen's estimates of the scarcity of each edition and, with its issuance, the modern collector's plate market was born.

Antique dealers and gift shops around the country were soon quoting Jensen's prices. Word spread over the next two years and, as collectors who owned the more recent issues became aware of the value of those earlier plates, the scramble to complete their collections was on: the resulting prices were quickly bid up well beyond those of Svend Jensen's early lists.

(14-R59-1.38) "A Peaceful Motif"
1945 Royal Copenhagen *Christmas*

(14-R59-1.55) "The Little Mermaid at Wintertime"
1962 Royal Copenhagen *Christmas*

(18-L3-1.1) "Deux Oiseaux"
1965 Lalique *Annual*

Two early winners on the budding plate market were the 1945 Royal Copenhagen *Christmas* issue, "A Peaceful Motif" (Bradex number **14-R59-1.38**), and the 1951 Royal Copenhagen *Christmas* plate, "Christmas Angel" **(14-R59-1.44)**, both by Ricard Böcher. Issued at $4.00 and $5.00 respectively, both plates were trading as high as $300.00 by 1959.

By 1960, the older plates were getting scarce, and more and more collectors were asking for current editions of the Danish Christmas plates. Recognizing this demand, antique dealers began to sell current plate editions—even though they could hardly be considered antiques; new issues began to appear in gift shops as well; and new collectors began to look for earlier issues, creating a circular pattern of back-issue trading among dealers.

Some enterprising dealers found they could bypass American distributors and deal directly with sources in Denmark. In 1960, Earl Falack of Edward's 5th Avenue in New York found some Danish dealers still blithely unaware of the growing demand across the Atlantic. He recalls that random Royal Copenhagen back-issues could still be purchased in lots of 1,000 or even 2,000 at $2.00 to $5.00 a plate.

In 1962, a combination of factors—demand from Americans who had visited Copenhagen, Scandinavians nostalgic about their homeland, and the growing army of plate collectors and other people who were simply attracted to the plate itself—created a sensational sellout of Royal Copenhagen's "The Little Mermaid at Wintertime" **(14-R59-1.55)**. Issued at $11.00, it immediately rose in market price, appreciating even more rapidly when word leaked out that the mold had broken before the entire edition had been completed. By spring of 1963, the plate had shot up to about $30.00 in Denmark and $50.00 in the U.S. Little more than a decade later, it brought $190.00 in Denmark and $160.00 in the U.S. Last year, this plate sold at $200.00 and is still among the most popular of the Royal Copenhagen series.

The success of "Little Mermaid" spurred an increased demand for back-issues in the series, followed by rapid price increases. Excited by the appreciation of this issue, casual collectors turned into avid seekers of plates with similar market promise.

CRYSTAL SHATTERS MARKET

In 1965, the French maker Lalique—whose fine crystalware was selling in shops where Danish plates were unheard of—introduced an etched crystal plate showing two entwined birds. Entitled "Deux Oiseaux" **(18-L3-1.1)**, the plate shattered the previously accepted boundaries of plate collecting: it was not porcelain, not blue-and-white, not Danish, not even a Christmas plate. It was simply called an "annual" (the series continued for twelve years to 1976), and its market success firmly established limited-edition plates as true "collector's

items." By 1968, "Deux Oiseaux" traded at $100.00— four times its $25.00 issue price. By 1973 it brought $965.00; by the end of 1974 it traded at $1,740.00; and at the close of trading in 1983 the plate had last traded on the Bradford Exchange at $1,475.00—5,900% of issue price.

News of the success of "Deux Oiseaux" was late in reaching Europe because the plate was distributed only in North America. But eventually European makers and collectors alike learned of its precedent-shattering reception in the U.S., and were alerted to the profits to be made in limited-edition plates.

In 1967, Bareuther of Germany introduced a *Christmas* series **(22-B7-1)** to commemorate its one hundredth anniversary; in 1968 its Danish Church *Christmas* series **(22-D5-1)** began, followed by a *Father's Day* series **(22-B7-2)** in 1969.

Rörstrand of Sweden **(76-R54-1)** and Porsgrund of Norway **(54-P62-1)** both re-entered the market in 1968 with *Christmas* series that were successful in their own countries as well as the United States. Konigliche Porzellan-Manufaktur Berlin (KPM), some 45 years after discontinuing its first collector's plates, re-entered the market in 1969 with a new *Christmas* series.

Despite the growing success of collector's plates, Bing & Grøndahl issued the first Mother's Day plate, "Dog and Puppies" **(14-B36-3.1)** in 1969 with remarkable caution. The success of "Little Mermaid" had inspired manufacturers to expand their edition sizes, which in turn had softened the market throughout the mid-1960s. So "Dog and Puppies" was given only a modest production run.

American collectors, however, were becoming increasingly aware of the high market prices commanded by back-issue Bing & Grøndahl plates. Given the opportunity to acquire a first issue from the world's most prominent collector's plate manufacturer, they scrambled to buy it at the U.S. issue price of $9.75. Their hunches paid off when the U.S. allocation sold out within weeks and the price jumped to $25.00. By Christmas, the figure was already $65.00. Four years later, in 1974, it was priced at $245.00. At the end of 1983, "Dog and Puppies" had last traded on the Bradford Exchange at $445.00.

However, Danish collectors had little immediate interest in the first Mother's Day plate. In the spring of 1969, Michigan antique dealer, Jon Nielsen, returning from a Danish buying trip, could still purchase 18 plates at a gift shop in the Copenhagen airport for $3.50 each. The manager said he had 125 more if Nielsen wanted them. Nielsen did. Other American dealers also bought the plates in bulk and resold them to U.S. collectors, making "Dog and Puppies" virtually unobtainable anywhere in Europe. The scarcity continued over the decade and explains why the plate's 1983 market price in Germany,

for example, was still almost one-third higher than its price in the United States.

Danish indifference to "Dog and Puppies" didn't last long, however. The shortage caused by the drain of plates to the U.S. market soon became evident in Denmark, and the price of the plate rose sharply. By late summer of 1969 it brought the equivalent of $30.00 in Denmark, and $50.00 by Christmas. The plate continued to rise throughout the 1970s and late in 1983 brought up to 3500 Kroner (about $350.00).

WEDGWOOD PLATE SPARKS BRITISH MARKET
Later that same year, Wedgwood of England issued its first *Christmas* plate, "Windsor Castle" **(26-W90-1.1)**, intended mainly for export to the North American market. Response was quick and enthusiastic: the entire allocation sold out immediately, and within a year the plate was trading at twice its $25.00 U.S. issue price.

(14-B36-3.1) "Dog and Puppies"
1969 Bing & Grøndahl *Mother's Day*

(26-W90-1.1) "Windsor Castle"
1969 Wedgwood *Christmas*

(22-R55-2.1) "Maria and Child"
1971 Rosenthal *Wiinblad Christmas*

(22-G54-1.1) "Heavenly Angel"
1971 Goebel *Hummel Annual*

(22-S12-1.1) "Angel in a Christmas Setting"
1971 Schmid *Hummel Christmas*

Wedgwood shifted 40% of its English allocation to the U.S. to meet this sudden demand abroad, only to learn to their surprise that "Windsor Castle" was just as well received by the home market. British dealers who were able to get the plate immediately sold it to customers at 20% above its £4.20 ($10.00) issue price. By Christmas, 1969, the figure had jumped to £20.00 ($48.00), nearly five times the issue price. Further speculation pushed "Windsor Castle" up to £100.00 ($240.00) by spring and £130.00 ($312.00) by the end of 1970. On the strength of the fabulous success of this one plate, the English collector's plate market was born.

With booming demand for plates on both sides of the Atlantic, more and more manufacturers began to produce editions to meet it. In 1970 Kaiser and Berlin Design in Germany, Haviland in France, Belleek in Northern Ireland, Santa Clara in Spain, Orrefors in Sweden, and Lenox, Pickard, and Reed & Barton in the U.S. all started making collector's plates. And most remarkable—all were successful.

The Franklin Mint, another U.S. producer, made history in 1970 by issuing the first silver collector's plate, "Bringing Home the Tree" **(84-F64-1.1)** with commissioned artwork by Norman Rockwell, and it, too, was a runaway success, doubling in market price from $100.00 to $200.00 in the first year.

The excitement spread north into Canada where thousands of new collectors vied with those of the U.S. for the most popular issues. Wedgwood's 1969 "Windsor Castle" was the first big winner in Canada. Spurred by U.S. trading, the 1969 Royal Copenhagen *Christmas* plate **(14-R59-1.62)** also inspired delayed but extraordinary demand and was priced late in 1970 at triple its $14.00 Canadian issue price.

The thousands of new Canadian collectors also added fuel to the growing "boom" on the U.S. side of the border. In 1971, still more makers, Furstenberg of Germany, Gorham of the U.S., and Lladró of Spain all entered the U.S. market. Haviland & Parlon of France began a unique and successful series based on medieval tapestries **(18-H8-1)**. Older makers such as Royal Copenhagen and Wedgwood introduced *Mother's Day* series **(14-R59-2** and **26-W90-2)**. Rosenthal began a new *Christmas* series **(22-R55-2)** by Danish artist Bjørn Wiinblad, which was at first overlooked by German collectors but did well on the Danish and U.S. markets. Veneto Flair in Italy entered the market with a hand-made single issue **(38-V22-1)**.

Also in 1971, two German makers, Goebel **(22-G54-1)** and Schmid **(22-S12-1)**, introduced series in which both first issues were the same design by the late Sister Maria Innocentia Hummel who had become widely known for her stylized portrayals of children. Both series were highly successful, but the coincidence sparked lawsuits concerning the rights to Hummel works. The Siessen Convent near Stuttgart, Germany, where Sister Hummel

had resided, claimed sole ownership of all her creations and had contracted with Goebel to reproduce them in figurines and plates. Viktoria Hummel, the Sister's mother, disputed the claim and granted permission for production of works in her possession to Schmid.

In 1974, the West German Federal Supreme Court ruled that the convent would have rights to all Hummel creations after April 22, 1931—the day Berta Hummel entered the convent and took the name of Sister Maria Innocentia; her family would maintain rights to all works completed before Berta took her vows. Litigation was still pending in 1983 as Goebel alleged that Schmid's advertising of Hummel works by "Sister Berta" knowingly misconstrued their secular origin. Meanwhile, both plate series continued despite the controversy.

Back in the United States, the new surge in plate supply still did not keep up with collector demand; as the number of collectors and dealers increased, market prices continued to rise. In December, 1971, the *Wall Street Journal* ran an article inspired by the spectacular price rise of the first Franklin Mint *Rockwell Christmas* plate with the headline "While You Were Going Under, Granny Got in at $100, Got out at $450." Reporter Scott R. Schmedel also singled out the 1969 Wedgwood *Christmas* plate which was then selling for about $200.00—800% of issue price. To show this could be only temporary inflation, Mr. Schmedel quoted a serious Wedgwood collector who predicted its value would fall back and stabilize around $80.00. Instead, it held its price and rose to $250.00 at the end of 1983. The *Wall Street Journal* article and others like it were widely reprinted and set the stage for 1972 as the year of the speculator.

THE "CRASH OF '72"

As prices continued to rise in early 1972, still more makers leapt into the market, some of them less than reputable. Plates of poor design and quality were rushed into production. Thousands of new dealers and collectors began speculating with little or no knowledge of plates or of the market. New "mints" sprang up to mass-produce silver plates on the heels of the Franklin Mint's success. One, the George Washington Mint, introduced *six* new silver plates in 1972 alone.

Another, the Lincoln Mint, advertised its silver plate, "Collies," with pictures of an acid-etched plate, and thousands were sold before the plate was produced. Prices rose dramatically, but the actual plate was *stamped,* not etched, and many collectors were sadly disillusioned as the price of the issue plummeted.

Suddenly dealers all over the country found themselves overstocked as prices for the 1972 silver plates fell below issue. As the year ended, all other plates began to fall on the heels of the silver crash. In 1973 dealers panicked, and the speculator-collectors, many of whom had gone into part-time business as "bedroom dealers," saw their visions of quick riches vanish.

1972 "Collies"
The plate that set off the "crash of '72"

(18-D15-1.1) "The Secret Contract"
1973 D'Arceau-Limoges *Lafayette Legacy*

After the "crash of '72"—so-called because unsold 1972 issues still glutted the market in 1973—the following year became the year of the "shake-out." Several "mints" closed their doors. Some 100,000 fewer silver plates were issued in 1973 than in 1972, and thousands of those in existence were melted down. Established makers cut back production dramatically, and the bedroom dealers disappeared.

The effect of the U.S. "crash of '72" spread to Denmark. Overproduction of traditional lines by Bing & Grøndahl and Royal Copenhagen, coupled with a host of new issues from competitors, glutted the market there as well. With little potential for appreciation on their purchases, many collectors dropped out of the market, and dealers found themselves hopelessly overstocked.

In the midst of the bear market of 1973, American interest was rekindled by two new series from Europe. One for the American Bicentennial, the *Lafayette Legacy Collection* from D'Arceau-Limoges **(18-D15-1)** in France,

(26-R62-2.1) "Colette and Child"
1973 Royal Doulton *Mother and Child*

(84-G58-3.1) "Tiny Tim"
1974 Gorham *Rockwell Christmas*

(84-R70-1.1) "Scotty Gets His Tree"
1974 Rockwell Society *Christmas*

was unavailable to U.S. dealers. But the plates were imported directly from France by enough individual American collectors to become the most sought-after of all U.S. Bicentennial issues. The first issue was quoted at $36.00—two times its $14.82 issue price—in late 1983.

"Colette and Child" **(26-R62-2.1)** from Royal Doulton was the first plate by artist Edna Hibel and helped lead the market toward recovery, selling out immediately and climbing to $355.00—888% of its $40.00 issue price— within two years of its appearance. And as marginal plates disappeared from trading, established plates gradually regained their market strength.

The Canadian, German, and United Kingdom markets were relatively untouched by the American crash. In 1973 Carl Sorvin for Hutschenreuther introduced a series specifically for Canadian collectors. His *Canadian Christmas* —produced in West Germany exclusively for Canadian distribution—was well received and rose moderately in aftermarket trading.

As the U.S. market recovered in 1974 and 1975, it felt for the firt time a "reverse demand" from European collectors and dealers. When news of the American recovery slowly spread in Europe, plates that had originated there but had languished in their home markets— such as the Rörstrand *Christmas* series **(76-R54-1)** in Sweden—were bid up even higher in the American market when European dealers and their agents began buying them up for resale back in Europe. The Rosenthal *Wiinblad Christmas* series **(22-R55-2)** had gone relatively unnoticed in Germany when it was introduced in 1971. But, "Maria mit Kind" **(22-R55-2.1)**, the first issue, was bid up in the U.S. and Denmark because it was a radical departure from traditional plate art.

As this news began to reach the German market via magazine articles in 1973 and 1974, a brisk new aftermarket developed in which German dealers and individual collectors bought plates abroad at sharply appreciating prices and resold them to German collectors— many of whom were willing to pay even higher prices to obtain the scarce first issue. This in turn caused a scarcity on the U.S. market and drove the price up even further. In December of 1983, "Maria mit Kind" was priced in the U.S. at $1,300.00—1,300% of its $100.00 issue price; in Germany at DM3,400.00 ($1,231.80) 2,345% of its DM145.00 issue price.

THE MARKET MATURES

The U.S. market's recovery proved that even a dramatic crash could not permanently stifle collector demand and speculator optimism. In 1974 both Gorham **(84-G58-3)** and the Rockwell Society of America **(84-R70-1)** introduced series for Christmas with the artwork of Norman Rockwell. Within a year, each first issue had doubled in market price.

In 1975, D'Arceau-Limoges came out with *Nöel Vitrail Christmas* series **(18-D15-2)** in stained-glass style on translucent Limoges porcelain. It, too, sold out quickly and within a year had doubled in market price.

In contrast, the Danish market continued to be sluggish as makers failed to cut back edition sizes fast enough to react to the glut of plates issued in 1972-1973.

In Great Britain "Victorian Boy and Girl" **(26-R62-7.1)**, the 1976 first issue in Royal Doulton's *Valentine's Day* series, proved to be a new market catalyst, reminiscent of Wedgwood's "Windsor Castle" seven years earlier. It sold out within days of its introduction and more than doubled in price during its first year on the market.

In the recovering Canadian market, the first plate to generate exceptional excitement was the 1977 first issue in the Wedgwood *Blossoming of Suzanne* series **(26-W90-4.1)**, "Innocence," by the English painter, Mary Vickers. The plate sold out in Canada in less than a month. Issued at $60.00, it shot up to $225.00 in some areas as dealers scrambled to meet the sharp demand. And some six months later, dealers were still buying plates on the U.S. market for resale in Canada.

This in turn drove up the price of "Innocence" in the U.S. where it went to triple the issue price by mid-summer of 1978. The Canadian price finally leveled off in the same range.

New materials began to appear in 1976. "Rigoletto" **(38-V90-1.1)** the first *Grand Opera* plate in high relief from Italy's Studio Dante di Volteradici, was the first plate in a material called ivory alabaster. It almost tripled in price within a year, and ended 1983 at $100.00— almost three times its $35.00 issue price. "Brown's Lincoln" **(84-R69-1.1)** was also issued in 1976, the first *Famous Americans* plate from River Shore and the first copper collector's plate. It initially soared on the secondary market, ending 1983 at $90.00—225% of its $40.00 issue price. "She Walks in Beauty" **(84-I31-1.1)** was

(38-V90-1.1) "Rigoletto"
1976 Studio Dante di Volteradici *Grand Opera*

(84-R69-1.1) "Brown's Lincoln"
1976 River Shore *Famous Americans*

(18-D15-2.1) "Flight into Egypt"
1975 D'Arceau-Limoges *Nöel Vitrail*

(84-I31-1.1) "She Walks in Beauty"
1977 Incolay *Romantic Poets*

(84-R70-3.2) "The Cobbler"
1978 Rockwell Society *Heritage*

(16-A69-1.3) "Lemminkainen's Chase"
1978 Arabia *Kalevala*

718% of issue price; in Canada at C$240.00—up to 814%; in Germany at DM282.00 (U.S. $102.15)—at 627%; and in England at £75.00 (U.S. $107.15)—605% of its issue price.

The German-made 1978 Goebel *Hummel Annual* "Happy Pastime" **(22-G54-1.8)**, ended 1983 priced in the U.S. at $90.00—or 138% of issue price; in Canada at C$185.00—or 233%; and in England at £67.00 (U.S. $95.70)—or 170% of issue. The Finnish-made 1978 Arabia *Kalevala* "Lemminkainen's Chase" **(16-A69-1.3)**, ended 1983 priced in the U.S. at $50.00—or 128% of issue price; in Germany at DM165.00 (U.S. $59.80)—up to 176% and in England at £33.50 (U.S. $47.85)—177% of issue.

The "world market" was also evident in reports from countries previously considered beyond the realm of plate collecting, such as South Africa, Australia, and Japan. This was due in part to the worldwide marketing by Bing & Grøndahl and Royal Copenhagen as well as the growing number of local magazine and newspaper articles describing the phenomenal growth of plate collecting in North America over the past decade.

THE 1980s—VARIED AND VOLATILE

But as the 1970s ended, there was cause for concern about the U.S. market. The sharp increase in the number of new plate issues in 1979 and a six-month-long decline in the U.S. Market Bradex (the Bradford Exchange index of overall market performance) over the second half of the year were reminiscent of the gathering clouds of 1972 before the crash. A few market watchers saw the beginning of a possible collapse.

But others were quick to point out that the slide came off a two-year bull market (suggesting short-term profit-taking rather than a true downturn) and that despite the slide the Market Bradex had registered a net nine-point gain for the year. There were already signs that, far from panicking, collectors were quietly filling out their collections at bargain prices.

In fact, by the end of 1981, the market had regained considerable strength. The U.S. Market Bradex rose to a record high, and manufacturer optimism was again borne out by the introduction of an unusually large number of new issues from virtually every major maker in the U.S. and abroad. The year 1982 saw a continuation of this industry-wide optimism with almost 500 new issues introduced over the twelve-month period. The number of collectors actively buying and selling plates in the U.S. alone increased by more than 600,000, bringing the U.S. total to over five and one half million by the end of 1982. Strong attendance at regional plate conventions confirmed the optimism shared by manufacturers, dealers, and collectors.

The year ended on a positive note with a rise in the Market Bradex and the introduction of the Bradford

issued in 1977, the first *Romantic Poets* plate from Incolay Studios of California and the first cameo-style collector's plate. It was traded in December, 1983, at $190.00—317% of its $60.00 issue price.

The late 1970s also brought a "world market" closer to reality with issues of various national origins traded simultaneously on several markets. Thus the U.S. made 1978 Rockwell Society *Heritage* issue, "The Cobbler" **(84-R70-3.2)**, ended 1983 in the U.S. at $140.00—or

Exchange Instaquote™ trading system.

In 1983 attendance at regional plate conventions continued to grow along with the number of regional shows. The year saw an estimated 397,000 collectors enter the U.S. market, bringing the total to 6 million in the United States alone. And more than 580 new issues were released.

The collector's plate market has undergone remarkable changes since Harald Bing created the world's first limited-edition plate eighty-nine years ago. Today, computer technology enables collectors thousands of miles apart to trade plates quickly and efficiently. Entire publications are devoted to the plate market, and thousands of enthusiastic collectors gather at regional conventions to evaluate new issues and meet with leading artists and manufacturers. Less than a century after it began as a Christmas tradition, plate collecting has grown into the world's most traded art form, and the only art form with a recognized secondary market for the orderly buying and selling of issues.

The 1983 Plate of the Year, "Annie and Sandy," 1983
issue in the Edwin M. Knowles *Annie* series

1983—THE YEAR IN REVIEW

Compiled by the Staff of The Bradford Exchange Market Information Center

Nineteen eighty-three was William Chambers' year. A newcomer to the collector's plate medium, the Illinois artist made market history when "Annie and Sandy" **(84-K41-5.1)**, his first limited-edition plate, walked off with the two top honors of the year—Plate of the Year and New Edition of the Year. It was the first time both of these coveted awards had gone to the same plate.

Already well known in the U.S. as an illustrator and prize-winning portraitist, Chambers burst upon the collector's plate scene in January when "Annie and Sandy," the first issue in his *Annie* series **(84-K41-5)**, was introduced by Edwin M. Knowles. The plate, based on the famous comic strip and movie characters, was an immediate hit and was trading at $25.00 by October; by December, collectors were paying $60.00 for "Annie and Sandy," and it closed the year up 216% from the original issue price of $19.00.

Even though the final figures were conclusive, the race for both awards went to the wire. Another Knowles plate ("Bathsheba and Solomon" **[84-K41-6.1]**) was a serious contender for top honors, and heavy trading in both issues during November and December left the outcome in doubt until complete 1983 figures were in. When the dust settled, however, market history had been made: "Annie and Sandy," the big winner of 1983, had posted the greatest appreciation of *any* plate during the year (Plate of the Year) and the greatest appreciation of any plate in its year of issue (New Edition of the Year).

Chambers' accomplishment was even more remarkable in light of the fact that "Annie and Sandy" was his first collector's plate: at the beginning of 1983, he was a complete unknown on the collector's plate market. But collectors loved the *Annie* series, and Chambers was virtually mobbed by enthusiastic fans from California to New York whenever he made personal appearances at collectors' conventions or dealer open houses.

But William Chambers wasn't the only news in 1983. The plate market saw heavy profit-taking as collectors cashed in their older "blue chip" issues, setting market

(84-K41-6.1) "Bathsheba and Solomon"
1983 Edwin M. Knowles *Biblical Mothers*

sales records in the process. For example, one collector favorite, Norman Rockwell's "The Toy Maker" **(84-R70-3.1)**, was selling in July at $250.00, nearly twenty times its original $14.50 issue price.

One result of the selloff was a significant drop in the Market Bradex* (the quote-price/issue-price ratio of twelve well- established series), which closed the year at 299, down 44 points from a year earlier. Overall, declines outnumbered advances, 492 to 313. Although this was the first time since February 1978 that the Market Bradex had fallen below 300, exchange analysts were not concerned: the list of series that make up the Market Bradex is due for re-evaluation and is expected to be updated to include newer series in 1984.

MARKET, DOLLAR VOLUME UP

But if the Market Bradex was off from 1982 levels, other important indicators emphatically were not: primary and secondary market volume on the U.S. exchange was up 20%, to a record 3,331,555 plates traded; dollar volume set an all-time high, up 19% at $82,025,924; and there were a record 46 "million-dollar weeks."

An estimated 400,000 new collectors entered the market, bringing the U.S. total to a record 6 million-plus collectors, another indication of overall market strength. And even though the inflationary economy of the past several years evidently made some manufacturers more conservative, 585 new issues were introduced to the market in 1983, the second-highest number of new issues in market history.

(84-R70-3.1) "The Toy Maker"
1977 Rockwell Society *Heritage*

*The U.S. Market Bradex is based on the quote-price/issue-price ratio of issues in these key series: Bing & Grøndahl *Christmas* **(14-B36-1)** (since 1951), Bing & Grøndahl *Mother's Day* **(14-B36-3)**, Royal Copenhagen *Christmas* **(14-R59-1)** (since 1951), D'Arceau-Limoges *Christmas* **(18-D15-2)**, Goebel *Hummel Annual* **(22-G54-1)**, Schmid *Hummel Christmas* **(22-S12-1)**, Royal Doulton *Mother and Child* **(26-R62-2)**, Wedgwood *Christmas* **(26-W90-1)**, Fairmont *DeGrazia Holiday* **(84-F4-1)**, Reco *McClelland's Mother Goose* **(84-R60-2)**, Rockwell Society *Mother's Day* **(84-R70-2)** and *Heritage* **(84-R70-3)**.

ROCKWELLS STILL DOMINATE MARKET

Sales of Rockwell collector's plates since the death of Norman Rockwell on November 8, 1978, were of continuing interest to serious collectors—particularly those

CHART OF THE 1983 U.S. MARKET BRADEX

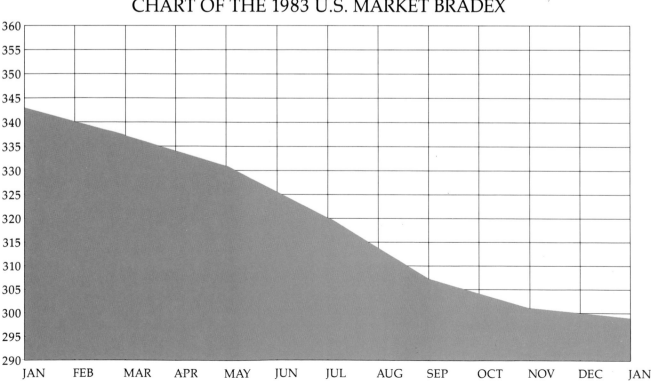

| | JAN | FEB | MAR | APR | MAY | JUN | JUL | AUG | SEP | OCT | NOV | DEC | JAN |

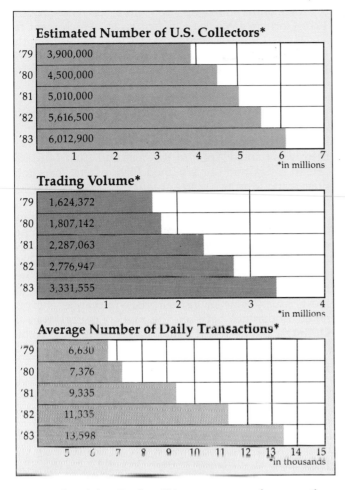

Estimated Number of U.S. Collectors*

'79	3,900,000	
'80	4,500,000	
'81	5,010,000	
'82	5,616,500	
'83	6,012,900	

1 2 3 4 5 6 7
*in millions

Trading Volume*

'79	1,624,372
'80	1,807,142
'81	2,287,063
'82	2,776,947
'83	3,331,555

1 2 3 4
*in millions

Average Number of Daily Transactions*

'79	6,630
'80	7,376
'81	9,335
'82	11,335
'83	13,598

5 6 7 8 9 10 11 12 13 14 15
*in thousands

Heritage series. Of the twelve Bradex-listed Rockwell series, the *Heritage* **(84-R70-3)** collection was still the front-runner at the end of 1983, out-trading the *Rockwell's Rediscovered Women* series by 25.8%. Exchange analysts were confident that interest in Rockwell plates would continue to boom, and predicted that Rockwell series would continue to make strong showings.

ANAHEIM SHOW BREAKS RECORDS

Among the year's highlights were six major conventions, beginning with the first California Plate Collectors' Convention, held February 18-20 in Anaheim and sponsored by the Southern California Association of Plate Collector Clubs (SCAPCC). More than 22,000 collectors and 150 limited-edition plate producers attended the show, making it the largest plate convention in history. The Swap'n'Sell held during the show was the biggest in plate collecting history, as well. Some 5,000 plates, with asking prices ranging from $10.00 to $4,000.00, were offered for sale during the seven-hour event, and collectors paid a total of $174,397 for 2,008 plates (658 different issues, about half of them Bradex-listed). Although most of the trades were in the $25.00 price range, a fair number sold for $50.00 or more. The

(84-R70-4.1) "Dreaming in the Attic"
1981 Rockwell Society *Rockwell's Rediscovered Women*

who realized that Rockwell issues account for more than half the total number of annual transactions on the exchange. As in previous years, Norman Rockwell plates—and especially those from the Rockwell Society of America—continued to dominate the market in 1983, accounting for more than 55% of the total trading volume on the exchange, only a slight drop from the 1982 figure of 58%.

From 1978 to 1981, the Rockwell Society's *Heritage* **(84-R70-3)** plates were the unquestioned market leaders, accounting for as much as 66% of total Rockwell trading. In 1981, however, that record fell when a new Rockwell series (also from the Rockwell Society **[84-R70-0]**) made a dramatic market debut. "Dreaming in the Attic" **(84-R70-4.1)**, the first issue in the Society's *Rockwell's Rediscovered Women* series, was an unprecedented success (according to exchange analysts, it is the single most sought-after Rockwell issue of all time), and within a year plates in that series were indisputably leading the market in trading volume.

In 1983 the Rockwell Society introduced another new series, *Rockwell's Light Campaign* **(84-R70-6)**, which was an immediate success, quickly moving up to third position in overall trading volume, outdistanced only by the Society's *Rockwell's Rediscovered Women* **(84-R70-4)** and

1st California Plate Collectors' Convention

(84-G58-5.1) "Los Niños"
1976 Gorham *DeGrazia Children*

(OTC) "6213 at Rest"
1983 Christian Bell

top trade of the show was "Los Niños" **(84-G58-5.1)**, the 1976 Gorham *DeGrazia Children* issue, which went for $1,750.00. Other collector favorites were plates from the Rockwell Society of America **(84-R70-0)**, Fairmont **(84-F4-0)**, Knowles **(84-K41-0)**, Reco **(84-R60-0)**, and Goebel **(22-G54-0)**.

In voting for the first annual Silver Chalice awards, members of more than 100 collector's clubs nationwide honored two top plate-artists at the Anaheim show: Sue Etém was named Artist of the Year and Alan Murray's "Heart of a Child" was named Plate of the Year. Both Etém's and Murray's plates are OTC issues.

Collector's plates by a "favorite son," the late Arizona artist Ted DeGrazia, led Swap'n'Sell trading at another convention, the second Southwest Plate Collectors Show (Phoenix, Arizona), sponsored by the Arizona Plate Collectors' Club and held March 18-20. DeGrazia issues have always done well in the Southwest and demand for these issues came as no surprise. Exchange analysts noted similarities between the market performance of DeGrazia and Rockwell issues: both continued to be bid up significantly after the artists' deaths.

The 5th Annual Canadian Plate Fair, held in Toronto, Ontario, June 10-12, attracted over 6,000 collectors, 30 artists, and 30 exhibitors, and featured yet another successful Swap'n'Sell. Of the 1,634 plates registered for sale, 729 sold for a total of $64,783. The most actively traded plates were "Little Boy Blue" **(84-R60-2.2)**, the 1980 Reco *McClelland's Mother Goose* plate; "The Ship Builder" **(84-R70-3.4)**, the 1980 Rockwell Society *Heritage* plate; "Little Miss Muffet" **(84-R60-2.3)**, the 1981 Reco *McClelland's Mother Goose* plate; and "The Lighthouse Keeper's Daughter" **(84-R70-3.3)**, the 1979 Rockwell Society *Heritage* plate.

A highlight of the Toronto Fair was the announcement by the Canadian Association of Limited Edition Dealers (CALED) that "The Frog King" **(22-K4-5.1)**, the 1982 Kaiser *Classic Fairy Tales* plate, had earned Plate of the Year honors. Also of particular interest to Canadian collectors was a plate created especially for the show. "6213 at Rest" (OTC) by Ted Xaras for Christian Bell depicted the last Canadian National Railway steam engine in regular service in the Toronto area, and was issued in an edition limited to only 1,000 plates. The entire edition sold out during the show at the issue price of $25.00; by year-end the plate was trading at $200.00.

SOUTH BEND SHOW ATTRACTS 14,000

From July 8 to 10, the oldest plate show of all was held in South Bend, Indiana. The ninth International Plate Collector's Convention, sponsored by Watson's Collector's Club and the National Association of Limited Edition Dealers (NALED), attracted more than 14,000 collectors—a healthy 27% jump in attendance from the previous year. More than 174 exhibitors and 90 artists

attended, including Sven Vestergaard, creator of Royal Copenhagen's new *Motherhood* collection **(14-R59-4)**; Studio Dante di Volteradici's Alberto Santangela, noted Italian sculptor and creator of the new *Ghiberti Doors* series **(38-V90-3)**; and Gene Boyer, creator of Crown Parian's *American Folk Heroes* series **(84-C72-2)**. Goebel **(22-G54-0)**, the West German maker perhaps best known for its M. I. Hummel plates and figurines, shipped a facsimile of its Roedenthal factory to the show—complete with four artists and craftsmen and a simulated kiln; Anri's **(38-A54-0)** master carver Georg Mahlknecht demonstrated his skill as a woodcarver.

As always, makers used the South Bend show to introduce new releases; almost sixty new plates were previewed. Five NALED awards were announced, including Manufacturer of the Year (Pickard China **[84-P29-0]**); Plate of the Year ("Heart of a Child" [OTC], the 1982 Ernst Enterprises *Little Misses Young and Fair* plate by Alan Murray); Artist of the Year (Sue Etém); and Collectible of the Year ("Heart of a Child"). Swap'n'Sell, a regular feature of the South Bend show, was successful as usual. Of the 5,884 items registered for sale, 2,376 were sold for a total sales volume of $122,718.

Two Massachusetts conventions (the 2nd Annual Eastern States Plate and Collectible Show, held October 1-2 in Worcester, and Convention '83, sponsored by the Northeast Regional Chapter of the Rockwell Society of America, held October 8-9 in Lenox) rounded out the year's scheduled plate shows.

THE YEAR AT A GLANCE

January trading got the year off to a strong start, with total exchange activity up 233% from the previous month (December 1982) and dollar volume up 177% over the same period. A market record was set when the highest single week's dollar volume in the history of the ex-

change—$2.9 million—was recorded in the fourth week. "Annie and Sandy" **(84-K41-5.1)** from Knowles' *Annie* series was introduced to the market and almost immediately began to generate strong collector demand; Rockwells continued strong, accounting for 53% of the month's total transactions.

By February, however, the Market Bradex had begun to decline and was down 6 points (to 337) at the end of the month. Responding to record-high market prices, collectors began to sell off plates in older, "blue-chip" series, particularly Goebel Hummel *Annual* **(22-G54-1)**, Schmid Hummel *Christmas* **(22-S12-1)**, and Rockwell Society *Heritage* **(84-R70-3)** issues. As a result, seven of the twelve key indicator series declined; five advanced, led by Fairmont's *DeGrazia Holiday* series **(84-F4-1)**, up 6%. Advancing issues outnumbered declines 141 to 136, with the greatest gain posted by "Touching the Sky" **(84-P19-1.1)**, the 1982 plate in Pemberton & Oakes'

(84-P19-1.1) "Touching the Sky"
1982 Pemberton & Oakes *Wonder of Childhood*

9th International Plate Collector's Convention

(84-R70-3.7) "The Painter"
1983 Rockwell Society *Heritage*

(16-A69-1.1) "Vainamoinen's Sowing"
1976 Arabia *Kalevala*

Wonder of Childhood series, which climbed 37% to $26.00. Continuing the strong market record of Rockwell Society issues, "Waiting at the Dance" **(84-R70-4.5)**, the 1983 plate in the *Rockwell's Rediscovered Women* series, was the most sought-after issue, followed by "The Painter" **(84-R70-3.7)**, the Society's 1983 *Heritage* plate. Ted De-Grazia's "Merry Little Indian" **(84-F4-4.5)** from Fairmont's *DeGrazia's Children* series came on strong, jumping 34% in February to close at $130.00, up $33.00 from its 1982 high. Another DeGrazia plate, Gorham's 1976 "Los Niños" **(84-G58-5.1)**, climbed $25.00 and was trading at $900.00 by the end of the month.

Also in February, *Plate World* magazine announced that a poll of its readers voted John McClelland "America's favorite plate artist" for the second year in a row.

COMPUTERIZED TRADING BEGINS

On February 1, Bradford Exchange chairman J. Roderick MacArthur cut the red ribbon to open Bradford's new, fully computerized Trading Floor. "With our new Trading Floor and its new Bradford Exchange *Instaquote* trading system, we have created a real-time, two-sided auction market for collector's plates," MacArthur said. The *Instaquote* system enables collectors and dealers to receive up-to-the-minute bid/ask information on more than 1,100 Bradex-listed plates and some 3,500 over-the-counter issues.

The Collectors Platemakers Guild announced that its traveling mall shows would be cancelled due to a lack of participation and funding by Guild members. The shows, which featured new issues from major makers, a display showing how plates are made, and an exhibit of "firsts" in plate collecting, had been quite popular in 1982 when they visited shopping malls in cities across the country.

During March, Rockwell sales on the exchange rose again, accounting for 61% of all transactions, and Rockwell Society issues continued to dominate the market, with two new plates—"The Painter" **(84-R70-3.7)** (*Heritage* series) and "Add Two Cups and a Measure of Love" **(84-R70-2.8)** (*Mother's Day* series)—leading the way.

By April, the Market Bradex had dropped another 6 points (to 331). Eight of the twelve key indicator series declined, two remained steady, with the two remaining series advancing only slightly. Overall, advancing issues outnumbered declines 138 to 124, with "Touching the Sky" **(84-P19-1.1)**, the 1982 plate in the Pemberton & Oakes *Wonder of Childhood* series, the top gainer for the second consecutive period (up 35%, to $35.00). Total exchange activity was up 20% from March, and Rockwell sales accounted for a hefty 71% of exchange transactions. The *Age of Steam* series **(8-C30-1)** from Christian Bell Porcelain of Canada was added to the U.S. Bradex (all plates were still at issue price), bringing to twelve the total number of countries represented.

Among the plates making strong showings were "Vainamoinen's Sowing" **(16-A69-1.1)**, the 1976 plate in Arabia's *Kalevala* series, which jumped $25.00 in April to close at $200.00; Ted DeGrazia's 1976 "Los Niños" **(84-G58-5.1)** by Gorham, up $150.00 to $1,050.00; the 1983 issue in Fairmont's *Playful Memories* series, "Jamie" **(84-F4-10.3)**, up 17.6% to $50.00; and Haviland & Parlon's 1979 *Christmas* plate, "Madonna of the Eucharist" **(18-H8-2.8)**, which closed the month at $102.00, up 13.3% from the previous December.

The May 5 death of Frank B. Knight, publisher of *The Plate Collector* magazine, was a loss to the plate collecting world. Knight, a respected figure in the collecting community, had published various magazines and

newsletters through the years. He introduced *The Plate Collector* in 1972.

Also in May, Frode Bahnsen, artist since 1980 for Grande Copenhagen's *Christmas* plate series **(14-G65-1)**, died in Copenhagen. Holder of the Knight of Dannebrog Award from the Queen of Denmark and longtime chief sculptor of the Danish Royal Mint, Bahnsen was considered an unrivaled master of his craft and was generally considered the most honored Danish artist of his generation.

Total exchange activity was down slightly more than 10% in May from the same period in 1982. Collector attention focused on "Annie and Sandy" **(84-K41-5.1)**, the first plate in Knowles' *Annie* series, and "The Painter" **(84-R70-3.7)**, the 1983 plate in the Rockwell Society *Heritage* series. Both plates were still at issue price. Although all four weeks were "million-dollar" weeks, total exchange dollar-volume was down 8.8% from May of 1982 and Rockwell trading fell to 41.3% of total transactions in May.

The June Market Bradex was down 11 points, closing at 320. Eight of the twelve key indicator series declined, two advanced, and two remained steady. Exchange analysts felt that the decline was again primarily the result of profit-taking by collectors who were cashing in their blue-chip plates. "Mary, Mary" **(84-R60-2.1)**, for example, the first issue in Reco's *McClelland's Mother Goose* series (one of the Bradex key indicators) started out the year trading at $273.00, but had slipped twenty points by June, to $253.00, and closed out the year trading at $230.00, down 15.8%. Another "blue chip" that sustained a substantial overall loss in 1983 was Pickard's "Girl with Watering Can" **(84-P29-4.1)**, the 1978 first issue in the *Children of Renoir* series, which steadily slid in value from a January-February high of $214.00 to a December low of $150.00, down 29.9% (but still three times its original issue price of $50.00).

For the fifth consecutive bi-monthly period, Fairmont's *DeGrazia Holiday* series **(84-F4-1)** led advances (up 4.8%). Schmid's *Hummel Christmas* **(22-S12-1)** topped

Frode Bahnsen

(84-R60-2.1) "Mary, Mary"
1979 Reco *McClelland's Mother Goose*

Frank B. Knight

(84-P29-4.1) "Girl with a Watering Can"
1978 Pickard *Children of Renoir*

Frances Hook

(84-R70-4.7) "Standing in the Doorway"
1983 Rockwell Society *Rockwell's Rediscovered Women*

(84-R70-2.8) "Add Two Cups and a Measure of Love"
1983 Rockwell Society *Mother's Day*

the list of declining series, dropping 3.7%, and declines outnumbered advances 185 to 111 with River Shore's 1978 *Famous Americans* "Brown's Peace Corps" **(84-R69-1.3)** posting the heaviest loss (down 42.9% to $40.00). Pemberton & Oakes' "Touching the Sky" **(84-P19-1.1)** continued to climb, closing at $43.00 in heavy trading.

MARKET RALLIES IN JUNE

The market rallied briefly in June, thanks in large part to continued heavy demand for Knowles' "Annie and Sandy" **(84-K41-5.1)** plate. "Vainamoinen's Sowing" **(16-A69-1.1)**, the first issue in Arabia's *Kalevala* series and one of the few square plates on the market, continued its steady upward climb, appreciating another $30.00 to close the month at $230.00; so did Gorham's "Los Niños" **(84-G58-5.1)**, which was trading at $1,100.00 (up $50.00), and Fairmont's "Jamie" **(84-F4-10.3)**, which went up 30% in June to close at $65.00.

The total number of transactions on the exchange rose 20.5% from May (and were up an extraordinary 87.1% from June 1982). Leading trading activity was the sixth plate in the Rockwell Society's *Rockwell's Rediscovered Women* series, "Gossiping in the Alcove" **(84-R70-4.6)**. "Little Bo Peep" **(84-R60-2.5)**, the 1983 plate in Reco's *McClelland's Mother Goose* series, ranked second.

The death of children's artist Frances Hook on July 23 at the age of seventy saddened the many collectors who admired her limited-edition plates, prints, and figurines. Hook was best-known for her portraits of dreamy-eyed children, and at the time of her death eleven Hook plates (all OTC) had been released by Roman, Inc.

By July, total exchange activity was up 28.1% from June of 1983. All four weeks were "million-dollar" weeks and total exchange dollar volume was up 28.8% from the previous month. The most sought-after plate was "Standing in the Doorway" **(84-R70-4.7)**, the 1983 Rockwell Society *Rockwell's Rediscovered Women* issue, followed by "Little Bo Peep" **(84-R60-2.5)**, the 1983 Reco *McClelland's Mother Goose* issue. Rockwell trading accounted for 41.2% of total July transactions.

The August Market Bradex was down another 13 points to 307, as eight of the twelve key indicator series declined. For the sixth consecutive bi-monthly Bradex reporting period, advances were led by Fairmont's *De-Grazia Holiday* series **(84-F4-1)** (up 1.8%). The Rockwell Society's *Heritage* series **(84-R70-3)** suffered the biggest decline (down 4.4%) due to heavy profit-taking in "The Toy Maker" **(84-R70-3.1)** which had traded as high as $260.00 earlier in the year. ("The Toy Maker" was at $235.00 by the end of the month and continued to lose ground, closing the year down 18.7% at $213.00); overall declines outnumbered advances 216 to 125.

The 1977 first issue in Knowles' *Wizard of Oz* series, "Over the Rainbow" **(84-K41-1.1)**, posted the heaviest loss of any single issue (down 28.2% to $140.00). Advances were headed by the 1983 Rockwell Society *Moth-*

er's Day plate, "Add Two Cups and a Measure of Love" **(84-R70-2.8)** (up 73.3% to $52.00 through June-August reporting). Heinrich/Villeroy & Boch's 1980 "The Snow Maiden" **(22-H18-1.1)**, first issue in the *Russian Fairy Tales* collection, posted a $30.00 increase to close the month at $120.00, up 71.4% over its $70.00 issue price. Total exchange activity was up 18.6% from August 1982 and collectors bought heavily into two newly released issues: "Flirting in the Parlor" **(84-R70-4.8)**, the eighth plate in the Rockwell Society's *Rockwell's Rediscovered Women* series, and an early 1983 Christmas release, "Santa in the Subway" **(84-R70-1.10)**, the Society's *Christmas* plate.

By August, the leading candidates for Plate of the Year were "Touching the Sky" **(84-P19-1.1)**, the 1982 plate in Pemberton & Oakes' *Wonder of Childhood* series, up 268.4% to $70.00, followed by "Add Two Cups and a Measure of Love" **(84-R70-2.8)**, the 1983 plate in the Rockwell Society *Mother's Day* series, up 103.9% since January to $52.00, and "The Grand Finale" **(84-K41-1.8)**, the last plate in Knowles' *Wizard of Oz* collection, up 87.5% to $45.00.

At the same time, a number of plates—none of them the eventual winner—were in the running for New Edition of the Year honors: Rockwell Society's "Add Two Cups and a Measure of Love"; "Michele et Sylvie" **(18-D15-8.1)**, the 1983 plate in D'Arceau-Limoges' *Cambier Mother's Day* series, up 37% to $45.00, and "Spring Innocence" **(84-P19-1.2)**, the 1983 plate in Pemberton & Oakes' *Wonder of Childhood* series, up 31.6% to $25.00. At this point in the year, "Annie and Sandy" **(84-K41-5.1)**, which eventually won in both categories, was still trading at issue price.

"BRADEX" IS TEN YEARS OLD

Another plate market milestone was reached in September when the Bradford Exchange *Current Quotations* (the "Bradex") marked its tenth anniversary. When this bi-monthly market report on trading activity first appeared in 1973, it listed only 159 plates by 38 producers. In contrast, the September-October 1983 issue included more than 1,100 plates from 62 makers—a testament to the growth of the collector's plate market in the last decade.

Total exchange activity and total dollar volume were both down 4% from the previous month. "This Is the Room That Light Made" **(84-R70-6.1)**, the first plate in the Rockwell Society's *Rockwell's Light Campaign* series, was still trading at issue price and continued to generate strong collector demand, as did "Working in the Kitchen" **(84-R70-4.9)**, the ninth plate in the Rockwell Society's *Rockwell's Rediscovered Women* series. Rockwell trading increased to 61.4% of total transactions.

By October, the Market Bradex had fallen to 301, down a total of 42 points for the year and 6 points since August. Seven of the twelve key indicator series declined, three advanced, and two remained steady. The top advancing series was D'Arceau-Limoges' *Christmas*

(84-R70-1.10) "Santa in the Subway"
1983 Rockwell Society *Christmas*

First bi-monthly Bradford Exchange
Current Quotations (September, 1973)

(84-K41-4.3) "The Cookie Tasting"
1982 Edwin M. Knowles *Csatari Grandparent Plate*

(18-D15-2), up 1.8%; declines were again led by the Rockwell Society's *Heritage* series, down 3.9%. Overall declining issues outnumbered advances, 214 to 129, and the plate that posted the greatest gain was the 1982 Knowles *Csatari Grandparent Plate*, "The Cookie Tasting" **(84-K41-4.3)**, which doubled in value (to $50.00).

(84-R70-6.2) "Grandpa's Treasure Chest"
1984 Rockwell Society *Rockwell's Light Campaign*

François Ganeau

(14-B36-1.1) "Behind the Frozen Window"
1895 Bing & Grøndahl *Christmas*

Heading the list of declining issues was the 1982 Pemberton & Oakes *Wonder of Childhood* plate, "Touching the Sky" **(84-P19-1.1)**, a drop which exchange analysts considered a reaction to the heavy speculation which had forced its price up earlier in the year. Apparently, many dealers overbought and, by September, were willing to sell at devalued prices. In most cases they still made a profit: "Touching the Sky" closed the month at $50.00, down 28.6% from its August high, but still up substantially over its trading price earlier in the year (it was trading at $26.00 in February, and at $35.00 in April). Total exchange activity was up 27.1% from September.

FOURTH ROCKWELL POSTCARD DISCOVERED
The Rockwell Society surprised the plate collecting world in late October when it announced that artwork for a fourth *Rockwell on Tour* **(84-R70-5)** plate had been discovered, and that a fourth plate would be added to the collection. This unusual series, based on hand-painted and-colored postcards that Rockwell sent to a few close friends during a 1927 tour of Europe, had originally been announced in 1982 as a three-plate series.

Leading candidates for Plate of the Year as of October were "The Cookie Tasting" **(84-K41-4.3)**, the 1982 Knowles *Csatari Grandparent Plate* (up 150% from issue price) and "Spring Innocence" **(84-P19-1.2)**, the 1983 plate in Pemberton & Oakes' *Wonder of Childhood* series (up 136.8% from issue price). October front-runners for New Edition of the Year were "Spring Innocence" and "Add Two Cups and a Measure of Love" **(84-R70-2.8)**, the 1983 plate in the Rockwell Society's *Mother's Day* series, which had already appreciated 111.8% to $54.00. Meanwhile, "Annie and Sandy" **(84-K41-5.1)**, the plate which eventually earned both Plate of the Year and New Edition of the Year honors, was just beginning its climb in value on the secondary market, closing the month at $25.00, up 31.6% from its $19.00 issue price.

By November, the most heavily traded plate was "Grandpa's Treasure Chest" **(84-R70-6.2)**, the second issue in the Rockwell Society's *Rockwell's Light Campaign* series, followed by "Santa in the Subway" **(84-R70-1.10)**, the 1983 Rockwell Society *Christmas* plate. Both were still at issue price. Rockwell trading accounted for 56.2% of total transactions for the month.

In Paris, artist François Ganeau died on November 5 at the age of 71. He was best-known to U.S. audiences for his landmark *Women of the Century* series of collector's plates **(18-D15-3)**. Introduced in 1976 by D'Arceau-Limoges, the series was available by subscription only, and was one of the first collector's plate series ever available in North America.

"BEHIND THE FROZEN WINDOW"
SELLS FOR $4,000
Easily setting a 1983 market record for the single highest trade, "Behind the Frozen Window" **(14-B36-1.1)**—the landmark 1895 Bing & Grøndahl *Christmas* plate—was

sold in November by a New York dealer to a Texas collector for $4,000.00. Of the approximately 500 "Frozen Window" plates believed to have been made, only 13 are known to exist, and those are traded very infrequently.

The December Market Bradex was down another 2 points to 299, putting it below the 300 mark for the first time since February 1978. Ten key indicator series advanced, but two declined, weighing the index down. The top advancing series was D'Arceau-Limoges' *Christmas* **(18-D15-2)**, up 15.5%; declines, led by Royal Doulton's *Mother and Child* **(26-R62-2)** down 3%, outnumbered advances for the fourth consecutive bi-monthly period, 248 to 148. It should be noted here that the Market Bradex is constantly absorbing new issues in the various key indicator series, and since they seldom appreciate dramatically in market value in their first few weeks in the market, this weighs the average down and pulls the Market Bradex down. This can occur despite the fact that individual plates may have appreciated. So it is not surprising to see ten key indicator series advancing with the addition of new issues and the Market Bradex declining overall. Even one plate can pull the calculation down significantly if its decline is great enough.

The top advancing issue was the issue which earned both Plate of the Year and New Edition of the Year honors in 1983, "Annie and Sandy" **(84-K41-5.1)**. Since October, when it closed at $25.00, this first issue in Knowles' *Annie* series had jumped another $35.00 to close out the year at $60.00—an appreciation of 215.8% in its year of issue. Other 1983 plates which made strong showings were "Juliana" **(26-R62-11.4)**, from Royal Doulton's *Portraits of Innocence* series (up 31.6% for the year, at $125.00), "Girl with Seabirds" **(84-A72-1.5)**, from the Artists of the World *Children of Aberdeen* series

(84-R70-5.4) "Die Walk am Rhein"
1984 Rockwell Society *Rockwell on Tour*

(up 33.3%, at $80.00), "Heavenly Blessings" **(84-F4-1.8)**, from Fairmont's DeGrazia *Holiday* series (up 115.4%, at $140.00), and "Jamie" **(84-F4-10.3)**, from Fairmont's *Playful Memories* series, which posted an overall 64.7% gain and closed the year at $70.00.

The 1982 plate in Fairmont's *DeGrazia Children* series, "Merry Little Indian" **(84-F4-4.5)**, made a strong last-quarter showing (it closed the year at $225.00 for a total 1983 gain of 132%); so did "Los Niños" **(84-G58-5.1)**, the 1976 Gorham *DeGrazia Children* plate which was trading at $1,400.00 by year-end, a gain of 60% for the year.

Total exchange activity and dollar volume were up 21% and 8.5% respectively above December 1982 levels, with the just-released "Die Walk am Rhein" (84-

THE TOP TWENTY GAINERS FOR 1983

YEAR	MAKER	SERIES	PLATE	% UP	TO
1983	Knowles	*Annie*	"Annie and Sandy"	215.8%	$ 60.00
1983	Knowles	*Biblical Mothers*	"Bathsheba and Solomon"	178.5%	110.00
1983	Rockwell Society	*Rockwell on Tour*	"Walking through Merrie Englande"	175.0%	44.00
1982	Knowles	*Csatari Grandparent*	"The Cookie Tasting"	150.0%	50.00
1982	Fairmont	*DeGrazia Children*	"Merry Little Indian"	132.0%	225.00
1983	Rockwell Society	*Mother's Day*	"Add Two Cups and Love"	127.5%	58.00
1983	Fairmont	*DeGrazia Holiday*	"Heavenly Blessings"	115.4%	140.00
1982	di Volteradici	*Grand Opera*	"Pagliacci"	112.5%	85.00
1982	Pemberton & Oakes	*Wonder of Childhood*	"Touching the Sky"	110.6%	40.00
1980	Knowles	*Wizard of Oz*	"The Grand Finale"	108.3%	50.00
1982	Georges Boyer	*Alice in Wonderland*	"Alice and the White Rabbit"	103.0%	75.00
1979	Knowles	*Wizard of Oz*	"Wonderful Wizard of Oz"	100.0%	50.00
1984	Fairmont	*DeGrazia Children*	"Pink Papoose"	92.3%	125.00
1973	Kaiser	*Mother's Day*	"Cats"	85.7%	26.00
1983	Pemberton & Oakes	*Wonder of Childhood*	"Spring Innocence"	84.2%	35.00
1982	Reco	*McClelland's Mother Goose*	"Little Jack Horner"	83.7%	45.00
1983	D'Arceau-Limoges	*Cambier Mother's Day*	"Michele et Sylvie"	82.7%	60.00
1982	D'Arceau-Limoges	*Christmas*	"The Annunciation"	78.9%	55.00
1982	Knowles	*Gone With the Wind*	"Mammy Lacing Scarlett"	78.7%	42.00
1980	Heinrich/Villeroy & Boch	*Russian Fairy Tales*	"Snow Maiden"	73.3%	130.00

THE TEN GREATEST DECLINING ISSUES OF 1983

YEAR	MAKER	SERIES	PLATE	% DOWN	TO
1979	Anna-Perenna	*Triptych*	"Byzantine Triptych"	63.2%	$125.00
1977	River Shore	*Famous Americans*	"Brown's Rockwell"	61.5%	50.00
1976	River Shore	*Famous Americans*	"Brown's Lincoln"	59.1%	90.00
1970	Franklin Mint	*Christmas*	"Bringing Home the Tree"	57.1%	150.00
1978	River Shore	*Famous Americans*	"Brown's Peace Corps"	57.1%	30.00
1972	Wedgwood	*Mothers*	"The Sewing Lesson"	55.9%	15.00
1978	Viletta	*Nutcracker Ballet*	"Clara and the Nutcracker"	51.6%	30.00
1979	Schmid	*Hummel Mother's Day*	"Cherub's Gift"	48.6%	18.00
1980	Pickard	*Children of Renoir*	"The Artist's Son Jean"	47.7%	45.00
1979	Königszelt Bayern	*Hedi Keller Christmas*	"The Adoration"	46.4%	75.00
1976	Pickard	*Annual Christmas*	"Alba Madonna"	44.9%	130.00

R70-5.4), the surprise fourth plate in the Rockwell Society's *Rockwell on Tour* collection, leading in trading volume.

DISAPPOINTMENTS AND SURPRISES

Most market analysts agreed on the five most disappointing issues of 1983, all from the U.S.

Issued at $60.00, "Wondering" (84-F4-4.6), sixth plate in the Fairmont/Artists of the World's *DeGrazia Children* series, fell short of expectations, although it had nearly doubled in value and was trading at $115.00 by year-end. Market observers based their predictions of even greater gains on the heavy trading in DeGrazia issues since the artist's death in September 1982, and the success of the previous *DeGrazia Children* issue ("Merry Little Indian" [84-F4-4.5]), which had been named New Edition of the Year for 1982. "Wondering" had appreciated 53.3% in 1982, closing that year at $92.00.

Another new issue which surprised analysts with its lackluster performance was Fairmont/Hackett's "Randy" (84-F4-10.4), from the *Playful Memories* series. The first issue in that series ("Renée" [84-F4-10.1]), was named Plate of the Year for 1982, leading to speculation that the entire series would do well. However, "Randy" closed the year at $55.00, up only 22.2% from its $45.00 issue price.

"Daddy Warbucks" (84-K41-5.2), the second plate in Knowles' *Annie* series, was another instance where a plate failed to live up to the promise of its predecessor (in this case, the highly successful "Annie and Sandy" [84-K41-5.1]). Although "Daddy Warbucks" came on the market early in the year, the edition was not sold-out by year-end, and the plate was still trading at the $19.00 issue price.

Still another disappointment was Reco's "Little Bo Peep" (84-R60-2.5) from the *McClelland's Mother Goose* series. Although the series has been a top market performer since its introduction in 1979 and has been a key indicator series since February 1982, "Little Bo Peep"—a 1983 issue—closed out the year still trading at its $24.50 issue price.

A series that provided its share of excitement was the Rockwell Society's *Rockwell's Light Campaign* collection (84-R70-6). "This Is the Room That Light Made" (84-R70-6.1), the first issue in the series, failed to generate the same collector interest—or trading volume—as previous first issues in the Rockwell Society series. When it closed out the year still trading at the issue price of $19.50, it had to be considered a major disappointment.

Hard on its heels, however, came a big surprise: the immediate collector demand which made the *next* issue in the series, "Grandpa's Treasure Chest" (84-R70-6.2), a consistently strong trader from the time it was introduced in late summer. (It is officially listed as a 1984 issue.)

Exchange analysts also pointed to Ted DeGrazia's "Los Niños" (84-G58-5.1) as a major surprise. The plate, the first issue in Gorham's two-plate *DeGrazia Children* series, came on the market in 1976 at the issue price of $35.00. At the time of his death in September 1982, it had already climbed to $840.00; it skyrocketed in value throughout 1983, closing out the year at $1,400.00, 4,000% of issue price.

LISTINGS AND DELISTINGS

Lack of consistent trading volume on the exchange led to the delisting of eleven series from the Bradex by the close of the year: Svend Jensen's *Christmas* and *Mother's Day* series (Denmark), Kaiser's *Anniversary* (Germany), Lihs-Lindner's *Christmas* (Germany), Schmid's *Ferrandiz Mother and Child* (Germany), Royal Worcester's *Doughty Birds* (Great Britain), Veneto Flair's *Dogs* (Italy), Fairmont's *Spencer's Special Requests* (U.S.A.), Kern's *Runci Mother's Day* (U.S.A.), Gorham's *Spencer Annual* (U.S.A.), and International's *Bicentennial* (U.S.A.).

Four series were added to the Bradex at year's end: Christian Bell's *Age of Steam* (8-C30-1) (Canada), Royal Copenhagen's *Motherhood* (14-R59-4) (Denmark), Reco's *Days Gone By* (84-R60-8) (U.S.A.), and Vague Shadows' *The Chieftains I* (84-V3-2) (U.S.A.).

INTERNATIONAL NEWS

CANADA. Nineteen eighty-three was also a year of profit-taking in the Canadian marketplace, and al-

(8-C30-1.1) "Symphony in Steam"
1981 Christian Bell *Age of Steam*

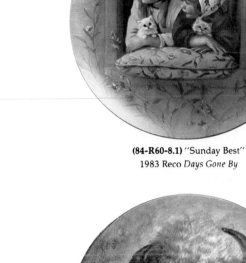

(84-R60-8.1) "Sunday Best"
1983 Reco *Days Gone By*

(14-R59-4.1) "Mother Robin and Babies"
1982 Royal Copenhagen *Motherhood*

(84-V3-2.1) "Chief Sitting Bull"
1979 Vague Shadows *The Chieftains I*

though the Market Bradex closed the year at 287 (down 33 points) observers had confidence in the basic strength of the market. Exchange analysts noted a subtle trend away from the old, traditional European plates, especially the Christmas blue-and-white issues, and an increasing interest in "made in Canada" issues such as Christian Bell Porcelain's *Age of Steam* series **(8-C30-1)**. Overall, declines outnumbered advances 206 to 159.

Trading on both the secondary market, as monitored by the Bradford Exchange, Ltd., in London, Ontario, and on the primary market, as reported by the Bradford Exchange AG Canadian agent in Don Mills, Ontario, showed a dramatic increase in dollar volume: up 46% (nearly $6 million) from the previous year, with unit volume increasing to an average of 1,658 primary and secondary market transactions a day. Equally important, the estimated number of Canadian collectors topped the 900,000 mark, an increase of approximately 67,000 in one year.

Canadian Plate of the Year honors went to "Melanie"

(84-K41-3.3) "Melanie"
1980 Edwin M. Knowles *Gone With the Wind*

(22-K4-2.13) "Titmice Family"
1983 Kaiser *Mother's Day*

(22-K46-3.1) "The Music"
1982 Königszelt Bayern *Sulamith's Love Song*

(84-K41-3.3), the 1980 plate in Knowles' *Gone With the Wind* series, which appreciated 165.6% (to $85.00). The runner-up was "Symphony in Steam," the 1981 plate in Christian Bell's *Age of Steam* series, which appreciated 140% (to $240.00). The 1983 Kaiser *Mother's Day* plate, "Titmice Family" **(22-K4-2.13)**, (which Kaiser sells as "Tender Care" in the U.S.), earned Canadian New Edition of the Year honors for showing the greatest percentage of appreciation in its year of issue—37.5% (to $55.00). "Michele et Sylvie" **(18-D15-8.1)**, the first issue in D'Arceau-Limoges' *Cambier Mother's Day* series, came in second with 11.3% appreciation (to $60.00).

GERMANY. Market analysts noted a definite trend away from traditional blue-and-white plates to newer (and usually European-made) issues in full color. No one artist dominated the market. However, two new series that were in particular demand were Königszelt Bayern's *Sulamith's Love Song* **(22-K46-3)** and D'Arceau-Limoges' *Les Douze Sites Parisiens de Louis Dali* **(18-D15-6)**. On the secondary market, the most-traded issue was "The Tycoon" **(84-R70-3.6)**, the 1982 plate in the Rockwell Society's *Heritage* series.

A poll of German collectors ranked "Bathsheba and Solomon" **(84-K41-6.1)**, first plate in Knowles' *Biblical Mothers* series, and "Adoration of the Magi" **(38-V90-3.1)**, first plate in Knowles' *Ghiberti Doors* collection, their first and second choices, respectively, as the most significant new issues of the year. Although these editions were still trading at issue price at year-end, analysts expect prices to increase significantly once the editions are sold out and plates begin trading on the secondary market.

There are strong indications that the recession is ending in Germany, and the words "made in Germany" are becoming increasingly important to German collectors. The number of German makers producing collector's plates designed specifically for the domestic market increased significantly, and by year-end German makers had announced plans to introduce at least ten new plate series in 1984.

SWITZERLAND. Reflecting strong collector interest, six new plate series were added to the Swiss Bradex: Pemberton & Oakes' *Wonder of Childhood* **(84-P19-1)**, Kaiser's *Classic Fairy Tales* **(22-K4-5)**, Studio Dante di Volteradici's *Ghiberti Doors* **(38-V90-3)**, and Knowles' *Annie* **(84-K41-5)** and *Biblical Mothers* **(84-K41-6)** series, and the Rockwell Society of America's *Rockwell's Light Campaign* **(84-R70-6)**. According to a survey of Swiss collectors, Königszelt Bayern's "The Music" **(22-K46-3.1)**, Knowles' "Bathsheba and Solomon" **(84-K41-6.1)**, and Studio Dante di Volteradici's "Adoration of the Magi" **(38-V90-3.1)** were ranked one-two-three as the most important plates to be introduced during 1983. As in Germany, it was expected that prices would appreciate significantly once these editions sell out. Based on the strength of the Swiss economy (unemployment rate

of 1%, inflation rate of 2%), observers predict a strong year ahead for the collector's plate market.

UNITED KINGDOM. Favorite series and issues in the U.K. during 1983 included the 1980 Heinrich/Villeroy & Boch *Russian Fairy Tales* issue, "The Snow Maiden" **(22-H18-1.1)**, and their 1979 *Flower Fairies* issue, "Lavender Fairy" **(22-H18-2.1)**, which appreciated 33.3% and 21.6% respectively during the year; D'Arceau-Limoges' *Christmas* series **(18-D15-2)**, which appreciated 12.5%; Reco's *McClelland's Mother Goose* series **(84-R60-2)**, which appreciated 5.6%; and the Rockwell Society's *Heritage* series **(84-R70-3)**, which appreciated 5.1% in 1983.

There were, of course, disappointments, particularly in three plates which had been expected to perform well: "Cinderella" **(18-L52-2.1)**, the 1983 plate in Limoges-Turgot's *Quellier's Morals of Perrault* series; "Daddy Warbucks" **(84-K41-5.2)**, the 1983 *Annie* plate from Knowles; and "Lillie Langtry" **(84-P29-5.3)**, the 1983 plate in Pickard's *Oleg Cassini's Most Beautiful Women of All Time* series.

DENMARK. The first Danish Bradex, listing 24 series and 345 issues from seven countries, made its debut on September 1, 1983, when the Bradford Exchange formally announced the opening of the Danish exchange in Copenhagen.

(22-H18-1.1) "The Snow Maiden"
1980 Heinrich/Villeroy & Boch *Russian Fairy Tales*

ARRANGEMENT OF THE LISTINGS

The Bradford Book of Collector's Plates is the official directory of all major issues regularly traded in the market. It is used to locate and identify all plates quickly and accurately. The plates are arranged by:

Country of plate's origin in alphabetical order.
Plate Maker within each country, also in alphabetical order.
Plate Series of each maker in chronological order beginning with the maker's first series.
Individual Plates in each series, also in chronological order beginning with the first plate.

To speed identification, each plate is listed by its Bradex number. *These numbers are in sequence but not necessarily consecutive.* The number on the upper outer corner of each page indicates the first plate listed on that page.

THE BRADEX NUMBER

of a plate is made up of four identifiers.
(The number used as an example here is that of the 1904 Bing & Grøndahl *Christmas* plate)

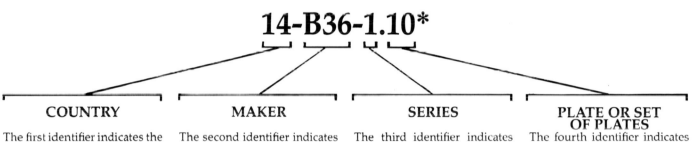

14-B36-1.10*

COUNTRY	MAKER	SERIES	PLATE OR SET OF PLATES
The first identifier indicates the country of origin. The number **14** is for Denmark. A list of countries with their Bradex numbers is in the Table of Contents.	The second identifier indicates the plate maker. The combination **B36** is for Bing & Grøndahl. A list of makers with their Bradex numbers is in the Table of Contents.	The third identifier indicates the maker's series, listed in chronological order. The number **1** is for Bing & Grøndahl's first series, the *Christmas* series. A list of series by type and name with their Bradex numbers is in the Appendixes on page **367**.	The fourth identifier indicates the individual plate (or set of plates) within each series, listed in chronological order. The number **10** is for the tenth plate in the Bing & Grøndahl *Christmas* series, *View of Copenhagen from Frederiksberg Hill*, the 1904 issue. A list of plate titles with their Bradex numbers is in the Appendixes on page **367**.

Bradex numbers are indexed by *Makers and Sponsors, Plate Titles and Series by Type,* and *Plate Artists* in the Indexes. A Glossary of Commonly Used Terms is provided in the Appendixes.

*Plates issued in sets use an additional successive digit to indicate their identification within the set (see ANNA-PERENNA **22-A3-3.1-1**).

LOCATION OF OTHER INFORMATION

Information on history and trademarks is included in each maker's listing; artist, medium, plate diameter, hanging provisions, edition limits, and numbering appear with each series listing; Bradex number, plate title, artist, issue price, and 1983 high, low, and close price information are found below each plate in the series. The listings are complete to 1984 issues, except where the maker did not provide information by press time. Typical edition limits given by makers may be defined as follows:

Edition size limited to 10,000 means the maker established 10,000 plates as the maximum to be produced in the edition, and each plate may or may not be numbered.

Edition size undisclosed, limited by period of issue means the edition was limited to the number of plates produced during an announced time period; each plate may or may not be numbered.

Edition size undisclosed, limited by year of issue means the edition was limited to the number of plates produced during the year of issue; each plate may or may not be numbered.

Founded in 1979, Christian Bell Porcelain Ltd. traces its name to founder Horst S. Muller's great-grandfather, Christian Bell, a prominent figure in the white-ware industry of Siebenbürgen in pre-World War I Austria-Hungary.

The firm's first collector's plate series, *Preserving a Way of Life*, (not U.S. Bradex-listed) began in 1980. Their *Age of Steam* series began in 1981 and celebrates the vital role of the railroads in Canada's national heritage.

Theodore "Ted" Xaras holds a B.F.A. in illustration from Philadelphia College of Art, as well as a M.F.A. in painting from the Tyler School of Art in Philadelphia. His interest in railroads is evidenced throughout his work, which includes a cover for *Time* magazine and various other books and railroad magazines.

CANADA
CHRISTIAN BELL
Mount Forest, Ontario

Age of Steam Series
Artist: Theodore Xaras. Artist's signature appears on front

Hard-paste porcelain

Diameter: 24.1 centimeters (9½ inches)

No hanger

Edition size limited to 15,000

Numbered, without certificate through 1982, with certificate thereafter

8-C30-1.1
1981 *Symphony in Steam*
Prices: Issue $65.00; 1983 High $100.00;
Low $65.00; Close $100.00; Up $35.00

8-C30-1.2
1982 *Brief Encounter*
Prices: Issue $65.00; 1983 High $65.00;
Low $65.00; Close $65.00; No Change

8-C30-1.3
1983 *No Contest*
Prices: Issue $65.00; 1983 High $65.00;
Low $65.00; Close $65.00; No Change

8-C30-1.4
1984 *Timber Country*
Issue price: $65.00

Bing & Grøndahl, Denmark's second oldest existing porcelain maker (after Royal Copenhagen), was established in 1853 by Frederick Vilhelm Grøndahl and Meyer and Jacob Bing. Grøndahl, a young sculptor previously employed by Royal Copenhagen, supplied the artistic talent while the Bing brothers provided financial backing. Although Grøndahl died before the manufactory's third year of operation, his name was retained in honor of his contribution. Bing & Grøndahl has continued under the leadership of the Bing family for five generations.

The world's first collector's plate, "Behind the Frozen Window," was issued by Bing & Grøndahl in 1895. This began its *Christmas* series which has been produced each year without interruption despite wars and economic crises. Plates in this series are now the most widely collected of all plates in the market. In 1969 Bing & Grøndahl issued the first Mother's Day plate, "Dog and Puppies." Their *Moments of Truth* series started in 1984.

Besides limited-edition collector's plates, Bing & Grøndahl makes a variety of porcelain articles, including figurines and tableware. Many of their porcelain works can be found in museums around the world, and they have achieved the distinction of appointment to the royal courts of Denmark, Sweden, and Great Britain. This distinction is symbolized by the crown which is part of their trademark.

The artist for the very first collector's plate was Frans August Hallin, a Swede who moved to Copenhagen in 1885. After Harald Bing named him chief designer in 1895, Hallin created a distinctive item for the maker's Christmas giftware line—"Behind the Frozen Window." Its success assured his niche in history. He also designed the Christmas plates for 1896 and 1897. From 1897 until 1929 he served as manager of Bing & Grøndahl's exhibitions abroad, and in 1924 rose to the position of Assisting Director of the maker's artware line. Hallin retired in 1934 and died in Copenhagen in 1947.

Artist Henry Thelander's association with Bing & Grøndahl is unparalleled on the collector's plate market. The 1984 issue marks his twenty-second consecutive design for the *Christmas* series. He also has designed every Bing & Grøndahl *Mother's Day* issue—sixteen in all. A self-taught artist, Thelander has spent his five-decade-long career living and working in Copenhagen, London, and Stockholm, benefiting from the variety of cultures and artistic influences. Known as the "equivalent of a poet laureate" in the field of Danish visual arts, he has designed government-sponsored postage stamps and posters. His celebrated series of paintings commemorating the kingdom's eight-hundredth anniversary is displayed in the Copenhagen town hall.

Christmas Series

Artist: as indicated

True underglaze-decorated porcelain hand-painted in Copenhagen blue on bas-relief

Diameter: 17.8 centimeters (7 inches)

Pierced foot rim

Edition size undisclosed, limited by year of issue

Not numbered, without certificate; individually initialed on back by each painter

14-B36-1.1
1895 *Behind the Frozen Window*
Artist: Frans August Hallin
Prices: Issue $.50; 1983 High $4100.00
Low $4000.00; Close $4000.00;
Down $100.00

14-B36-1.2
1896 *New Moon over Snow-covered Trees*
Artist: Frans August Hallin
Prices: Issue $.50; 1983 High $2000.00;
Low $1975.00; Close $2000.00; Up $25.00

14-B36-1.3
1897 *Christmas Meal of the Sparrows*
Artist: Frans August Hallin
Prices: Issue $.75; 1983 High $1300.00,
Low $1270.00; Close $1270.00;
Down $30.00

14-B36-1.4
1898 *Christmas Roses and Christmas Star*
Artist: Fanny Garde
Prices: Issue $.75; 1983 High $725.00;
Low $650.00; Close $650.00; Down $75.00

14-B36-1.5
1899 *The Crows Enjoying Christmas*
Artist: Dahl Jensen
Prices: Issue $.75; 1983 High $1440.00;
Low $1320.00; Close $1440.00; Up $120.00

14-B36-1.6
1900 *Church Bells Chiming in Christmas*
Artist: Dahl Jensen
Prices: Issue $.75; 1983 High $780.00;
Low $760.00; Close $780.00; No Change

14-B36-1.7
1901 *The Three Wise Men from the East*
Artist: S. Sabra
Prices: Issue $1.00; 1983 High $425.00;
Low $400.00; Close $400.00; Down $15.00

14-B36-1.8
1902 *Interior of a Gothic Church*
Artist: Dahl Jensen
Prices: Issue $1.00; 1983 High $375.00;
Low $350.00; Close $350.00; Down $25.00

14-B36-1.9
1903 *Happy Expectation of Children*
Artist: Margrethe Hyldahl
Prices: Issue $1.00; 1983 High $275.00;
Low $200.00; Close $200.00; Down $75.00

14-B36-1.10
1904 *View of Copenhagen from Frederiksberg Hill*
Artist: Cathinka Olsen
Prices: Issue $1.00; 1983 High $124.00;
Low $100.00; Close $124.00; Up $4.00

14-B36-1.11
1905 *Anxiety of the Coming Christmas Night*
Artist: Dahl Jensen
Prices: Issue $1.00; 1983 High $130.00;
Low $127.00; Close $130.00; Up $3.00

14-B36-1.12
1906 *Sleighing to Church on Christmas Eve*
Artist: Dahl Jensen
Prices: Issue $1.00; 1983 High $105.00;
Low $99.00; Close $105.00; Up $6.00

14-B36-1.13
1907 *The Little Match Girl*
Artist: E. Plockross
Prices: Issue $1.00; 1983 High $130.00;
Low $120.00; Close $120.00; Down $10.00

14-B36-1.14
1908 *St. Petri Church of Copenhagen*
Artist: Povl Jorgensen
Prices: Issue $1.00; 1983 High $87.00;
Low $75.00; Close $83.00; Down $4.00

14-B36-1.15
1909 *Happiness over the Yule Tree*
Artist: Aarestrup
Prices: Issue $1.50; 1983 High $110.00;
Low $90.00; Close $95.00; Down $15.00

14-B36-1.16
1910 *The Old Organist*
Artist: C. Ersgaard
Prices: Issue $1.50; 1983 High $95.00;
Low $89.00; Close $95.00; Up $6.00

14-B36-1.17
1911 *First It Was Sung by Angels to Shepherds in the Fields*
Artist: H. Moltke
Prices: Issue $1.50; 1983 High $95.00;
Low $85.00; Close $85.00; Down $10.00

14-B36-1.18
1912 *Going to Church on Christmas Eve*
Artist: Einar Hansen
Prices: Issue $1.50; 1983 High $90.00;
Low $90.00; Close $90.00; No Change

14-B36-1.19
1913 *Bringing Home the Yule Tree*
Artist: Th. Larsen
Prices: Issue $1.50; 1983 High $98.00;
Low $90.00; Close $98.00; Up $2.00

14-B36-1.20
1914 *Royal Castle of Amalienborg,
Copenhagen*
Artist: Th. Larsen
Prices: Issue $1.50; 1983 High $79.00;
Low $65.00, Close $75.00; Down $4.00

14-B36-1.21
1915 *Chained Dog Getting Double Meal
on Christmas Eve*
Artist: Dahl Jensen
Prices: Issue $1.50; 1983 High $123.00;
Low $115.00; Close $123.00; Up $3.00

14-B36-1.22
1916 *Christmas Prayer of the Sparrows*
Artist: J. Bloch Jorgensen
Prices: Issue $1.50; 1983 High $95.00;
Low $95.00; Close $95.00; No Change

14-B36-1.23
1917 *Arrival of the Christmas Boat*
Artist: Achton Friis
Prices: Issue $1.50; 1983 High $86.00;
Low $75.00; Close $75.00; Down $11.00

14-B36-1.24
1918 *Fishing Boat Returning Home
for Christmas*
Artist: Achton Friis
Prices: Issue $1.50; 1983 High $88.00;
Low $80.00; Close $85.00; Down $3.00

14-B36-1.25
1919 *Outside the Lighted Window*
Artist: Achton Friis
Prices: Issue $2.00; 1983 High $86.00;
Low $82.00; Close $86.00; Up $4.00

14-B36-1.26
1920 *Hare in the Snow*
Artist: Achton Friis
Prices: Issue $2.00; 1983 High $85.00;
Low $65.00; Close $65.00; Down $20.00

14-B36-1.27
1921 *Pigeons in the Castle Court*
Artist: Achton Friis
Prices: Issue $2.00; 1983 High $70.00;
Low $60.00; Close $60.00; Down $9.00

14-B36-1.28
1922 *Star of Bethlehem*
Artist: Achton Friis
Prices: Issue $2.00; 1983 High $75.00;
Low $60.00; Close $60.00; Down $15.00

14-B36-1.29
1923 *Royal Hunting Castle, the Ermitage*
Artist: Achton Friis
Prices: Issue $2.00; 1983 High $58.00;
Low $50.00; Close $50.00; Down $3.00

14-B36-1.30
1924 *Lighthouse in Danish Waters*
Artist: Achton Friis
Prices: Issue $2.50; 1983 High $74.00;
Low $65.00; Close $65.00; Down $7.00

14-B36-1.31
1925 *The Child's Christmas*
Artist: Achton Friis
Prices: Issue $2.50; 1983 High $87.00;
Low $80.00; Close $80.00; Down $7.00

14-B36-1.32
1926 *Churchgoers on Christmas Day*
Artist: Achton Friis
Prices: Issue $2.50; 1983 High $75.00;
Low $66.00; Close $66.00; Down $9.00

14-B36-1.33
1927 *Skating Couple*
Artist: Achton Friis
Prices: Issue $2.50; 1983 High $112.00;
Low $106.00; Close $112.00; No Change

14-B36-1.34
1928 *Eskimo Looking at Village Church
in Greenland*
Artist: Achton Friis
Prices: Issue $2.50; 1983 High $72.00;
Low $50.00; Close $50.00; Down $20.00

14-B36-1.35
1929 *Fox Outside Farm on Christmas Eve*
Artist: Achton Friis
Prices: Issue $2.50; 1983 High $82.00;
Low $70.00; Close $70.00; Down $8.00

BING & GRØNDAHL
Copenhagen

14-B36-1.36
1930 *Yule Tree in Town Hall Square of Copenhagen*
Artist: H. Flugenring
Prices: Issue $2.50; 1983 High $115.00;
Low $100.00; Close $100.00; Down $15.00

14-B36-1.37
1931 *Arrival of the Christmas Train*
Artist: Achton Friis
Prices: Issue $2.50; 1983 High $89.00;
Low $75.00; Close $75.00; Down $14.00

14-B36-1.38
1932 *Lifeboat at Work*
Artist: H. Flugenring
Prices: Issue $2.50; 1983 High $92.00;
Low $88.00; Close $92.00; Up $4.00

14-B36-1.39
1933 *The Korsor-Nyborg Ferry*
Artist: H. Flugenring
Prices: Issue $3.00; 1983 High $72.00;
Low $56.00; Close $72.00; Up $9.00

14-B36-1.40
1934 *Church Bell in Tower*
Artist: Immanuel Tjerne
Prices: Issue $3.00; 1983 High $73.00;
Low $65.00; Close $73.00; No Change

14-B36-1.41
1935 *Lillebelt Bridge Connecting Funen with Jutland*
Artist: Ove Larsen
Prices: Issue $3.00; 1983 High $68.00;
Low $64.00; Close $64.00; Down $4.00

14-B36-1.42
1936 *Royal Guard Outside Amalienborg Castle in Copenhagen*
Artist: Ove Larsen
Prices: Issue $3.00; 1983 High $78.00;
Low $73.00; Close $78.00; Up $5.00

14-B36-1.43
1937 *Arrival of Christmas Guests*
Artist: Ove Larsen
Prices: Issue $3.00; 1983 High $80.00;
Low $70.00; Close $70.00; Down $10.00

14-B36-1.44
1938 *Lighting the Candles*
Artist: Immanuel Tjerne
Prices: Issue $3.00; 1983 High $124.00;
Low $100.00; Close $100.00; Down $24.00

14-B36-1.45
1939 *Ole Lock-Eye, the Sandman*
Artist: Immanuel Tjerne
Prices: Issue $3.00; 1983 High $165.00;
Low $155.00; Close $165.00; Up $10.00

14-B36-1.46
1940 *Delivering Christmas Letters*
Artist: Ove Larsen
Prices: Issue $4.00; 1983 High $170.00;
Low $156.00; Close $170.00; Up $1.00

14-B36-1.47
1941 *Horses Enjoying Christmas Meal in Stable*
Artist: Ove Larsen
Prices: Issue $4.00; 1983 High $345.00;
Low $315.00; Close $345.00; Up $30.00

14-B36-1.48
1942 *Danish Farm on Christmas Night*
Artist: Ove Larsen
Prices: Issue $4.00; 1983 High $153.00;
Low $138.00; Close $150.00; Up $12.00

14-B36-1.49
1943 *The Ribe Cathedral*
Artist: Ove Larsen
Prices: Issue $5.00; 1983 High $171.00;
Low $150.00; Close $150.00; Down $21.00

14-B36-1.50
1944 *Sorgenfri Castle*
Artist: Ove Larsen
Prices: Issue $5.00; 1983 High $118.00;
Low $108.00; Close $110.00; Up $2.00

14-B36-1.51
1945 *The Old Water Mill*
Artist: Ove Larsen
Prices: Issue $5.00; 1983 High $142.00;
Low $135.00; Close $135.00; Down $7.00

14-B36-1.52
1946 *Commemoration Cross in Honor of Danish Sailors Who Lost Their Lives in World War II*
Artist: Margrethe Hyldahl
Prices: Issue $5.00; 1983 High $90.00;
Low $85.00; Close $90.00; Up $5.00

14-B36-1.53
1947 *Dybbol Mill*
Artist: Margrethe Hyldahl
Prices: Issue $5.00; 1983 High $86.00;
Low $76.00; Close $76.00; Down $10.00

14-B36-1.54
1948 *Watchman, Sculpture of Town Hall,*
Copenhagen
Artist: Margrethe Hyldahl
Prices: Issue $5.50; 1983 High $80.00;
Low $70.00; Close $80.00; Up $5.00

14-B36-1.55
1949 *Landsoldaten, 19th Century*
Danish Soldier
Artist: Margrethe Hyldahl
Prices: Issue $5.50; 1983 High $94.00;
Low $76.00; Close $76.00; Down $18.00

14-B36-1.56
1950 *Kronborg Castle at Elsinore*
Artist: Margrethe Hyldahl
Prices: Issue $5.50; 1983 High $145.00;
Low $145.00; Close $145.00; No Change

14-B36-1.57
1951 *Jens Bang, New Passenger Boat*
Running Between Copenhagen
and Aalborg
Artist: Margrethe Hyldahl
Prices: Issue $6.00; 1983 High $111.00;
Low $102.00; Close $111.00; Up $9.00

14-B36-1.58
1952 *Old Copenhagen Canals at*
Wintertime with Thorvaldsen Museum
in Background
Artist: Borge Pramvig
Prices: Issue $6.00; 1983 High $84.00;
Low $78.00; Close $84.00; Up $6.00

14-B36-1.59
1953 *Royal Boat in Greenland Waters*
Artist: Kjeld Bonfils
Prices: Issue $7.00; 1983 High $100.00;
Low $84.00; Close $100.00; Up $16.00

14-B36-1.60
1954 *Birthplace of Hans Christian*
Andersen, with Snowman
Artist: Borge Pramvig
Prices: Issue $7.50; 1983 High $110.00;
Low $95.00; Close $110.00; Up $15.00

14-B36-1.61
1955 *Kalundborg Church*
Artist: Kjeld Bonfils
Prices: Issue $8.00; 1983 High $112.00;
Low $105.00; Close $105.00; Down $7.00

14-B36-1.62
1956 *Christmas in Copenhagen*
Artist: Kjeld Bonfils
Prices: Issue $8.50; 1983 High $144.00;
Low $138.00; Close $144.00; Up $4.00

14-B36-1.63
1957 *Christmas Candles*
Artist: Kjeld Bonfils
Prices: Issue $9.00; 1983 High $155.00;
Low $140.00; Close $155.00; Up $9.00

14-B36-1.64
1958 *Santa Claus*
Artist: Kjeld Bonfils
Prices: Issue $9.50; 1983 High $110.00;
Low $105.00; Close $105.00; Down $5.00

14-B36-1.65
1959 *Christmas Eve*
Artist: Kjeld Bonfils
Prices: Issue $10.00; 1983 High $130.00;
Low $120.00; Close $120.00; Down $10.00

14-B36-1.66
1960 *Danish Village Church*
Artist: Kjeld Bonfils
Prices: Issue $10.00; 1983 High $184.00;
Low $180.00; Close $184.00; Up $4.00

14-B36-1.67
1961 *Winter Harmony*
Artist: Kjeld Bonfils
Prices: Issue $10.50; 1983 High $111.00;
Low $100.00; Close $104.00; Down $7.00

14-B36-1.68
1962 *Winter Night*
Artist: Kjeld Bonfils
Prices: Issue $11.00; 1983 High $88.00;
Low $80.00; Close $82.00; Down $2.00

14-B36-1.69
1963 *The Christmas Elf*
Artist: Henry Thelander
Prices: Issue $11.00; 1983 High $127.00;
Low $120.00; Close $120.00; Down $2.00

14-B36-1.70
1964 *The Fir Tree and Hare*
Artist: Henry Thelander
Prices: Issue $11.50; 1983 High $56.00;
Low $44.00; Close $44.00; Down $12.00

14-B36-1.71
1965 *Bringing Home the Christmas Tree*
Artist: Henry Thelander
Prices: Issue $12.00; 1983 High $60.00;
Low $55.00; Close $55.00; Down $5.00

14-B36-1.72
1966 Home for Christmas
Artist: Henry Thelander
Prices: Issue $12.00; 1983 High $57.00;
Low $50.00; Close $50.00; Down $7.00

14-B36-1.73
1967 Sharing the Joy of Christmas
Artist: Henry Thelander
Prices: Issue $13.00; 1983 High $45.00;
Low $40.00; Close $45.00; Up $5.00

14-B36-1.74
1968 Christmas in Church
Artist: Henry Thelander
Prices: Issue $14.00; 1983 High $44.00;
Low $44.00; Close $44.00; No Change

14-B36-1.75
1969 Arrival of Christmas Guests
Artist: Henry Thelander
Prices: Issue $14.00; 1983 High $34.00;
Low $30.00; Close $30.00; Down $4.00

14-B36-1.76
1970 Pheasants in the Snow at Christmas
Artist: Henry Thelander
Prices: Issue $14.50; 1983 High $25.00;
Low $20.00; Close $20.00; Down $5.00

14-B36-1.77
1971 Christmas at Home
Artist: Henry Thelander
Prices: Issue $15.00; 1983 High $20.00;
Low $20.00; Close $20.00; No Change

14-B36-1.78
1972 Christmas in Greenland
Artist: Henry Thelander
Prices: Issue $16.50; 1983 High $16.00;
Low $14.00; Close $16.00; Up $2.00

14-B36-1.79
1973 Country Christmas
Artist: Henry Thelander
Prices: Issue $19.50; 1983 High $28.00;
Low $25.00; Close $25.00; Down $3.00

14-B36-1.80
1974 Christmas in the Village
Artist: Henry Thelander
Prices: Issue $22.00; 1983 High $22.00;
Low $16.00; Close $22.00; Up $2.00

14-B36-1.81
1975 *The Old Water Mill*
Artist: Henry Thelander
Prices: Issue $27.50; 1983 High $24.00;
Low $24.00; Close $24.00; No Change

14-B36-1.82
1976 *Christmas Welcome*
Artist: Henry Thelander
Prices: Issue $27.50; 1983 High $30.00;
Low $24.00; Close $24.00; Down $6.00

14-B36-1.83
1977 *Copenhagen Christmas*
Artist: Henry Thelander
Prices: Issue $29.50; 1983 High $26.00;
Low $20.00; Close $26.00; Up $1.00

14-B36-1.84
1978 *A Christmas Tale*
Artist: Henry Thelander
Prices: Issue $32.00; 1983 High $32.00;
Low $25.00; Close $30.00; Down $2.00

14-B36-1.85
1979 *White Christmas*
Artist: Henry Thelander
Prices: Issue $36.50; 1983 High $39.00;
Low $29.00; Close $29.00; Down $10.00

14-B36-1.86
1980 *Christmas in the Woods*
Artist: Henry Thelander
Prices: Issue $42.50; 1983 High $45.00;
Low $40.00; Close $40.00; Down $3.00

14-B36-1.87
1981 *Christmas Peace*
Artist: Henry Thelander
Prices: Issue $49.50; 1983 High $50.00;
Low $42.00; Close $42.00; Down $8.00

14-B36-1.88
1982 *The Christmas Tree*
Artist: Henry Thelander
Prices: Issue $54.50; 1983 High $54.50;
Low $54.50; Close $54.50; No Change

14-B36-1.89
1983 *Christmas in the Old Town*
Artist: Henry Thelander
Prices: Issue $54.50; 1983 High $54.50;
Low $54.50; Close $54.50; No Change

14-B36-1.90
1984 *The Christmas Letter*
Artist: Henry Thelander
Issue price: $54.50

Mother's Day Series

Artist: Henry Thelander

True underglaze-decorated porcelain hand-painted in Copenhagen blue on bas-relief

Diameter: 15.2 centimeters (6 inches)

Pierced foot rim

Edition size undisclosed, limited by year of issue

Not numbered, without certificate; individually initialed on back by each painter

14-B36-3.1
1969 *Dog and Puppies*
Prices: Issue $9.75; 1983 High $445.00;
Low $435.00; Close $445.00; Up $7.00

14-B36-3.2
1970 *Bird and Chicks*
Prices: Issue $10.00; 1983 High $40.00;
Low $40.00; Close $40.00; No Change

14-B36-3.3
1971 *Cat and Kitten*
Prices: Issue $11.00; 1983 High $22.00;
Low $17.00; Close $17.00; Down $5.00

14-B36-3.4
1972 *Mare and Foal*
Prices: Issue $12.00; 1983 High $19.00;
Low $19.00; Close $19.00; No Change

14-B36-3.5
1973 *Duck and Ducklings*
Prices: Issue $13.00; 1983 High $22.00;
Low $22.00; Close $22.00; No Change

14-B36-3.6

DENMARK
BING & GRØNDAHL
Copenhagen

14-B36-3.6
1974 *Bear and Cubs*
Prices: Issue $16.50; 1983 High $24.00;
Low $22.00; Close $22.00; Down $2.00

14-B36-3.7
1975 *Doe and Fawns*
Prices: Issue $19.50; 1983 High $22.00;
Low $22.00; Close $22.00; No Change

14-B36-3.8
1976 *Swan Family*
Prices: Issue $22.50; 1983 High $25.00;
Low $25.00; Close $25.00; No Change

14-B36-3.9
1977 *Squirrel and Young*
Prices: Issue $23.50; 1983 High $26.00;
Low $22.00; Close $25.00; Up $1.00

14-B36-3.10
1978 *Heron*
Prices: Issue $24.50; 1983 High $26.00;
Low $24.00; Close $24.00; Down $2.00

14-B36-3.11
1979 *Fox and Cubs*
Prices: Issue $27.50; 1983 High $29.00;
Low $25.00; Close $28.00; Down $1.00

14-B36-3.12
1980 *Woodpecker and Young*
Prices: Issue $29.50; 1983 High $30.00;
Low $30.00; Close $30.00; No Change

14-B36-3.13
1981 *Hare and Young*
Prices: Issue $36.50; 1983 High $40.00;
Low $40.00; Close $40.00; No Change

14-B36-3.14
1982 *Lioness and Cubs*
Prices: Issue $39.50; 1983 High $45.00;
Low $39.50; Close $45.00; Up $5.50

BING & GRØNDAHL
Copenhagen

14-B36-3.15
1983 *Raccoon and Young*
Prices: Issue $39.50; 1983 High $45.00;
Low $39.50; Close $45.00; Up $5.50

14-B36-3.16
1984 *Stork and Nestlings*
Issue price: $39.50

Moments of Truth Series

Artist: Kurt Ard. Artist's signature appears on front

Porcelain

Diameter: 21.1 centimeters
(8⁵/₁₆ inches)

Pierced foot rim

Edition size undisclosed, limited by period of issue

Numbered with certificate

14-B36-7.1
1984 *Home Is Best*
Issue price: undetermined
at press time

Grande Copenhagen plates are produced at the Eslau porcelain factory near Copenhagen. Grande Copenhagen began its *Christmas* series of plates depicting Danish winter scenes in 1975.

Artists for Grande Copenhagen *Christmas* plates prior to 1980 are undisclosed. The artist for the 1980, 1981, 1982, and 1983 issues is Frode Bahnsen of Aarhus, Jutland, Denmark. Bahnsen studied sculpture, ceramics, and drawing at the Copenhagen Royal Academy of Art, and subsequently worked for the Royal Mint in Copenhagen, rising to the position of head sculptor in 1968. Among the many places where his works have been exhibited are the Charlottenborg Art Exhibition in Copenhagen, F.I.D.M.E. (Federal International Danish Medal Exhibitions), and the National Museum of Copenhagen. In 1978 he was titled knight of Dannebrog by the Queen of Denmark.

GRANDE COPENHAGEN
Copenhagen

Christmas Series

Artist: as indicated

True underglaze-decorated porcelain hand-painted in Copenhagen blue on bas-relief

Diameter: 18.4 centimeters (7¼ inches)

Pierced foot rim

Edition size undisclosed, limited by year of issue

Not numbered, without certificate through 1979; numbered with certificate thereafter

14-G65-1.1
1975 *Alone Together*
Artist: Undisclosed
Prices: Issue $24.50; 1983 High $32.00; Low $30.00; Close $30.00; Down $2.00

14-G65-1.2
1976 *Christmas Wreath*
Artist: Undisclosed
Prices: Issue $24.50; 1983 High $28.00; Low $27.00; Close $27.00; Down $1.00

14-G65-1.3
1977 *Fishwives at Gammelstrand*
Artist: Undisclosed
Prices: Issue $26.50; 1983 High $28.00; Low $28.00; Close $28.00; No Change

14-G65-1.4
1978 *Hans Christian Andersen*
Artist: Undisclosed
Prices: Issue $32.50; 1983 High $33.00; Low $33.00; Close $33.00; No Change

14-G65-1.5
1979 *Pheasants in the Snow*
Artist: Undisclosed
Prices: Issue $34.50; 1983 High $35.00; Low $35.00; Close $35.00; No Change

14-G65-1.6
1980 *The Snow Queen in the Tivoli*
Artist: Frode Bahnsen
Prices: Issue $39.50; 1983 High $45.00; Low $41.00; Close $45.00; Up $4.00

14-G65-1.7
1981 *Little Match Girl in Nyhavn*
Artist: Frode Bahnsen
Prices: Issue $42.50; 1983 High $43.00; Low $42.50; Close $43.00; Up $.50

14-G65-1.8
1982 *The Shepherdess and the Chimney Sweep*
Artist: Frode Bahnsen
Prices: Issue $45.00; 1983 High $52.00; Low $45.00; Close $52.00; Up $7.00

14-G65-1.9
1983 *The Little Mermaid Near Kronborg*
Artist: Frode Bahnsen
Prices: Issue $45.00; 1983 High $45.00;
Low $45.00; Close $45.00; No Change

14-G65-1.9 "Little Mermaid Near Kronborg"
1983 Grande Copenhagen *Christmas*
Detail from true underglaze-decorated porcelain hand-painted in Copenhagen blue on bas-relief.

The Royal Copenhagen Porcelain Manufactory, Denmark's oldest existing porcelain maker, was established by Franz Henrich Muller with the support of Denmark's queen dowager, Juliane Marie, in January 1775. Since the 1760s, members of the Danish royal family had been interested in the white hard-paste porcelain made in China, but it was not until 1772 that Muller, a Danish pharmacist and chemist, was able to duplicate the fine porcelain. In 1779 "The Danish Porcelain Factory," as Royal Copenhagen was then called, came under royal control.

The Danish Court controlled the firm from 1779 to 1867, a period in its history that is still symbolized by the crown in its trademark. The three wavy lines under the crown, part of the factory trademark since 1775, pay tribute to Denmark's tradition as a seafaring nation and represent Denmark's three ancient waterways: the Sound, the Great Belt, and the Little Belt. In 1867 the factory was sold and has continued under private ownership. It is still a supplier to the royal court in Denmark.

The first Royal Copenhagen *Christmas* plate was issued in 1908, and the series has continued every year since then. From the beginning, the motif for each year's *Christmas* plate has been selected from suggestions submitted by employees of the Royal Copenhagen factory. Until 1941, small quantities of plates in the *Christmas* series were created with the word "Christmas" translated into other languages to meet the demand from non-Danish collectors. The Royal Copenhagen *Mother's Day* series, started in 1971, ended in 1982.

In 1982, their *Motherhood* series started with artwork by Sven Vestergaard.

Christian Thomsen, designer of the first Royal Copenhagen collector's plate, served an apprenticeship as a wood-carver before joining the firm in 1898. His porcelain creations won a silver medal in a Milan exhibit in 1908 and a gold medal in a Brussels exhibit in 1910. His work now hangs in the Museum of Decorative Arts in Copenhagen. Arnold Krog innovated the famed cobalt-blue underglaze design technique which has become a tradition in Danish plate making. He worked for Royal Copenhagen from 1884 to 1916, rising to art director and taking the Grand Prix for decorative art in Paris in 1900. Krog's most famous creation is his fountain located in The Hague, The Netherlands. Artist Kai Lange has been with Royal Copenhagen since the age of seventeen and, after more than half a century with the firm, is regarded as one of the most knowledgeable artists working in the porcelain medium today. The first Kai Lange design selected for the annual *Christmas* plate was for the 1940 issue, and since 1963 every plate, except the 1976 issue, has been a Kai Lange creation. Kamma Svenson, artist for the first two *Mother's Day* issues, has gained a world following for her illustrations of Danish literary scenes. Since 1950 she has worked as an illustrator for *Politiken*, one of the two largest Copenhagen newspapers. Her work, "Russian Dolls," was reproduced as a UNICEF Christmas card. The Royal Academy of Fine Arts has sponsored numerous exhibitions of her work. Ib Spang Olsen, artist for the *Mother's Day* series, is a recipient of the Danish Children's Book Prize.

ROYAL COPENHAGEN
Copenhagen

Christmas Series

Artist: as indicated. Artist's name appears on back since 1955

True underglaze-decorated porcelain hand-painted in Copenhagen blue on bas-relief

Diameter: 15.2 centimeters (6 inches) for 1908 to 1910; 17.8 centimeters (7 inches) thereafter

Pierced foot rim

Edition size undisclosed, limited by year of issue

Not numbered, without certificate; individually initialed on back by each painter

14-R59-1.1
1908 *Madonna and Child*
Artist: Christian Thomsen
Prices: Issue $1.00; 1983 High $1830.00;
Low $1750.00; Close $1800.00;
Down $30.00

14-R59-1.2
1909 *Danish Landscape*
Artist: St. Ussing
Prices: Issue $1.00; 1983 High $170.00;
Low $155.00; Close $170.00; Up $10.00

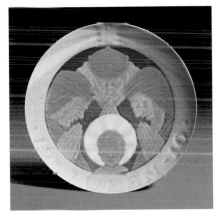

14-R59-1.3
1910 *The Magi*
Artist: Christian Thomsen
Prices: Issue $1.00; 1983 High $145.00;
Low $140.00; Close $140.00; Down $5.00

14-R59-1.4
1911 *Danish Landscape*
Artist: Oluf Jensen
Prices: Issue $1.00; 1983 High $132.00;
Low $120.00; Close $120.00; Down $12.00

14-R59-1.5
1912 *Elderly Couple by Christmas Tree*
Artist: Christian Thomsen
Prices: Issue $1.00; 1983 High $150.00;
Low $138.00; Close $138.00; Down $12.00

14-R59-1.6
1913 *Spire of Frederik's Church,*
Copenhagen
Artist: A. Boesen
Prices: Issue $1.50; 1983 High $145.00;
Low $135.00; Close $135.00; Down $10.00

14-R59-1.7
1914 *Sparrows in Tree at Church of the*
Holy Spirit, Copenhagen
Artist: A. Boesen
Prices: Issue $1.50; 1983 High $127.00;
Low $115.00; Close $115.00; Down $12.00

14-R59-1.8
1915 *Danish Landscape*
Artist: Arnold Krog
Prices: Issue $1.50; 1983 High $206.00;
Low $150.00; Close $206.00; Up $33.00

14-R59-1.9
1916 *Shepherd in the Field on
Christmas Night*
Artist: Ricard Bôcher
Prices: Issue $1.50; 1983 High $95.00;
Low $95.00; Close $95.00; No Change

14-R59-1.10
1917 *Tower of Our Savior's Church,
Copenhagen*
Artist: Oluf Jensen
Prices: Issue $2.00; 1983 High $86.00;
Low $70.00; Close $70.00; Down $16.00

14-R59-1.11
1918 *Sheep and Shepherds*
Artist: Oluf Jensen
Prices: Issue $2.00; 1983 High $96.00;
Low $85.00; Close $85.00; Down $11.00

14-R59-1.12
1919 *In the Park*
Artist: Oluf Jensen
Prices: Issue $2.00; 1983 High $96.00;
Low $83.00; Close $83.00; Down $13.00

14-R59-1.13
1920 *Mary with the Child Jesus*
Artist: G. Rode
Prices: Issue $2.00; 1983 High $84.00;
Low $78.00; Close $80.00; Up $2.00

14-R59-1.14
1921 *Aabenraa Marketplace*
Artist: Oluf Jensen
Prices: Issue $2.00; 1983 High $75.00;
Low $75.00; Close $75.00; No Change

14-R59-1.15
1922 *Three Singing Angels*
Artist: Ellinor Selschau
Prices: Issue $2.00; 1983 High $80.00;
Low $75.00; Close $75.00; Down $3.00

14-R59-1.16
1923 *Danish Landscape*
Artist: Oluf Jensen
Prices: Issue $2.00; 1983 High $92.00;
Low $75.00; Close $75.00; Down $17.00

14-R59-1.17
1924 *Christmas Star over the Sea and
Sailing Ship*
Artist: Benjamin Olsen
Prices: Issue $2.00; 1983 High $110.00;
Low $105.00; Close $105.00; Down $5.00

14-R59-1.18
1925 *Street Scene from Christianshavn,*
Copenhagen
Artist: Oluf Jensen
Prices: Issue $2.00; 1983 High $88.00;
Low $85.00; Close $88.00; Up $3.00

14-R59-1.19
1926 *View of Christianshavn Canal,*
Copenhagen
Artist: Ricard Bocher
Prices: Issue $2.00; 1983 High $88.00;
Low $72.00; Close $72.00; Down $16.00

14-R59-1.20
1927 *Ship's Boy at the Tiller on*
Christmas Night
Artist: Benjamin Olsen
Prices: Issue $2.00; 1983 High $152.00;
Low $152.00; Close $152.00; No Change

14-R59-1.21
1928 *Vicar's Family on Way to Church*
Artist: G. Rode
Prices: Issue $2.00; 1983 High $75.00;
Low $75.00; Close $75.00; No Change

14-R59-1.22
1929 *Grundtvig Church, Copenhagen*
Artist: Oluf Jensen
Prices: Issue $2.00; 1983 High $85.00;
Low $80.00; Close $80.00; Down $5.00

14-R59-1.23
1930 *Fishing Boats on the Way*
to the Harbor
Artist: Benjamin Olsen
Prices: Issue $2.50; 1983 High $90.00;
Low $80.00; Close $80.00; Down $10.00

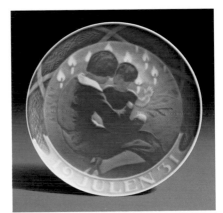

14-R59-1.24
1931 *Mother and Child*
Artist: G. Rode
Prices: Issue $2.50; 1983 High $90.00;
Low $75.00; Close $75.00; Down $15.00

14-R59-1.25
1932 *Frederiksberg Gardens with Statue*
of Frederik VI
Artist: Oluf Jensen
Prices: Issue $2.50; 1983 High $102.00;
Low $80.00; Close $80.00; Down $15.00

14-R59-1.26
1933 *The Great Belt Ferry*
Artist: Benjamin Olsen
Prices: Issue $2.50; 1983 High $125.00;
Low $110.00; Close $110.00; Down $15.00

14-R59-1.27
1934 *The Hermitage Castle*
Artist: Oluf Jensen
Prices: Issue $2.50; 1983 High $122.00;
Low $122.00; Close $122.00; No Change

14-R59-1.28
1935 *Fishing Boat off Kronborg Castle*
Artist: Benjamin Olsen
Prices: Issue $2.50; 1983 High $144.00;
Low $135.00; Close $144.00; Up $9.00

14-R59-1.29
1936 *Roskilde Cathedral*
Artist: Ricard Böcher
Prices: Issue $2.50; 1983 High $140.00;
Low $135.00; Close $135.00; Down $3.00

14-R59-1.30
1937 *Christmas Scene in Main Street,
Copenhagen*
Artist: Nils Thorsson
Prices: Issue $2.50; 1983 High $141.00;
Low $135.00; Close $135.00; Down $6.00

14-R59-1.31
1938 *Round Church in Osterlars on
Bornholm*
Artist: Herne Nielsen
Prices: Issue $3.00; 1983 High $258.00;
Low $200.00; Close $200.00; Down $58.00

14-R59-1.32
1939 *Expeditionary Ship in the Pack-Ice
of Greenland*
Artist: Sv. Nic. Nielsen
Prices: Issue $3.00; 1983 High $215.00;
Low $200.00; Close $200.00; Down $15.00

14-R59-1.33
1940 *The Good Shepherd*
Artist: Kai Lange
Prices: Issue $3.00; 1983 High $368.00;
Low $300.00; Close $300.00; Down $68.00

14-R59-1.34
1941 *Danish Village Church*
Artist: Th. Kjolner
Prices: Issue $3.00; 1983 High $320.00;
Low $312.00; Close $312.00; Down $8.00

14-R59-1.35
1942 *Bell Tower of Old Church in Jutland*
Artist: Nils Thorsson
Prices: Issue $4.00; 1983 High $398.00;
Low $350.00; Close $350.00; Down $48.00

14-R59-1.36
1943 Flight of Holy Family into Egypt
Artist: Nils Thorsson
Prices: Issue $4.00; 1983 High $500.00;
Low $450.00; Close $450.00; Down $50.00

14-R59-1.37
1944 Typical Danish Winter Scene
Artist: Viggo Olsen
Prices: Issue $4.00; 1983 High $170.00;
Low $163.00; Close $170.00; Up $7.00

14-R59-1.38
1945 A Peaceful Motif
Artist: Ricard Böcher
Prices: Issue $4.00; 1983 High $392.00;
Low $360.00; Close $360.00; Down $32.00

14-R59-1.39
1946 Zealand Village Church
Artist: Nils Thorsson
Prices: Issue $4.00; 1983 High $155.00;
Low $155.00; Close $155.00; No Change

14-R59-1.40
1947 The Good Shepherd
Artist: Kai Lange
Prices: Issue $4.50; 1983 High $200.00;
Low $198.00; Close $200.00; Up $2.00

14-R59-1.41
1948 Nodebo Church at Christmastime
Artist: Th. Kjolner
Prices: Issue $4.50; 1983 High $174.00;
Low $170.00; Close $170.00; Down $4.00

14-R59-1.42
1949 Our Lady's Cathedral, Copenhagen
Artist: Hans H. Hansen
Prices: Issue $5.00; 1983 High $180.00;
Low $165.00; Close $165.00; Down $15.00

14-R59-1.43
1950 Boeslunde Church, Zealand
Artist: Viggo Olsen
Prices: Issue $5.00; 1983 High $200.00;
Low $185.00; Close $185.00; Down $15.00

14-R59-1.44
1951 Christmas Angel
Artist: Ricard Böcher
Prices: Issue $5.00; 1983 High $325.00;
Low $300.00; Close $300.00; Down $18.00

14-R59-1.45
1952 *Christmas in the Forest*
Artist: Kai Lange
Prices: Issue $5.00; 1983 High $130.00;
Low $120.00; Close $120.00; Down $10.00

14-R59-1.46
1953 *Frederiksberg Castle*
Artist: Th. Kjolner
Prices: Issue $6.00; 1983 High $120.00;
Low $114.00; Close $120.00; Up $6.00

14-R59-1.47
1954 *Amalienborg Palace, Copenhagen*
Artist: Kai Lange
Prices: Issue $6.00; 1983 High $145.00;
Low $124.00; Close $145.00; Up $5.00

14-R59-1.48
1955 *Fano Girl*
Artist: Kai Lange
Prices: Issue $7.00; 1983 High $210.00;
Low $193.00; Close $193.00; Down $17.00

14-R59-1.49
1956 *Rosenborg Castle, Copenhagen*
Artist: Kai Lange
Prices: Issue $7.00; 1983 High $185.00;
Low $160.00; Close $160.00; Down $25.00

14-R59-1.50
1957 *The Good Shepherd*
Artist: Hans H. Hansen
Prices: Issue $8.00; 1983 High $117.00;
Low $117.00; Close $117.00; No Change

14-R59-1.51
1958 *Sunshine over Greenland*
Artist: Hans H. Hansen
Prices: Issue $9.00; 1983 High $140.00;
Low $135.00; Close $135.00; Down $5.00

14-R59-1.52
1959 *Christmas Night*
Artist: Hans H. Hansen
Prices: Issue $9.00; 1983 High $145.00;
Low $120.00; Close $120.00; Down $25.00

14-R59-1.53
1960 *The Stag*
Artist: Hans H. Hansen
Prices: Issue $10.00; 1983 High $185.00;
Low $155.00; Close $155.00; Down $27.00

14-R59-1.54
1961 *Training Ship Danmark*
Artist: Kai Lange
Prices: Issue $10.00; 1983 High $186.00;
Low $150.00; Close $152.00; Down $28.00

14-R59-1.55
1962 *The Little Mermaid at Wintertime*
Artist: Undisclosed
Prices: Issue $11.00; 1983 High $217.00;
Low $190.00; Close $200.00; Down $13.00

14-R59-1.56
1963 *Hojsager Mill*
Artist: Kai Lange
Prices: Issue $11.00; 1983 High $98.00;
Low $85.00; Close $85.00; Down $13.00

14-R59-1.57
1964 *Fetching the Christmas Tree*
Artist: Kai Lange
Prices: Issue $11.00; 1983 High $78.00;
Low $75.00; Close $75.00; Down $1.00

14-R59-1.58
1965 *Little Skaters*
Artist: Kai Lange
Prices: Issue $12.00; 1983 High $70.00;
Low $60.00; Close $60.00; Down $10.00

14-R59-1.59
1966 *Blackbird at Christmastime*
Artist: Kai Lange
Prices: Issue $12.00; 1983 High $52.00;
Low $48.00; Close $52.00; Up $1.00

14-R59-1.60
1967 *The Royal Oak*
Artist: Kai Lange
Prices: Issue $13.00; 1983 High $45.00;
Low $40.00; Close $45.00; Up $5.00

14-R59-1.61
1968 *The Last Umiak*
Artist: Kai Lange
Prices: Issue $13.00; 1983 High $36.00;
Low $33.00; Close $36.00; Up $3.00

14-R59-1.62
1969 *The Old Farmyard*
Artist: Kai Lange
Prices: Issue $14.00; 1983 High $36.00;
Low $34.00; Close $34.00; Down $2.00

14-R59-1.63
1970 Christmas Rose and Cat
Artist: Kai Lange
Prices: Issue $14.00; 1983 High $40.00;
Low $33.00; Close $40.00; Up $7.00

14-R59-1.64
1971 Hare in Winter
Artist: Kai Lange
Prices: Issue $15.00; 1983 High $27.00;
Low $23.00; Close $27.00; Up $4.00

14-R59-1.65
1972 In the Desert
Artist: Kai Lange
Prices: Issue $16.00; 1983 High $24.00;
Low $20.00; Close $20.00; Down $3.00

14-R59-1.66
1973 Train Homeward Bound for Christmas
Artist: Kai Lange
Prices: Issue $22.00; 1983 High $29.00;
Low $25.00; Close $27.00; No Change

14-R59-1.67
1974 Winter Twilight
Artist: Kai Lange
Prices: Issue $22.00; 1983 High $25.00;
Low $22.00; Close $25.00; Up $3.00

14-R59-1.68
1975 Queen's Palace
Artist: Kai Lange
Prices: Issue $27.50; 1983 High $23.00;
Low $20.00; Close $23.00; Up $3.00

14-R59-1.69
1976 Danish Watermill
Artist: Sven Vestergaard
Prices: Issue $27.50; 1983 High $45.00;
Low $25.00; Close $30.00; Down $15.00

14-R59-1.70
1977 Immervad Bridge
Artist: Kai Lange
Prices: Issue $32.00; 1983 High $30.00;
Low $28.00; Close $30.00; Up $2.00

14-R59-1.71
1978 Greenland Scenery
Artist: Kai Lange
Prices: Issue $35.00; 1983 High $36.00;
Low $33.00; Close $36.00; Up $2.00

14-R59-1.72
1979 *Choosing the Christmas Tree*
Artist: Kai Lange
Prices: Issue $42.50; 1983 High $60.00;
Low $45.00; Close $60.00; Up $15.00

14-R59-1.73
1980 *Bringing Home the Christmas Tree*
Artist: Kai Lange
Prices: Issue $49.50; 1983 High $53.00;
Low $45.00; Close $45.00; Down $8.00

14-R59-1.74
1981 *Admiring the Christmas Tree*
Artist: Kai Lange
Prices: Issue $52.50; 1983 High $53.00;
Low $50.00; Close $50.00; Down $2.50

14-R59-1.75
1982 *Waiting for Christmas*
Artist: Kai Lange
Prices: Issue $54.50; 1983 High $63.00;
Low $54.50; Close $63.00; Up $8.50

14-R59-1.76
1983 *Merry Christmas*
Artist: Kai Lange
Prices: Issue $54.50; 1983 High $54.50;
Low $54.50; Close $54.50; No Change

14-R59-1.77
1984 *Jingle Bells*
Artist: Kai Lange
Issue price: $54.50

Mother's Day Series

Artist: as indicated

True underglaze-decorated
porcelain hand-painted in
Copenhagen blue on bas-relief

Diameter: 15.9 centimeters
(6¼ inches)

Pierced foot rim

Edition size undisclosed, limited
by year of issue

Not numbered, without certificate;
individually initialed on back by
each painter

14-R59-2.1
1971 *American Mother*
Artist: Kamma Svensson
Prices: Issue $12.50; 1983 High $15.00;
Low $13.00; Close $13.00; Down $2.00

14-R59-2.2
1972 *Oriental Mother*
Artist: Kamma Svensson
Prices: Issue $14.00; 1983 High $9.00;
Low $8.00; Close $8.00; No Change

14-R59-2.3
1973 *Danish Mother*
Artist: Arne Ungermann
Prices: Issue $16.00; 1983 High $17.00;
Low $12.00; Close $12.00; Down $5.00

14-R59-2.4
1974 *Greenland Mother*
Artist: Arne Ungermann
Prices: Issue $16.50; 1983 High $18.00;
Low $15.00; Close $15.00; Down $3.00

14-R59-2.5
1975 *Bird in Nest*
Artist: Arne Ungermann
Prices: Issue $20.00; 1983 High $19.00;
Low $17.00; Close $19.00; No Change

14-R59-2.6
1976 *Mermaids*
Artist: Arne Ungermann
Prices: Issue $20.00; 1983 High $20.00;
Low $16.00; Close $20.00; Up $1.00

14-R59-2.7
1977 *The Twins*
Artist: Arne Ungermann
Prices: Issue $24.00; 1983 High $26.00;
Low $20.00; Close $20.00; Down $2.00

14-R59-2.8
1978 *Mother and Child*
Artist: Ib Spang Olsen
Prices: Issue $26.00; 1983 High $25.00;
Low $24.00; Close $25.00; Up $1.00

14-R59-2.9
1979 *A Loving Mother*
Artist: Ib Spang Olsen
Prices: Issue $29.50; 1983 High $28.00;
Low $25.00; Close $25.00; Down $3.00

14-R59-2.10
1980 *An Outing with Mother*
Artist: Ib Spang Olsen
Prices: Issue $37.50; 1983 High $35.00;
Low $30.00; Close $30.00; Down $5.00

14-R59-2.11
1981 *Reunion*
Artist: Ib Spang Olsen
Prices: Issue $39.00; 1983 High $35.00;
Low $35.00; Close $35.00; No Change

DENMARK
ROYAL COPENHAGEN
Copenhagen

14-R59-2.12
1982 *The Children's Hour*
Artist: Ib Spang Olsen
Prices: Issue $39.50; 1983 High $45.00;
Low $39.50; Close $45.00; Up $5.50
Series Closed

Motherhood Series

Artist: Sven Vestergaard

True underglaze-decorated
porcelain hand-painted in
Copenhagen blue on bas-relief

Diameter: 15.2 centimeters
(6 inches)

Pierced foot rim

Edition size undisclosed, limited
by year of issue

Not numbered, without certificate

14-R59-4.1
1982 *Mother Robin with Babies*
Issue price: $29.50

14-R59-4.2
1983 *Mother Cat and Kitten*
Issue price: $29.50

14-R59-4.3
1984 *Mare with Foal*
Issue price: $29.50

ARABIA
FINLAND

In 1873 Arabia was founded as a subsidiary of the Swedish firm Rörstrand (see Sweden, RÖR-STRAND). The factory was located on the outskirts of Helsinki, a site chosen in hopes of supplying the growing markets for ceramics in Finland and the Russian Empire. Early products included dinner services, pitchers, and mugs, almost all based on Rörstrand designs.

In 1884 Arabia was reorganized as a Finnish company, Arabia Aktiefabrik, and developed its own designs from that time on. The company won a gold medal at the Paris World Exhibition in 1900, and is the only pottery producing both household and art ceramics in Finland today.

To celebrate the one-hundredth anniversary of the firm in 1973, Arabia produced a limited-edition anniversary plate. Its success, in turn, led to the introduction in 1976 of an annual limited-edition series based on the Finnish national epic, the *Kalevala*.

Born in Hollola, Finland, Raija Uosikkinen is widely recognized as a master ceramicist. She studied at the Institute of Industrial Arts in Helsinki. In 1947 she joined the Arabia design department, and in 1952 she received a grant scholarship from the Arabia-Decora factory to study in Germany. She has taken subsequent study trips to Australia, England, Turkey, and Indonesia. A 1954 Helsinki exhibit was exclusively devoted to her creations. Her work, a distinctive contemporary folk art style, has also been exhibited at Brussels (1958), Milan (1960), and Sacramento (1961), where she won the prestigious Gold Medal.

ARABIA
Helsinki

Kalevala Series
Artist: Raija Uosikkinen
Stoneware
Diameter: 19 centimeters square
(7½ inches square)
Pierced foot rim
Edition size undisclosed
Not numbered, without certificate

16-A69-1.1
1976 *Vainamoinen's Sowing*
Prices: Issue $30.00; 1983 High $250.00;
Low $175.00; Close $250.00; Up $75.00

16-A69-1.2
1977 *Aino's Fate*
Prices: Issue $30.00; 1983 High $54.00;
Low $50.00; Close $50.00; Down $1.00

16-A69-1.3
1978 *Lemminkainen's Chase*
Prices: Issue $39.00; 1983 High $53.00;
Low $50.00; Close $50.00; Down $1.00

16-A69-1.4
1979 *Kullervo's Revenge*
Prices: Issue $39.50; 1983 High $40.00;
Low $39.50; Close $40.00; Up $.50

16-A69-1.5
1980 *Vainamoinen's Rescue*
Prices: Issue $45.00; 1983 High $70.00;
Low $65.00; Close $70.00; Up $2.00

16-A69-1.6
1981 *Vainamoinen's Magic*
Prices: Issue $49.50; 1983 High $61.00;
Low $57.00; Close $57.00; Down $4.00

16-A69-1.7
1982 *Joukahainen Shoots the Horse*
Prices: Issue $55.50; 1983 High $60.00;
Low $60.00; Close $55.50; Up $4.50

Maker had
no photo at
press time

16-A69-1.8
1983 *Lemminkainen's Escape*
Prices: Issue $60.00; 1983 High $60.00;
Low $60.00; Close $60.00; No Change

Porcelaine Georges Boyer of Limoges, France was founded in 1933 by Georges Boyer; his is the second generation of Boyers to work in porcelain. His father, Jean Boyer, originally worked for the house of Haviland before forming his own company, in which Georges worked as technical director. Today, the firm is managed by Gerard Boyer, son of Georges, thus continuing the family tradition.

Porcelaine Georges Boyer is the third-ranking company in the renowned porcelain center of Limoges, producing porcelain dinnerware as well as limited-edition collector's plates. The firm numbers among its efforts the production of extremely small limited-edition plate series based upon the works of Pierre Auguste Renoir and Maurice Utrillo. In 1982, Porcelaine Georges Boyer introduced its first collector's series for the United States market under its own name—the *Alice in Wonderland* series by British artist Sandy Nightingale.

Nightingale is known in Britain as a book illustrator for a number of well-established British publishing houses, including Pan, MacMillan and Hamlyn, and has exhibited her works in numerous British galleries. Her work on the *Alice in Wonderland* series allowed her to incorporate scenes from her parents' garden, and memories of her own childhood, in her first limited-edition work.

FRANCE
PORCELAINE GEORGES BOYER
Limoges

Alice in Wonderland Series
Artist: Sandy Nightingale

Overglaze-decorated porcelain
banded in 24k gold

Diameter: 21.6 centimeters
(8½ inches)

Attached back hanger

Edition size undisclosed, limited
by announced period of issue

Numbered with certificate

18-B61-1.1
1982 *Alice and the White Rabbit*
Prices: Issue $36.96; 1983 High $75.00;
Low $36.96; Close $75.00; Up $38.04

18-B61-1.2
1983 *Alice and the Caterpillar*
Prices: Issue $36.96; 1983 High $36.96;
Low $36.96; Close $36.96; No Change

18-B61-1.3
1983 *Alice and the Cheshire Cat*
Prices: Issue $36.96; 1983 High $36.96;
Low $36.96; Close $36.96; No Change

18-B61-1.4
1983 *Alice and the Mad Hatter*
Prices: Issue $36.96; 1983 High $36.96;
Low $36.96; Close $36.96; No Change

18-B61-1.5
1984 *Painting the Roses*
Issue price: $36.96

18-B61-1.6
1984 *Alice and the Croquet Game*
Issue price: $36.96

The hallmark of Henri d'Arceau L. & Fils is one of the most prestigious in the famous porcelain center of Limoges. The firm, which claims to adhere to the original "Grellet Standard" of 1768 for handcraftsmanship, is today directed by Gerard Boyer, a descendant of the founder.

The firm was commissioned by L' Association l'Esprit de Lafayette to produce the six-plate bicentennial series *Collection Le Patrimoine de Lafayette (Lafayette Legacy Collection)*, 1973-1975, which chronicles the role of the Marquis de Lafayette in America's War of Independence. The D'Arceau-Limoges *Christmas* series, *Noël Vitrail*, begun in 1975, was inspired by the stained-glass windows of the cathedral at Chartres. It ended in 1982. *Les Femmes du Siècle (Women of the Century)*, a twelve-plate series commissioned by the Chambre Syndicale de la Couture Parisienne, began in 1976 and ended in 1979. This series, recognized by the United Nations, depicts Western women's fashions from 1865 to 1965. Introduced in 1978 was *Les Jeunes Filles des Saisons (Girls of the Seasons)*, which ended in 1981, and in 1979 *Les Très Riches Heures (The Very Rich Hours)*, which adapts its artwork from an early fifteenth-century illuminated manuscript. In 1980, the firm, in collaboration with La Société de Paris et Son Histoire, issued Louis Dali's *Les Douze Sites Parisiens de Louis Dali (The Twelve Parisian Places of Louis Dali)* series, a collection of the artist's unique impressions of the famous city. In 1984 *Joséphine et Napoléon* was introduced with artwork by Claude Boulmé. Their *Cambier Mother's Day* series began in 1983 with artwork by French classicist Guy Cambier.

Among the artists who have designed works for D'Arceau-Limoges are the late André Restieau, world authority on the techniques of re-creating medieval stained glass coloration in porcelain; neo-Classicist Guy Cambier, winner of numerous awards from the Prix de la Jeune Peinture Méditerranée in 1955 to the Médaille d'or au Prix Leonardo da Vinci in 1972; and the late François Ganeau, resident consultant to the Theatre Comedie Française. In 1980 the noted Impressionist Louis Dali, a Fellow of the Salon de l'Ecole Française and the Salon des Independants, joined D'Arceau-Limoges artists with his *Les Douze Sites Parisiens de Louis Dali* series.

Collection Le Patrimoine de Lafayette

(The Lafayette Legacy Collection)

Artist: André Restieau. Artist's signature appears on front, initials on back

Overglaze-decorated porcelain

Diameter: 21.6 centimeters
(8½ inches)

Attached back hanger

Edition size undisclosed, limited by announced period of issue

Numbered with certificate

18-D15-1.1
1973 *The Secret Contract*
Prices: Issue $14.82; 1983 High $45.00;
Low $36.00; Close $36.00; Down $9.00

18-D15-1.2
1973 *The Landing at North Island*
Prices: Issue $19.82; 1983 High $53.00;
Low $51.00; Close $51.00; Down $2.00

18-D15-1.3
1974 *The Meeting at City Tavern*
Prices: Issue $19.82; 1983 High $44.00;
Low $42.00; Close $42.00; Down $2.00

18-D15-1.4
1974 *The Battle of Brandywine*
Prices: Issue $19.82; 1983 High $55.00;
Low $48.00; Close $48.00; Down $7.00

18-D15-1.5
1975 *The Messages to Franklin*
Prices: Issue $19.82; 1983 High $65.00;
Low $54.00; Close $54.00; Down $11.00

18-D15-1.6
1975 *The Siege at Yorktown*
Prices: Issue $19.82; 1983 High $48.00;
Low $47.00; Close $47.00; Down $1.00
Series Closed

Noël Vitrail
(Stained-glass Christmas)

Artist: André Restieau. Artist's signature appears on front, initials on back

Overglaze-decorated porcelain

Diameter: 21.6 centimeters (8½ inches)

Attached back hanger

Edition size undisclosed, limited by announced period of issue

Numbered with certificate

18-D15-2.1
1975 *La Fuite en Egypte*
(Flight into Egypt)
Prices: Issue $24.32; 1983 High $101.00;
Low $83.00; Close $95.00; Down $6.00

18-D15-2.2
1976 *Dans la Crêche*
(In the Manger)
Prices: Issue $24.32; 1983 High $39.00;
Low $34.00; Close $39.00; Up $5.00

18-D15-2.3
1977 *Le Refus d'Hèbergement*
(No Room at the Inn)
Prices: Issue $24.32; 1983 High $41.00;
Low $35.00; Close $40.00; Down $1.00

18-D15-2.4
1978 *La Purification*
(The Purification)
Prices: Issue $26.81; 1983 High $35.00;
Low $28.00; Close $35.00; Up $7.00

18-D15-2.5
1979 *L'Adoration des Rois*
(The Adoration of Kings)
Prices: Issue $26.81; 1983 High $36.00;
Low $30.00; Close $36.00; Up $6.00

18-D15-2.6
1980 *Joyeuse Nouvelle*
(Tidings of Great Joy)
Prices: Issue $28.74; 1983 High $42.00;
Low $29.00; Close $42.00; Up $13.00

18-D15-2.7
1981 *Guides par l'Etoile*
(Guided by the Star)
Prices: Issue $28.74; 1983 High $60.00;
Low $39.00; Close $60.00; Up $21.00

18-D15-2.8
1982 *L'Annunciation*
(The Annunciation)
Prices: Issue $30.74; 1983 High $55.00;
Low $30.74; Close $55.00; Up $24.26
Series Closed

FRANCE
D'ARCEAU-LIMOGES
Limoges

Les Femmes du Siècle
(The Women of the Century)

Artist: François Ganeau. Artist's signature appears on front, initials on back

Overglaze-decorated porcelain

Diameter: 21.6 centimeters (8½ inches)

Attached back hanger

Edition size undisclosed, limited by announced period of issue

Numbered with certificate

18-D15-3.1
1976 *Scarlet en Crinoline*
Prices: Issue $17.67; 1983 High $39.00;
Low $25.00; Close $25.00; Down $14.00

18-D15-3.2
1976 *Sarah en Tournure*
Prices: Issue $22.74; 1983 High $32.00;
Low $30.00; Close $30.00; Down $2.00

18-D15-3.3
1976 *Colette, la Femme Sportive*
Prices: Issue $22.74; 1983 High $29.00;
Low $25.00; Close $25.00; Down $4.00

18-D15-3.4
1976 *Léa, la Femme Fleur*
Prices: Issue $22.74; 1983 High $28.00;
Low $26.00; Close $26.00; Down $2.00

18-D15-3.5
1977 *Albertine, la Femme Liane*
Prices: Issue $22.74; 1983 High $28.00;
Low $26.00; Close $26.00; Down $2.00

18-D15-3.6
1977 *Edith, la Femme Pratique*
Prices: Issue $22.74; 1983 High $28.00;
Low $27.00; Close $27.00; Down $1.00

18-D15-3.7
1977 *Daisy, la Garçonne*
Prices: Issue $22.74; 1983 High $28.00;
Low $27.00; Close $27.00; Down $1.00

18-D15-3.8
1977 *Marlène, la Vamp*
Prices: Issue $22.74; 1983 High $28.00;
Low $25.00; Close $25.00; Down $3.00

18-D15-3.9
1978 Hélène, l'Intrépide
Prices: Issue $22.74; 1983 High $28.00;
Low $28.00; Close $28.00; No Change

18-D15-3.10
1978 Sophie, la Féminité Retrouvée
Prices: Issue $22.74; 1983 High $30.00;
Low $28.00; Close $30.00; Up $2.00

18-D15-3.11
1979 Françoise en Pantalon
Prices: Issue $22.74; 1983 High $30.00;
Low $28.00; Close $30.00; Up $2.00

18-D15-3.12
1979 Brigitte en Mini-jupe
Prices: Issue $22.74; 1983 High $30.00;
Low $28.00; Close $30.00; Up $2.00
Series Closed

Les Juenes Filles des Saisons
(The Girls of the Seasons)

Artist: Guy Cambier. Artist's signature appears on front

Overglaze-decorated porcelain banded in gold

Diameter: 24.8 centimeters (9¾ inches)

No hanger

Edition size limited to 15,000

Numbered with certificate

18-D15-4.1
1978 La Jeune Fille d'Eté
(Summer Girl)
Prices: Issue $105.00; 1983 High $125.00;
Low $120.00; Close $120.00; Down $5.00

18-D15-4.2
1979 La Jeune Fille d'Hiver
(Winter Girl)
Prices: Issue $105.00; 1983 High $110.00;
Low $108.00; Close $110.00; Up $2.00

FRANCE
D'ARCEAU-LIMOGES
Limoges

18-D15-4.3
1980 *La Jeune Fille du Printemps*
(Spring Girl)
Prices: Issue $105.00; 1983 High $110.00;
Low $109.00; Close $110.00; Up $1.00

18-D15-4.4
1981 *La Jeune Fille d'Automne*
(Autumn Girl)
Prices: Issue $105.00; 1983 High $160.00;
Low $145.00; Close $145.00; No Change
Series Closed

Les Très Riches Heures
(The Very Rich Hours)

Artist: Jean Dutheil. Artist's
signature appears on back

Overglaze-decorated porcelain

Diameter: 24.8 centimeters
(9¾ inches)

Attached back hanger

Edition size unannounced

Numbered with certificate

18-D15-5.1
1979 *Janvier (January)*
Prices: Issue $75.48; 1983 High $76.00;
Low $75.48; Close $76.00, Up $.52

18-D15-5.2
1980 *Avril (April)*
Prices: Issue $75.48; 1983 High $80.00;
Low $78.00; Close $80.00; Up $2.00

18-D15-5.3
1981 *Août (August)*
Prices: Issue $75.48; 1983 High $90.00;
Low $75.48; Close $90.00; Up $14.52

18-D15-5.4
1982 *Juin (June)*
Prices: Issue $75.48; 1983 High $75.48;
Low $75.48; Close $75.48; No Change

18-D15-5.5
1983 *Mai (May)*
Issue price: $75.48

Les Douze Sites Parisiens de Louis Dali *(The Twelve Parisian Places of Louis Dali)*

Artist: Louis Dali. Artist's signature appears on front

Overglaze-decorated porcelain

Diameter: 21.6 centimeters (8½ inches)

Attached back hanger

Edition size undisclosed, limited by announced period of issue

Numbered with certificate

18-D15-6.1
1980 *L'Arc de Triomphe (The Arch of Triumph)*
Prices: Issue $22.94; 1983 High $24.00; Low $24.00; Close $24.00; No Change

18-D15-6.2
1981 *La Cathedrale Notre-Dame (Notre Dame Cathedral)*
Prices: Issue $24.94; 1983 High $25.00; Low $24.94; Close $25.00; Up $.06

18-D15-6.3
1981 *La Place de la Concorde (Concord Place)*
Prices: Issue $24.94; 1983 High $25.00; Low $24.94; Close $25.00; Up $.06

18-D15-6.4
1981 *L'Église Saint-Pierre et le Sacré-Coeur de Montmartre (St. Peter's Church and Sacred Heart Basilica)*
Prices: Issue $26.83; 1983 High $27.00; Low $26.83; Close $27.00; Up $.17

18-D15-6.5
1982 *Le Marché aux Fleurs et la Conciergerie (The Flower Market and the Conciergerie)*
Prices: Issue $26.83; 1983 High $27.00; Low $26.83; Close $27.00; Up $.17

18-D15-6.6
1982 *La Pointe du Vert Galant et le Pont Neuf (Vert Galant Point and the New Bridge)*
Prices: Issue $26.83; 1983 High $30.00; Low $26.83; Close $30.00; Up $3.17

18-D15-6.7
1983 *Le Jardin des Tuileries (The Garden of the Tuileries)*
Prices: Issue $26.83; 1983 High $26.83; Low $26.83; Close $26.83; No Change

18-D15-6.8
1983 *Le Moulin Rouge (The Moulin Rouge)*
Prices: Issue $26.83; 1983 High $26.83; Low $26.83; Close $26.83; No Change

FRANCE
D'ARCEAU-LIMOGES
Limoges

18-D15-6.9
1983 *Le Pont Alexandre III*
(The Alexander III Bridge)
Prices: Issue $26.83; 1983 High $26.83;
Low $26.83; Close $26.83; No Change

18-D15-6.10
1983 *L'Opéra (The Opera)*
Prices: Issue $26.83; 1983 High $26.83;
Low $26.83; Close $26.83; No Change

18-D15-6.11
1983 *La Tour Eiffel*
(The Eiffel Tower)
Prices: Issue $26.83; 1983 High $26.83;
Low $26.83; Close $26.83; No Change

18-D15-6.12
1983 *L'Hôtel de Ville de Paris*
(The Hotel de Ville de Paris)
Prices: Issue $26.83; 1983 High $26.83;
Low $26.83; Close $26.83; No Change
Series Closed

Joséphine et Napoléon
(Josephine and Napoleon)

Artist: Claude Boulmé. Artist's
signature appears on front

Overglaze-decorated porcelain

Diameter: 21.6 centimeters
(8½ inches)

Edition size undisclosed, limited
by announced period of issue

Numbered with certificate

18-D15-7.1
1984 *L'Imperatrice Josephine*
(The Empress Josephine)
Issue Price: $29.32

18-D15-7.2
1984 *Bonaparte Traversant les Alpes*
(Bonaparte Crossing the Alps)
Issue price: $29.32

18-D15-8.1

Cambier Mother's Day Series

Artist: Guy Cambier. Artist's signature appears on front

Overglaze-decorated porcelain

Diameter: 21.6 centimeters (8½ inches)

No hanger

Edition size undisclosed, limited by year of issue

Numbered with certificate

18-D15-8.1
1983 *Michèle et Sylvie*
Prices: Issue $32.84; 1983 High $60.00;
Low $32.84; Close $60.00; Up $27.16

18-D15-8.2
1984 *Marie et Jacqueline*
Issue price: $32.84

18-D15-2.1 *"La Fuite en Egypte"*
(Flight into Egypt)
1975 D'Arceau-Limoges *Noël Vitrail*
Inspired by the stained-glass windows of
the cathedral at Chartres.

In 1839 David Haviland of New York City became the first American importer of Limoges porcelain made from white kaolin clay. When, in 1842, he realized that French factories would not adjust methods to meet the tastes of his American market, Haviland established his own pottery in Limoges.

In 1892 his son, Theodore, left the firm but remained in Limoges to set up Theodore Haviland & Company for production of porcelain dinnerware and decorative pieces. In the 1930s, Theodore Haviland & Company opened an American Haviland factory to produce tableware; the firm also bought the original Haviland & Company established by David Haviland.

All Haviland collector's plates are produced in Limoges, France. *The Twelve Days of Christmas* series, begun in 1970, is based on the carol of the same title. 1979 marked the beginning of the *Mille et Une Nuits* series based on the literary classic *One Thousand One Arabian Nights*.

Adept in a variety of styles, French painter Remy Hétreau is the principal artist for Haviland collector's plates, with two distinctively different series to his credit—from historical chronicle to delightful yuletide fantasy. Noted watercolorist Liliane Tellier, creator of the *Mille et Une Nuits* series, has an extensive following among connoisseurs of the medium. A native Parisienne, she studied watercolor and gouache at L'Ecole Camondo in Paris and refined her techniques in Sweden. Later she worked for the International Society for Education through Art as a consultant to UNESCO.

FRANCE
HAVILAND
Limoges

The Twelve Days of Christmas Series

Artist: Remy Hétreau. Artist's signature appears on back

Overglaze-decorated porcelain

Diameter: 21.3 centimeters (8³/₈ inches)

No hanger

Edition size limited to announced quantity of 30,000

Not numbered, without certificate

18-H6-1.1
1970 *A Partridge in a Pear Tree*
Prices: Issue $25.00; 1983 High $210.00; Low $160.00; Close $160.00; Down $50.00

18-H6-1.2
1971 *Two Turtle Doves*
Prices: Issue $25.00; 1983 High $57.00; Low $53.00; Close $53.00; Down $4.00

18-H6-1.3
1972 *Three French Hens*
Prices: Issue $27.50; 1983 High $22.00; Low $20.00; Close $20.00; Down $2.00

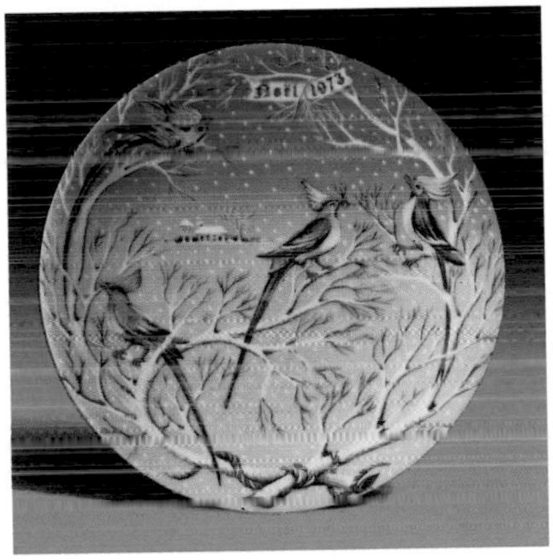

18-H6-1.4
1973 *Four Colly Birds*
Prices: Issue $28.50; 1983 High $34.00; Low $22.00; Close $22.00; Down $12.00

18-H6-1.5
1974 *Five Golden Rings*
Prices: Issue $30.00; 1983 High $28.00; Low $28.00; Close $28.00; No Change

18-H6-1.6
1975 *Six Geese A'Laying*
Prices: Issue $32.50; 1983 High $29.00; Low $25.00; Close $25.00; Down $3.00

18-H6-1.7
1976 *Seven Swans A'Swimming*
Prices: Issue $38.00; 1983 High $38.00; Low $35.00; Close $36.00; Down $1.00

18-H6-1.8
1977 *Eight Maids A'Milking*
Prices: Issue $40.00; 1983 High $52.00; Low $40.00; Close $40.00; Down $12.00

18-H6-1.9
1978 *Nine Ladies Dancing*
Prices: Issue $45.00; 1983 High $34.00;
Low $29.00; Close $34.00; Up $5.00

18-H6-1.10
1979 *Ten Lords A'Leaping*
Prices: Issue $50.00; 1983 High $56.00;
Low $45.00; Close $45.00; Down $10.00

18-H6-1.11
1980 *Eleven Pipers Piping*
Prices: Issue $55.00; 1983 High $52.00;
Low $52.00; Close $52.00; No Change

18-H6-1.12
1981 *Twelve Drummers Drumming*
Prices: Issue $60.00; 1983 High $60.00;
Low $56.00; Close $56.00; Down $4.00
Series Closed

Mille et Une Nuits
(1001 Arabian Nights)

Artist: Liliane Tellier. Artist's
signature appears on front

Porcelain banded in gold

Diameter: 24.1 centimeters
(9½ inches)

No hanger

Edition size undisclosed, limited
by period of issue

Numbered with certificate

18-H6-4.1
1979 *Le Cheval Magique*
(The Magic Horse)
Prices: Issue $54.50; 1983 High $55.00;
Low $54.50; Close $55.00; Up $.50

18-H6-4.2
1980 *Aladin et la Lampe Merveilleuse*
(Aladin and the Wonderful Lamp)
Prices: Issue $54.50; 1983 High $85.00;
Low $54.50; Close $85.00; Up $30.50

FRANCE
HAVILAND
Limoges

18-H6-4.3
1981 *Scheherazade*
Prices: Issue $54.50; 1983 High $54.50;
Low $54.50; Close $54.50; No Change

18-H6-4.4
1982 *Sinbad the Sailor*
Prices: Issue $54.50; 1983 High $54.50;
Low $54.50; Close $54.50; No Change
Series Closed

Haviland & Parlon is a chapter in the intricate Haviland porcelain story. In 1853 Robert Haviland left New York City to work for his brother David Haviland in Limoges (see France, HAVILAND). In 1870 Robert's son Charles Field Haviland also established a porcelain factory in Limoges and used "Ch. Field Haviland" as his trade name. After he retired in 1881, the firm was known by several different names until 1942, when Robert Haviland (Robert's great-grandson) purchased it. The firm is now known as Robert Haviland & C. Parlon but retains the "Ch. Field Haviland" trademark.

The *Tapestry* series, begun in 1971, reproduced six scenes from the French medieval tapestries, "The Hunt of the Unicorn," now hanging in the Cloisters of New York's Metropolitan Museum of Art. The *Christmas* series of famous Renaissance Madonnas began in 1972 and ended in 1979; a second *Tapestry* series of six plates began in 1977, reproducing scenes from "The Lady and the Unicorn" tapestries hanging in the Cluny Museum in Paris.

Designs for the *Christmas* series are taken from works by the great masters as indicated.

FRANCE
HAVILAND & PARLON
Limoges

Tapestry Series

Artist: Unknown. Reproduced from French medieval tapestries

Overglaze-decorated porcelain banded in gold

Diameter: 25.4 centimeters (10 inches)

No hanger

Edition size limited to announced quantity of 10,000

Not numbered, without certificate

18-H8-1.1
1971 *The Unicorn in Captivity*
Prices: Issue $35.00; 1983 High $186.00;
Low $158.00; Close $158.00; Down $28.00

18-H8-1.2
1972 *Start of the Hunt*
Prices: Issue $35.00; 1983 High $75.00;
Low $70.00; Close $70.00; Down $5.00

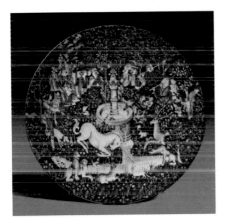

18-H8-1.3
1973 *Chase of the Unicorn*
Prices: Issue $35.00; 1983 High $155.00;
Low $120.00; Close $120.00; Down $35.00

18-H8-1.4
1974 *End of the Hunt*
Prices: Issue $37.50; 1983 High $133.00;
Low $117.00; Close $120.00; Down $13.00

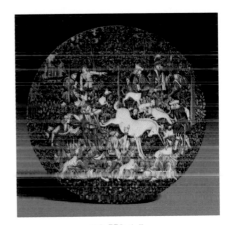

18-H8-1.5
1975 *The Unicorn Surrounded*
Prices: Issue $40.00; 1983 High $78.00;
Low $78.00; Close $78.00; No Change

18-H8-1.6
1976 *The Unicorn Is Brought
to the Castle*
Prices: Issue $42.50; 1983 High $60.00;
Low $58.00; Close $58.00; Down $2.00
Series Closed

Christmas Series

Artist: as indicated

Overglaze-decorated porcelain
banded in gold

Diameter: 25.4 centimeters
(10 inches)

No hanger

Edition size: as indicated

Numbered without certificate

18-H8-2.1
1972 Madonna and Child
Artist: Raphael/Edition: 5,000
Prices: Issue $35.00; 1983 High $148.00;
Low $100.00; Close $100.00; Down $44.00

18-H8-2.2
1973 Madonnina
Artist: Feruzzi/Edition: 5,000
Prices: Issue $40.00; 1983 High $102.00;
Low $87.00; Close $90.00; Down $12.00

18-H8-2.3
1974 Cowper Madonna and Child
Artist: Raphael/Edition: 5,000
Prices: Issue $42.50; 1983 High $83.00;
Low $65.00; Close $65.00; Down $18.00

18-H8-2.4
1975 Madonna and Child
Artist: Murillo/Edition: 7,500
Prices: Issue $42.50; 1983 High $58.00;
Low $45.00; Close $45.00; Down $13.00

18-H8-2.5
1976 Madonna and Child
Artist: Botticelli/Edition: 7,000
Prices: Issue $45.00; 1983 High $58.00;
Low $50.00; Close $50.00; Down $8.00

18-H8-2.6
1977 Madonna and Child
Artist: Bellini/Edition: 7,500
Prices: Issue $48.00; 1983 High $50.00;
Low $40.00; Close $40.00; Down $8.00

18-H8-2.7
1978 Madonna and Child
Artist: Fra Filippo Lippi/
Edition: 7,500
Prices: Issue $48.00; 1983 High $70.00;
Low $63.00; Close $65.00; Up $2.00

18-H8-2.8
1979 Madonna of the Eucharist
Artist: Botticelli/Edition: 7,500
Prices: Issue $49.50; 1983 High $150.00;
Low $90.00; Close $150.00; Up $60.00
Series Closed

FRANCE
HAVILAND & PARLON
Limoges

Lady and the Unicorn Series
Artist: Unknown. Reproduced from French medieval tapestries

Overglaze-decorated porcelain banded in gold

Diameter: 25.4 centimeters (10 inches)

No hanger

Edition size: as indicated

Not numbered, without certificate

18-H8-4.1
1977 To My Only Desire
Edition: 20,000
Prices: Issue $45.00; 1983 High $86.00;
Low $60.00; Close $60.00; Down $26.00

18-H8-4.2
1978 Sight
Edition: 20,000
Prices: Issue $45.00; 1983 High $48.00;
Low $41.00; Close $41.00; Down $7.00

18-H8-4.3
1979 Sound
Edition: 20,000
Prices: Issue $47.50; 1983 High $54.00;
Low $51.00; Close $51.00; Down $3.00

18-H8-4.4
1980 Touch
Edition: 15,000
Prices: Issue $52.50; 1983 High $103.00;
Low $103.00; Close $103.00; No Change

18-H8-4.5
1981 Scent
Edition: 10,000
Prices: Issue $59.00; 1983 High $65.00;
Low $62.00; Close $65.00; Up $3.00

18-H8-4.6
1982 Taste
Edition: 10,000
Prices: Issue $59.00; 1983 High $80.00;
Low $59.00; Close $80.00; Up $21.00
Series Closed

Réné Lalique, founder of the firm that bears his name, began his career as a goldsmith and jeweler in the late nineteenth century. His clients included such notables as Sarah Bernhardt and the dealers Cartier and Boucheron.

In 1902 his interests turned to glassmaking and he acquired a small glassworks at Clairfontaine, France. In 1909 he opened a glass factory near Paris where he produced bottles for the leading Parisian *parfumeurs*, and in 1918 he opened the present Lalique factory in Alsace. Here he began to produce glass items in the Art Deco style. His designs, usually created in pressed glass, are noted for the frosted and satin effects of the glass. Until his death in 1945, Lalique produced numerous commercial glass objects such as perfume bottles, vases and figurines.

Upon Réné's death in 1945, his son Marc—himself a noted artist—inherited the firm and served as its president until his death in 1977. The firm is currently headed by Marc's daughter, Marie-Claude. As Lalique's chief designer she created the *Annual* series of Lalique crystal collector's plates which began in 1965 and ended in 1976.

The third generation in a distinguished family of artists, Madame Lalique is known for her versatility, being an accomplished painter, sculptor, glassblower, and jewelry designer. She is a graduate of the Grand Chaumiere and L'Ecole Normale Superiore des Arts Decoratifs de Paris where she concentrated in the painting medium until her teacher, André Arbus, developed her appreciation of the Decorative Arts.

Annual Series

Artist: Marie-Claude Lalique

Full lead crystal with incised designs

Diameter: 21.6 centimeters (8½ inches)

No hanger

Edition size: as indicated. Announced between 5,000 and 8,000 from 1967 to 1975

Not numbered, without certificate; engraved "Lalique-France" on back

18-L3-1.1
1965 Deux Oiseaux (Two Birds)
Edition: 2,000
Prices: Issue $25.00; 1983 High $1650.00;
Low $1475.00; Close $1475.00;
Down $175.00

18-L3-1.2
1966 Rose de Songerie (Dream Rose)
Edition: 5,000
Prices: Issue $25.00; 1983 High $330.00;
Low $300.00; Close $300.00; Down $30.00

18-L3-1.3
1967 Ballet de Poisson (Fish Ballet)
Prices: Issue $25.00; 1983 High $280.00;
Low $200.00; Close $200.00; Down $80.00

18-L3-1.4
1968 Gazelle Fantaisie (Gazelle Fantasy)
Prices: Issue $25.00; 1983 High $130.00;
Low $100.00; Close $100.00; Down $30.00

18-L3-1.5
1969 Papillon (Butterfly)
Prices: Issue $30.00; 1983 High $120.00;
Low $100.00, Close $100.00; Down $18.00

18-L3-1.6
1970 Paon (Peacock)
Prices: Issue $30.00; 1983 High $112.00;
Low $105.00; Close $105.00; Down $5.00

18-L3-1.7
1971 Hibou (Owl)
Prices: Issue $35.00; 1983 High $86.00;
Low $80.00; Close $80.00; Down $6.00

18-L3-1.8
1972 Coquillage (Shell)
Prices: Issue $40.00; 1983 High $80.00;
Low $73.00; Close $75.00; Down $5.00

18-L3-1.9

18-L3-1.9
1973 Petit Geai (Jayling)
Prices: Issue $42.50; 1983 High $66.00;
Low $60.00; Close $60.00; Down $6.00

18-L3-1.10
1974 Sous d'Argent (Silver Pennies)
Prices: Issue $47.50; 1983 High $70.00;
Low $58.00; Close $70.00; Up $12.00

18-L3-1.11
1975 Duo de Poisson (Fish Duet)
Prices: Issue $50.00; 1983 High $80.00;
Low $73.00; Close $80.00; Up $7.00

18-L3-1.12
1976 Aigle (Eagle)
Prices: Issue $60.00; 1983 High $155.00;
Low $110.00; Close $110.00; Down $45.00
Series Closed

18-L3-1.1 "Deux Oiseaux"
1965 Lalique *Annual*
Detail from the world's first full-lead crystal collector's plate; note incised design of the entwined birds.

The porcelain house of Limoges-Turgot draws upon a tradition of porcelain making which began with A.-R.-J. Turgot, Baron de l'Aulne, Louis XVI's administrator for the Limousin province of which Limoges was the capital. When kaolin clay, the key ingredient in true hard-fire porcelain, was discovered in 1768 at the nearby town of Saint-Yrieix, it was largely due to Turgot's efforts that the Limoges porcelain industry was established and achieved world renown.

Les Enfants de Durand (Durand's Children Collection), began in 1978 and is the first proprietary series by Limoges-Turgot. The series ended in 1980. *Quellier's Morals of Perrault* series, by André Quellier, began in 1983.

The late artist, Paul Durand, achieved an international reputation for his illustrations of such children's classics as *The Three Musketeers* and *Treasure Island*. His art was personally chosen by General Charles de Gaulle to illustrate his 1969 Christmas message to French children. André Quellier, born in Paris in 1925, received his classical training at l'Ecole des Beaux Arts. His works have been shown in the major cities of the United States, Japan, the Soviet Union, Spain, and France. His numerous awards include the Prix de l'Institute, the Prix Casa Velasquez a Madrid, and the Medaille d'Or des Artists Française.

FRANCE
LIMOGES-TURGOT
Limoges

Les Enfants de Durand
(Durand's Children Collection)

Artist: Paul Durand. Artist's signature appears on front

Overglaze-decorated porcelain

Diameter: 20.3 centimeters (8 inches)

Attached back hanger

Edition size undisclosed, limited by year of issue

Numbered with certificate

18-L52-1.1
1978 Marie-Ange
Prices: Issue $36.40; 1983 High $42.00;
Low $38.00; Close $38.00; Down $4.00

18-L52-1.2
1979 Emilie et Philippe
Prices: Issue $36.40; 1983 High $45.00;
Low $40.00; Close $40.00; Down $5.00

18-L52-1.3
1980 Christiane et Fifi
Prices: Issue $36.40; 1983 High $51.00;
Low $45.00; Close $45.00; Down $5.00

18-L52-1.4
1980 Cecile et Raoul
Prices: Issue $36.40; 1983 High $70.00;
Low $65.00; Close $65.00; Down $3.00
Series Closed

Quellier's Morals of Perrault Series

Artist: André Quellier. Artist's signature appears on front

Overglaze-decorated porcelain

Diameter: 21.6 centimeters (8½ inches)

No hanger

Edition size undisclosed, limited by announced period of issue

Numbered with certificate

18-L52-2.1
1983 Cinderella
Prices: Issue $28.67; 1983 High $28.67;
Low $28.67; Close $28.67; No Change

18-L52-2.2
1984 Little Tom Thumb
Issue price: $28.67

Named for Anna Perenna, the Roman goddess associated with health, abundance, and the rebirth of spring, Anna-Perenna, Inc. was founded in 1977 by its president, Klaus D. Vogt, exclusively to produce high-quality limited-edition plates in hard-paste porcelain.

Two *Triptych* sets, inspired by the portable altar-pieces of the Middle Ages, were issued in 1979 and 1980. Each three-plate set reinterprets ancient Byzantine religious motifs. In 1979, Anna-Perenna introduced *Romantic Loves*, a four-plate series celebrating great romantic loves of history. Their four-plate series, *Uncle Tad's Cats*, began in 1979 and ended in 1981.

Frank Russell and Gertrude Barrer, the creators of the *Triptych* and the *Romantic Loves* series, are husband-and-wife co-workers who have blended their talents to become a successful art-producing team. They met at the Art Student's League in New York and, after five years of going their separate ways, reunited in New York's art center, Greenwich Village, working jointly in photography, lithographs, frescoes, serigraphs, ceramics, and sculpture. Their

work has been exhibited at the Art Institute of Chicago and the Whitney Museum of American Art, and hangs in the private collections of Cyrus Vance, Helmut Schmidt, and the U.N. Interfaith Chapel in New York. In 1980, their "Byzantine Triptych" was presented by Munich's Cardinal Ratzinger to Pope John Paul II during his pilgrimage to West Germany. Thaddeus Krumeich ("Uncle Tad") is master of the style known as *trompe l'oeil*, which he calls "magic realism." He has had shows throughout the United States, is represented in such private collections as those of Mrs. Paul Mellon, "Doc" Severinson, and His Excellency Seydou Traori, Mali Ambassador to the United States, and his work was selected for use in the 1980-81 series of UNICEF greeting cards.

The Triptych Series

Artist: Frank Russell and Gertrude Barrer. Artists' signatures appear on front

Hard-paste porcelain with hinged frame

Diameter: plates one and three, 21.6 cm. (8½ in.); plate two, 24.8 cm (9¾ in.); overall triptych, 88.9 cm. x 45.7 cm. (35 in. x 18 in.) for 1979 set; 83.8 cm. x 38.1 cm. (33 in. x 15 in.) for 1980 set

Attached back hanger

Edition size: 5,000 sets

Individually hand-numbered with certificate

A triptych is a set of three panels hinged side by side, bearing paintings or carvings usually on a religious theme and often used as a portable altarpiece.

22-A3-3.1-1
1979 *Gabriel*
Prices: Issue $325.00; 1983 High $340.00; Low $125.00; Close $125.00; Down $215.00

22-A3-3.1-2
1979 *Madonna and Child*
The Byzantine Triptych

22-A3-3.1-3
1979 *Michael*

22-A3-3.2-1
1980 *Saul*
Prices: Issue $350.00; 1983 High $350.00; Low $350.00; Close $350.00; No Change
Series Closed

22-A3-3.2-2
1980 *David*
The Jerusalem Triptych

22-A3-3.2-3
1980 *Solomon*

Romantic Loves Series

Artist: Frank Russell and Gertrude Barrer. Artists' signatures appear on front

Hard-paste porcelain banded in gold

Diameter: 25 centimeters (9⅞ inches)

Attached back hanger

Editions size limited to 7,500

Individually hand-numbered with certificate

22-A3-4.1
1979 *Romeo and Juliet*
Prices: Issue $95.00; 1983 High $99.00; Low $75.00; Close $75.00; Down $22.00

22-A3-4.2
1980 *Lancelot and Guinevere*
Prices: Issue $95.00; 1983 High $95.00; Low $95.00; Close $95.00; No Change

22-A3-4.3
1981 *Helen and Paris*
Prices: Issue $95.00; 1983 High $95.00; Low $95.00; Close $95.00; No Change

22-A3-4.4
1982 *Lovers of the Taj Mahal*
Prices: Issue $95.00; 1983 High $95.00; Low $95.00; Close $95.00; No Change
Series Closed

Uncle Tad's Cats Series

Artist: Thaddeus Krumeich. Artist's signature appears on front

Hard-paste porcelain

Diameter: 24.8 centimeters (9¾ inches)

Attached back hanger

Edition size limited to 5,000

Individually hand-numbered with certificate

22-A3-5.1
1979 *Oliver's Birthday*
Prices: Issue $75.00; 1983 High $190.00; Low $180.00; Close $190.00; Up $10.00

22-A3-5.2
1980 *Peaches and Cream*
Prices: Issue $75.00; 1983 High $87.00; Low $82.00; Close $85.00; Down $2.00

ANNA-PERENNA
Stuttgart

22-A3-5.3
1981 *Princess Aurora, Queen of the Night*
Prices: Issue $80.00; 1983 High $81.00;
Low $77.00; Close $77.00; Down $4.00

22-A3-5.4
1981 *Walter's Window*
Prices: Issue $85.00; 1983 High $85.00;
Low $80.00; Close $80.00; Down $5.00
Series Closed

The Bareuther & Company porcelain factory began to produce dinnerware, vases, and giftware in 1867. The small shop was established with a porcelain kiln and an annular brick kiln by sculptor Johann Matthaeus Ries. In 1884 Ries's son sold the shop to Oskar Bareuther who continued to produce fine tableware.

To observe the one-hundredth anniversary of the factory in 1967, Bareuther began a series of limited-edition *Christmas* plates. A *Father's Day* series, depicting the great castles of Germany, was started in 1969.

Hans Mueller, born in Waldsassen, Bavaria, was the son of a Bareuther artist. He studied engraving and painting at the porcelain academy in Selb, and in 1952 joined Bareuther as a porcelain painter. He was promoted to chief designer for the firm in 1968.

BAREUTHER
Waldsassen

Christmas Series

Artist: Hans Mueller, except 1971

Porcelain decorated in cobalt blue underglaze

Diameter: 20.3 centimeters (8 inches)

Pierced foot rim

Edition size limited to announced quantity of 10,000

Not numbered, without certificate

22-B7-1.1
1967 Stiftskirche
Prices: Issue $12.00; 1983 High $127.00;
Low $120.00; Close $125.00; Down $2.00

22-B7-1.2
1968 Kappl
Prices: Issue $12.00; 1983 High $42.00;
Low $40.00; Close $40.00; No Change

22-B7-1.3
1969 Christkindlesmarkt
Prices: Issue $12.00; 1983 High $20.00;
Low $18.00, Close $18.00; Down $2.00

22-B7-1.4
1970 Chapel in Oberndorf
Prices: Issue $12.50; 1983 High $18.00;
Low $15.00; Close $15.00; Down $3.00

22-B7-1.5
1971 Toys for Sale
From drawing by Ludwig Richter
Prices: Issue $12.75; 1983 High $21.00;
Low $21.00; Close $21.00; No Change

22-B7-1.6
1972 Christmas in Munich
Prices: Issue $14.50; 1983 High $49.00;
Low $35.00; Close $40.00; Down $8.00

22-B7-1.7
1973 Christmas Sleigh Ride
Prices: Issue $15.00; 1983 High $31.00;
Low $28.00; Close $28.00; Down $3.00

22-B7-1.8
1974 Church in the Black Forest
Prices: Issue $19.00; 1983 High $30.00;
Low $27.00; Close $28.00; Down $2.00

22-B7-1.9
1975 *Snowman*
Prices: Issue $21.50; 1983 High $29.00;
Low $27.00; Close $27.00; Down $2.00

22-B7-1.10
1976 *Chapel in the Hills*
Prices: Issue $23.50; 1983 High $34.00;
Low $25.00; Close $25.00; Down $9.00

22-B7-1.11
1977 *Story Time*
Prices: Issue $24.50; 1983 High $35.00;
Low $32.00; Close $35.00; No Change

22-B7-1.12
1978 *Mittenwald*
Prices: Issue $27.50; 1983 High $36.00;
Low $36.00; Close $36.00; No Change

22-B7-1.13
1979 *Winter Day*
Prices: Issue $35.00; 1983 High $40.00;
Low $39.00; Close $40.00; Up $1.00

22-B7-1.14
1980 *Miltenberg*
Prices: Issue $37.50; 1983 High $43.00;
Low $43.00; Close $43.00; No Change

22-B7-1.15
1981 *Walk in the Forest*
Prices: Issue $39.50; 1983 High $40.00;
Low $40.00; Close $40.00; No Change

22-B7-1.16
1982 *Bad Wimpfen*
Prices: Issue $39.50; 1983 High $40.00;
Low $39.50; Close $40.00; Up $.50

22-B7-1.17
1983 *The Night Before Christmas*
Prices: Issue $39.50; 1983 High $39.50;
Low $39.50; Close $39.50; No Change

BAREUTHER
Waldsassen

22-B7-1.18
1984 *Zeil on the River Main*
Issue price: $42.50

Father's Day Series

Artist: Hans Mueller

Porcelain decorated in cobalt blue underglaze

Diameter: 20.3 centimeters (8 inches)

Pierced foot rim

Edition size limited to announced quantity of 2,500

Not numbered, without certificate

22-B7-2.1
1969 *Castle Neuschwanstein*
Prices: Issue $10.50 ; 1983 High $55.00;
Low $45.00; Close $45.00; Down $7.00

22-B7-2.2
1970 *Castle Pfalz*
Prices: Issue $12.50; 1983 High $20.00;
Low $18.00; Close $18.00, Down $2.00

22-B7-2.3
1971 *Castle Heidelberg*
Prices: Issue $12.75; 1983 High $28.00;
Low $24.00; Close $28.00; Up $4.00

22-B7-2.4
1972 *Castle Hohenschwangau*
Prices: Issue $14.50; 1983 High $23.00;
Low $23.00; Close $23.00; No Change

22-B7-2.5
1973 *Castle Katz*
Prices: Issue $15.00; 1983 High $32.00;
Low $28.00; Close $30.00; No Change

22-B7-2.6
1974 Wurzburg Castle
Prices: Issue $19.00; 1983 High $52.00;
Low $50.00; Close $50.00; Down $2.00

22-B7-2.7
1975 Castle Lichtenstein
Prices: Issue $21.50; 1983 High $33.00;
Low $33.00; Close $33.00; No Change

22-B7-2.8
1976 Castle Hohenzollern
Prices: Issue $23.50; 1983 High $35.00;
Low $28.00; Close $28.00; Down $7.00

22-B7-2.9
1977 Castle Eltz
Prices: Issue $24.50; 1983 High $29.00;
Low $27.00; Close $28.00; Down $1.00

22-B7-2.10
1978 Castle Falkenstein
Prices: Issue $27.50; 1983 High $31.00;
Low $28.00; Close $30.00; Down $1.00

22-B7-2.11
1979 Castle Rheinstein
Prices: Issue $35.00; 1983 High $30.00;
Low $30.00; Close $30.00; No Change

22-B7-2.12
1980 Castle Cochem
Prices: Issue $37.50; 1983 High $40.00;
Low $35.00; Close $35.00; Down $5.00

22-B7-2.13
1981 Castle Gutenfels
Prices: Issue $39.50; 1983 High $42.00;
Low $40.00; Close $40.00; Down $2.00

22-B7-2.14
1982 Castle Zwingenberg
Prices: Issue $39.50; 1983 High $40.00;
Low $39.50; Close $40.00; Up $.50

GERMANY
BAREUTHER
Waldsassen

22-B7-2.15
1983 *Castle Lauenstein*
Prices: Issue $39.50; 1983 High $40.00;
Low $39.50; Close $40.00; Up $.50

22-B7-2.16
1984 *Castle Neuenstein*
Issue price: $42.50

Berlin Design's limited-edition plates, mugs, and other collectibles are manufactured by the Kaiser Porcelain Company (see Germany, KAISER), and are identified by the distinctive bear-and-crown symbol of the city of Berlin.

The *Christmas* series, introduced in 1970, depicts Yule festivities in German towns.

Their *Holiday Week of the Family Kappelmann* series began in 1984.

Artists for Berlin Design *Christmas* plates are not disclosed.

GERMANY
BERLIN DESIGN
Staffelstein

Christmas Series
Artist: Undisclosed

Porcelain decorated in cobalt blue underglaze

Diameter: 19.7 centimeters (7¾ inches)

Pierced foot rim

Edition size limited to 4,000 in 1970; 20,000 thereafter

Not numbered, without certificate

22-B20-1.1
1970 Christmas in Bernkastel
Prices: Issue $14.50; 1983 High $180.00; Low $158.00; Close $180.00; Up $22.00

22-B20-1.2
1971 Christmas in Rothenburg on Tauber
Prices: Issue $14.50; 1983 High $30.00; Low $28.00; Close $30.00; Up $2.00

22-B20-1.3
1972 Christmas in Michelstadt
Prices: Issue $15.00; 1983 High $35.00; Low $35.00; Close $35.00; No Change

22-B20-1.4
1973 Christmas in Wendelstein
Prices: Issue $20.00; 1983 High $44.00; Low $37.00; Close $44.00; Up $7.00

22-B20-1.5
1974 Christmas in Bremen
Prices: Issue $25.00; 1983 High $30.00; Low $30.00; Close $30.00; No Change

22-B20-1.6
1975 Christmas in Dortland
Prices: Issue $30.00; 1983 High $28.00; Low $25.00; Close $28.00; Up $3.00

22-B20-1.7
1976 Christmas Eve in Augsburg
Prices: Issue $32.00; 1983 High $35.00; Low $31.00; Close $35.00; Up $4.00

22-B20-1.8
1977 Christmas Eve in Hamburg
Prices: Issue $32.00; 1983 High $36.00; Low $33.00; Close $33.00; Down $1.00

22-B20-1.9

22-B20-1.9
1978 Christmas Market at the Dome of Berlin
Prices: Issue $36.00; 1983 High $38.00; Low $35.00; Close $38.00; Up $3.00

22-B20-1.10
1979 Christmas Eve in Greetsiel
Prices: Issue $47.50; 1983 High $52.00; Low $51.00; Close $52.00; Up $1.00

22-B20-1.11
1980 Christmas Eve in Miltenberg
Prices: Issue $55.00; 1983 High $61.00; Low $55.00; Close $61.00; Up $6.00

22-B20-1.12
1981 Christmas Eve in Hahnenklee
Prices: Issue $55.00; 1983 High $56.00; Low $53.00; Close $56.00; Up $3.00

22-B20-1.13
1982 Christmas Eve in Wasserburg
Prices: Issue $55.00; 1983 High $55.00; Low $55.00; Close $55.00; No Change

22-B20-1.14
1983 The Chapel in Oberndorf
Prices: Issue $55.00; 1983 High $55.00; Low $55.00; Close $55.00; No Change

22-B20-1.15
1984 Christmas Eve in Ramsau
Issue price: $55.00

BERLIN DESIGN
Staffelstein

*Holiday Week of the Family
Kappelmann Series*

Artist: Detlev Nitschke. Artist's
signature appears on front

Porcelain decorated in cobalt blue
underglaze

Diameter: 19 centimeters
(7½ inches)

Pierced foot rim

Edition size undisclosed, limited
by period of issue

Numbered with certificate

22-B20-4.1
1984 *Monday*
Issue price: undetermined
at press time

22-B20-4.2
1984 *Tuesday*
Issue price: undetermined
at press time

Goebel

W. Goebel Porzellanfabrik was
established in 1871 in Oeslau
by Franz-Detleff Goebel and his
son William. Headed by Wilhelm Goebel, who represents
the fifth generation of the
founding family, Goebel produces handcrafted figurines,
plates, dinnerware, and gift
items.

In 1935 Goebel introduced
the famous M. I. Hummel figurines based on sketches by the
Franciscan nun. In 1971, to
celebrate the one-hundredth
anniversary of the firm, Goebel
inaugurated an *Annual* series
of limited-edition plates with
the M. I. Hummel designs.

The Hummel *Anniversary*
series began in 1975, with a
new plate to be issued every five
years.

The late Sister Maria Innocentia Hummel (1909-1946),
in her years at the Franciscan
convent at Siessen, produced
stylized drawings of children—
quite often with a religious
theme—which Goebel has
translated into both porcelain
figurines and bas-relief stoneware plates.

GOEBEL
Oeslau

Hummel Annual Series

Artist: Sister M. I. Hummel.
Artist's signature appears on front

Stoneware with hand-painted bas-relief

Diameter: 19 centimeters
(7½ inches)

Pierced foot rim

Edition size undisclosed, limited by year of issue

Not numbered, without certificate

22-G54-1.1
1971 *Heavenly Angel*
Prices: Issue $25.00; 1983 High $810.00;
Low $750.00; Close $775.00; Down $35.00

22-G54-1.2
1972 *Hear Ye, Hear Ye*
Prices: Issue $30.00; 1983 High $90.00;
Low $75.00; Close $75.00; Down $15.00

22-G54-1.3
1973 *Globe Trotter*
Prices: Issue $32.50; 1983 High $211.00;
Low $150.00; Close $150.00; Down $61.00

22-G54-1.4
1974 *Goose Girl*
Prices: Issue $40.00; 1983 High $115.00;
Low $100.00; Close $100.00; Down $12.00

22-G54-1.5
1975 *Ride into Christmas*
Prices: Issue $50.00; 1983 High $96.00;
Low $90.00; Close $90.00; Down $6.00

22-G54-1.6
1976 *Apple Tree Girl*
Prices: Issue $50.00; 1983 High $92.00;
Low $92.00; Close $92.00; No Change

22-G54-1.7
1977 *Apple Tree Boy*
Prices: Issue $50.00; 1983 High $108.00;
Low $108.00; Close $108.00; No Change

22-G54-1.8
1978 *Happy Pastime*
Prices: Issue $65.00; 1983 High $105.00;
Low $90.00; Close $90.00; Down $15.00

22-G54-1.9
1979 Singing Lesson
Prices: Issue $90.00; 1983 High $80.00;
Low $65.00; Close $65.00; Down $15.00

22-G54-1.10
1980 School Girl
Prices: Issue $100.00; 1983 High $80.00;
Low $80.00; Close $80.00; No Change

22-G54-1.11
1981 Umbrella Boy
Prices: Issue $100.00; 1983 High $100.00;
Low $90.00; Close $90.00; Down $10.00

22-G54-1.12
1982 Umbrella Girl
Prices: Issue $100.00; 1983 High $100.00;
Low $100.00; Close $100.00; No Change

22-G54-1.13
1983 The Postman
Prices: Issue $108.00; 1983 High $108.00;
Low $108.00; Close $108.00; No Change

22-G54-1.14
1984 Little Helper
Issue price: $108.00

Hummel Anniversary Series

Artist: Sister M. I. Hummel.
Artist's signature appears on front

Stoneware with hand-painted bas-relief

Diameter: 25.4 centimeters
(10 inches)

Pierced foot rim

Edition size undisclosed, limited
by year of issue

Not numbered, without certificate

22-G54-3.1
1975 Stormy Weather
Prices: Issue $100.00; 1983 High $200.00;
Low $170.00; Close $170.00; Down $30.00

22-G54-3.2
1980 Spring Dance
Prices: Issue $225.00; 1983 High $165.00;
Low $135.00; Close $135.00; Down $30.00

22-G54-1.1 "Heavenly Angel"
1971 Goebel *Hummel Annual*
22-S12-1.1 "Angel in a Christmas Setting"
1971 Schmid *Hummel Christmas*
Hand-painted bas-relief stoneware and color transfer on hard-fire porcelain from Goebel and Schmid, respectively—two of Europe's most famous makers. Both series were highly successful, but the similarity of the design sparked controversy over the rights to Berta Hummel's work.

The history of Heinrich Porzellan dates from the opening by Franz Heinrich of a porcelain-painting studio in 1896 in Selb, Bavaria, near the Czechoslovakian border. In 1901, Heinrich established his own porcelain factory, Heinrich & Co., which produced fine table- and giftware. The firm remained under the control of the Heinrich family until 1976, when it was purchased by Villeroy & Boch. Heinrich creations are now distributed worldwide through Villeroy & Boch's marketing channels.

From 1980 thru 1983, Heinrich issued a twelve plate series of porcelain plates entitled *Russian Fairy Tales.* The *Fairies of the Fields and Flowers* series began in 1982.

Russian artist Boris Vasil'-evich Zvorykin was born in Moscow in 1872 and was one of the last great book illustrators of Czarist Russia. He was also noted for his murals in the Cathedral at Simferopol. Forced to leave Russia during the 1917 revolution, Zvorykin settled in Paris in 1920 and became an integral figure in an expatriate movement to retain the cultural heritage of Imperial Russia. He elaborately illustrated four books of Russian fairy tales. These books eventually found an American audience when Jacqueline Kennedy Onassis edited the manuscripts and published them under the title *The Firebird and Other Russian Fairy Tales.* Cicely Mary Barker was born in 1895 at Croydon, England. Her best-remembered works are the "Flower Fairy" books, first published in 1923. She was also known for designing a stained-glass window at St. André Church in Croydon and for the numerous cards she designed for charities.

GERMANY
HEINRICH/VILLEROY & BOCH
Selb

Russian Fairy Tales Series
Artist: Boris Zvorykin

Hard-paste porcelain banded in gold

Diameter: 21 centimeters (8¼ inches)

No hanger

Edition size limited to 27,500

Not numbered, with certificate

22-H18-1.1
1980 *The Snow Maiden*
Prices: Issue $70.00; 1983 High $130.00;
Low $75.00; Close $130.00; Up $55.00

22-H18-1.2
1980 *The Snow Maiden at the Court of Tsar Berendei*
Prices: Issue $70.00; 1983 High $110.00;
Low $74.00; Close $90.00; Up $16.00

22-H18-1.3
1980 *The Snow Maiden and Lel the Shepherd Boy*
Prices: Issue $70.00; 1983 High $90.00;
Low $72.00; Close $90.00; Up $18.00

22-H18-1.4
1981 *The Red Knight*
Prices: Issue $70.00; 1983 High $78.00;
Low $70.00; Close $78.00; Up $8.00

22-H18-1.5
1981 *Vassilissa and Her Stepsisters*
Prices: Issue $70.00; 1983 High $75.00;
Low $70.00; Close $75.00; Up $5.00

22-H18-1.6
1981 *Vassilissa Is Presented to the Tsar*
Prices: Issue $70.00; 1983 High $75.00;
Low $70.00; Close $75.00; Up $5.00

22-H18-1.7
1982 *In Search of the Firebird*
Prices: Issue $70.00; 1983 High $100.00;
Low $70.00; Close $100.00; Up $30.00

22-H18-1.8
1982 *Ivan and Tsarevna on the Grey Wolf*
Prices: Issue $70.00; 1983 High $100.00;
Low $70.00; Close $100.00; Up $30.00

22-H18-1.9
1982 *The Wedding of Tsarevna Elena the Fair*
Prices: Issue $70.00; 1983 High $85.00; Low $70.00; Close $85.00; Up $15.00

22-H18-1.10
1983 *Maria Morevna and Tsarevich Ivan*
Prices: Issue $70.00; 1983 High $70.00; Low $70.00; Close $70.00; No Change

22-H18-1.11
1983 *Koshchey Carries off Maria Morevna*
Prices: Issue $70.00; 1983 High $70.00; Low $70.00; Close $70.00; No Change

22-H18-1.12
1983 *Tsarevich Ivan and the Beautiful Castle*
Prices: Issue $70.00; 1983 High $70.00; Low $70.00; Close $70.00; No Change
Series Closed

Fairies of the Fields and Flowers Series

Artist: Cicely Mary Barker

Bone china banded in 24k gold

Diameter: 21.6 centimeters (8½ inches)

Attached back hanger

Edition size undisclosed, limited by announced period of issue

Numbered with certificate

22-H18-3.1
1982 *Ragged Robin*
Prices: Issue $49.00; 1983 High $55.00; Low $49.00; Close $55.00; Up $6.00

22-H18-3.2
1983 *Willow*
Prices: Issue $49.00; 1983 High $49.00; Low $49.00; Close $49.00; No Change

HEINRICH/VILLEROY & BOCH
Selb

22-H18-3.3
1984 *Elderberry*
Issue price: $49.00

22-H18-3.4
1984 *Vetch*
Issue price: $49.00

22-H18-3.5
1984 *Narcissus*
Issue price: $49.00

Hibel Studio was founded in 1976. Headquartered in Riviera Beach, Florida, the studio specializes in original stone lithographs, lithographs on porcelain, and limited-edition collector's plates. All artwork is approved by Edna Hibel, and plates are made by Kaiser Porcelain and Rosenthal China (see Germany, KAISER, ROSENTHAL).

Hibel Studio began its first series of collector's plates, the *David* series, in 1979. The four-plate series, with artwork by Edna Hibel, is based on the biblical story of King David.

Edna Hibel, at twenty-two, became the youngest living artist to have a painting in a major American museum when the Boston Museum purchased one of her canvases in 1939. She is an elected member of the Royal Society of Arts in London, and is one of the only living female artists with a U.S. museum devoted to her works. In 1979, she gave a one-woman show at the Monaco Fine Arts Gallery under the patronage of Prince Rainier and Princess Grace and won the "International Year of the Child" award in the United States. She held an internationally acclaimed show in 1980 at Castle Mainau in Germany sponsored by Count and Countess Lennart Bernadotte.

GERMANY
HIBEL STUDIO
Staffelstein

David Series
Artist: Edna Hibel. Artist's signature appears on front

Porcelain highlighted and banded in gold

Diameter: 25.7 centimeters (10⅛ inches)

Pierced foot rim

Edition size limited to 5,000

Numbered with certificate

22-H31-1.1
1979 *The Wedding of David and Bathsheba*
Prices: Issue $250.00; 1983 High $290.00; Low $200.00; Close $200.00; Down $90.00

22-H31-1.2
1980 *David, Bathsheba and Solomon*
Prices: Issue $275.00; 1983 High $275.00; Low $275.00; Close $275.00; No Change

22-H31-1.3
1982 *David the King*
Prices: Issue $275.00; 1983 High $275.00; Low $275.00; Close $275.00; No Change

22-H31-1.4
1983 *Bathsheba*
Prices: Issue $275.00; 1983 High $275.00; Low $275.00; Close $275.00; No Change
Series Closed

Hutschenreuther has produced limited-edition collector's plates since 1973, when they introduced their *Canada Christmas* series (not U.S. Bradex-listed). The *Love for All Seasons* series was issued in 1982 and 1983 and depicts six scenes of medieval romance as portrayed by the artist team of Charlotte and William Hallett.

Charlotte and William Hallett have worked together in a variety of artistic media, including silver, crystal, and painting. Charlotte studied fine art at the University of Bridgeport in Connecticut, and William Hallett graduated from the Vesper George School of Art in Boston. As a husband-and-wife artistic team, the Halletts have held numerous shows of their works, and list private individuals, major corporations, and royal families among their collectors.

GERMANY
HUTSCHENREUTHER
Selb

Love for All Seasons Series

Artist: Charlotte and William Hallett. Artists' signatures appear on back

Hard-paste porcelain with gold design on border

Diameter: 20.3 centimeters (8 inches)

Attached back hanger

Edition size limited to 10,000

Not numbered, without certificate

22-H82-6.1
1982 *The Minstrel Song*
Prices: Issue $125.00; 1983 High $125.00;
Low $125.00; Close $125.00; No Change

22-H82-6.2
1982 *Affection*
Prices: Issue $125.00; 1983 High $125.00;
Low $125.00; Close $125.00; No Change

22-H82-6.3
1982 *The Tournament*
Prices: Issue $125.00; 1983 High $125.00;
Low $125.00; Close $125.00; No Change

22-H82-6.4
1983 *The Falcon Hunt*
Prices: Issue $125.00; 1983 High $125.00;
Low $125.00; Close $125.00; No Change

22-H82-6.5
1983 *Winter Romance*
Prices: Issue $125.00; 1983 High $125.00;
Low $125.00; Close $125.00; No Change

22-H82-6.6
1983 *The Ride Out*
Prices: Issue $125.00; 1983 High $125.00;
Low $125.00; Close $125.00; No Change
Series Closed

Kaiser porcelain dates to 1872 when porcelain painter August Alboth set up his own workshop in Coburg. When he retired in 1899, his son Ernst moved the pottery to Bavaria. Marriage united the Alboth and Kaiser families in 1922, resulting in the ALKA trademark—a combination of the first two letters of both names.

In 1938 the firm purchased the old Bavarian pottery of Silbermann Brothers, which had been awarded a royal diploma in 1882 for its "magnificent" cobalt blue underglaze. The company opened its modern factory in Staffelstein in 1953 and in 1970 the trademark was changed to Kaiser Porcelain.

Long a producer of porcelain coffee sets, dinnerware, and figurines, Kaiser introduced its first series of limited-edition plates, the *Christmas* series, in 1970. The series ended in 1982. The *Mother's Day* series began in 1971 and ended in 1983. The *Classic Fairy Tales Collection* began in 1982.

Born in Karlsbad, Bohemia, Toni Schoener descended from a long family line of porcelain painters. He served his apprenticeship with Porzellanfabrik Altrohlau and Rosenthal Studios as a youth and studied at the Karlsbad School of Arts. Upon graduation, he returned to Porzellanfabrik Altrohlau where he became chief designer. After the ravages of World War II closed all German porcelain factories, Schoener devoted his talent to restoring war-damaged fresco paintings in cathedrals and churches. When stability returned, Schoener joined Kaiser Porcelain as chief designer. He retired officially in 1975, but continued to design plates for Kaiser until his death in 1978. Hungarian-born artist Nori Peter studied at the Academy of Fine Arts in Budapest. She fled Hungary to Canada following the uprising of 1956 and became fascinated by the native Eskimo and their habitat. She has gained wide acclaim for her paintings of their life. Gerda Neubacher, a native of Austria, studied art in Zurich, Switzerland. She has had major exhibitions in the United States and Canada at the Juliane Galleries, the Christel Galleries, and the O'Keefe Centre in Toronto; the National Art Center (to honour Queen Elizabeth II) in Ottawa; and the Galleria in Houston, Texas.

GERMANY
KAISER
Staffelstein

Christmas Series

Artist: as indicated

Porcelain decorated in cobalt blue underglaze

Diameter: 19 centimeters (7½ inches)

Pierced foot rim

Edition size undisclosed, limited by year of issue except 1974

Not numbered, without certificate

22-K4-1.1
1970 *Waiting for Santa Claus*
Artist: Toni Schoener
Prices: Issue $12.50; 1983 High $40.00;
Low $34.00; Close $34.00; Down $6.00

22-K4-1.2
1971 *Silent Night*
Artist: Kurt Bauer
Prices: Issue $13.50; 1983 High $25.00;
Low $25.00; Close $25.00; No Change

22-K4-1.3
1972 *Welcome Home*
Artist: Kurt Bauer
Prices: Issue $16.50; 1983 High $16.00;
Low $15.00; Close $16.00; Up $1.00

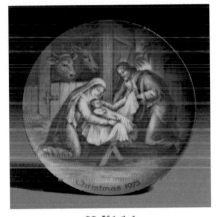

22-K4-1.4
1973 *Holy Night*
Artist: Toni Schoener
Prices: Issue $18.00; 1983 High $43.00;
Low $40.00; Close $43.00; Up $3.00

22-K4-1.5
1974 *Christmas Carolers*
Artist: Kurt Bauer/Edition: 8,000
Prices: Issue $25.00; 1983 High $34.00;
Low $34.00; Close $34.00; No Change

22-K4-1.6
1975 *Bringing Home the Christmas Tree*
Artist: Joann Northcott
Prices: Issue $25.00; 1983 High $28.00;
Low $25.00; Close $25.00; No Change

22-K4-1.7
1976 *Christ the Saviour Is Born*
Artist: Carlo Maratti
Prices: Issue $25.00; 1983 High $28.00;
Low $20.00; Close $20.00; Down $8.00

22-K4-1.8
1977 *The Three Kings*
Artist: Toni Schoener
Prices: Issue $25.00; 1983 High $16.00;
Low $16.00; Close $16.00; No Change

22-K4-1.9
1978 *Shepherds in the Field*
Artist: Toni Schoener
Prices: Issue $30.00; 1983 High $28.00;
Low $20.00; Close $20.00; Down $8.00

22-K4-1.10
1979 *Christmas Eve*
Artist: Hannelore Blum
Prices: Issue $32.00; 1983 High $24.00;
Low $23.00; Close $24.00; Up $1.00

22-K4-1.11
1980 *Joys of Winter*
Artist: Hannelore Blum
Prices: Issue $40.00; 1983 High $33.00;
Low $33.00; Close $33.00; No Change

22-K4-1.12
1981 *Most Holy Night*
Artist: Kurt Bauer
Prices: Issue $40.00; 1983 High $44.00;
Low $43.00; Close $43.00; No Change

22-K4-1.13
1982 *Bringing Home the Christmas Tree*
Artist: Kurt Bauer
Prices: Issue $40.00; 1983 High $40.00;
Low $35.00; Close $35.00; Down $5.00
Series Closed

Mother's Day Series

Artist: as indicated

Porcelain decorated in cobalt blue underglaze

Diameter: 19 centimeters
(7½ inches)

Pierced foot rim

Edition size undisclosed, limited by year of issue except 1974

Not numbered, without certificate

22-K4-2.1
1971 *Mare and Foal*
Artist: Toni Schoener
Prices: Issue $13.00; 1983 High $35.00;
Low $35.00; Close $35.00; No Change

22-K4-2.2
1972 *Flowers for Mother*
Artist: Toni Schoener
Prices: Issue $16.50; 1983 High $20.00;
Low $20.00; Close $20.00; No Change

KAISER
Staffelstein

22-K4-2.3
1973 *Cats*
Artist: Toni Schoener
Prices: Issue $17.00; 1983 High $26.00;
Low $14.00; Close $26.00; Up $12.00

22-K4-2.4
1974 *Fox*
Artist: Toni Schoener/Edition: 7,000
Prices: Issue $22.00; 1983 High $16.00;
Low $16.00; Close $16.00; No Change

22-K4-2.5
1975 *German Shepherd*
Artist: Toni Schoener
Prices: Issue $25.00; 1983 High $50.00;
Low $42.00; Close $50.00; Up $1.00

22-K4-2.6
1976 *Swan and Cygnets*
Artist: Toni Schoener
Prices: Issue $25.00; 1983 High $20.00;
Low $15.00; Close $15.00; Down $5.00

22-K4-2.7
1977 *Mother Rabbit and Young*
Artist: Toni Schoener
Prices: Issue $25.00; 1983 High $16.00;
Low $15.00; Close $15.00; Down $1.00

22-K4-2.8
1978 *Hen and Chicks*
Artist: Toni Schoener
Prices: Issue $30.00; 1983 High $15.00;
Low $15.00; Close $15.00; No Change

22-K4-2.9
1979 *A Mother's Devotion*
Artist: Nori Peter
Prices: Issue $32.00; 1983 High $24.00;
Low $24.00; Close $24.00; No Change

22-K4-2.10
1980 *Raccoon Family*
Artist: Joann Northcott
Prices: Issue $40.00; 1983 High $40.00;
Low $35.00; Close $38.00; Down $2.00

22-K4-2.11
1981 *Safe Near Mother*
Artist: Hannelore Blum
Prices: Issue $40.00; 1983 High $36.00;
Low $36.00; Close $36.00; No Change

22-K4-2.12
1982 *Pheasant Family*
Artist: Kurt Bauer
Prices: Issue $40.00; 1983 High $40.00;
Low $40.00; Close $40.00; No Change

22-K4-2.13
1983 *Tender Care*
Artist: Kurt Bauer
Prices: Issue $40.00; 1983 High $40.00;
Low $40.00; Close $40.00; No Change
Series Closed

Classic Fairy Tales Collection

Artist: Gerda Neubacher. Artist's signature appears on front

Porcelain banded in 24k gold

Diameter: 19.7 centimeters (7¾ inches)

Pierced foot rim

Edition size undisclosed, limited by announced period of issue

Numbered without certificate

22-K4-5.1
1982 *The Frog King*
Prices: Issue $39.50; 1983 High $50.00;
Low $39.50; Close $50.00; Up $10.50

22-K4-5.2
1983 *Puss in Boots*
Prices: Issue $39.50; 1983 High $39.50;
Low $39.50; Close $39.50; No Change

22-K4-5.3
1983 *Little Red Riding Hood*
Prices: Issue $39.50; 1983 High $39.50;
Low $39.50; Close $39.50; No Change

22-K4-5.4
1983 *Hansel and Gretel*
Prices: Issue $39.50; 1983 High $39.50;
Low $39.50; Close $39.50; No Change

22-K4-5.5
1984 *Cinderella*
Issue price: $39.50

22-K4-5.1 ''The Frog King''
1982 Kaiser *Classic Fairy Tales*
Kaiser's use of lithography and silk screen
transfer produces rich shades of deep purple
and green.

Königszelt Bayern entered the collector's plate market in 1979 with the first issue in its *Hedi Keller Christmas* series, more than a century after the creation of the first porcelain bearing the hallmark of Königszelt of Silesia. The likeness of Wilhelm I (1797-1888), king of Prussia and first sovereign of a united Germany, is incorporated in the hallmark of Königszelt Bayern—a tribute to his early patronage under which Bavarian porcelain began its rise to prominence among the porcelain creations of the world. In 1981 the *Grimm's Fairy Tales* series began in commemoration of the two-hundredth anniversary of the Grimm brothers' birth. *Sulamith's Love Song* series, created by Sulamith Wülfing, began in 1982.

Hedi Keller was born in Tuttlingen, a village near the Black Forest. She studied for three years at the Kunstakademie in Stuttgart, learning about the great masters—Titian, Rembrandt, and Brueghel—but later was influenced by Van Gogh and the French Impressionists, who discarded conventional ideas to seek a more personalized style. Her work has been exhibited in galleries in Berlin, Mun-ich, and Dusseldorf. Charles Gehm, a graduate of the Columbus Art School, is a prominent member of the Society of Illustrators and has gained a wide audience through his cover designs for Saul Bellow books. Sulamith Wülfing was born in 1901 in Elberfeld (now part of Wuppertal), Germany, and has lived in that area all of her life. She studied at the Art College in Wuppertal and is known for her numerous cards, books, and calendars.

KÖNIGSZELT BAYERN
Waldsassen

Hedi Keller Christmas Series
Artist: Hedi Keller. Artist's signature appears on front

Overglaze-decorated porcelain

Diameter: 24 centimeters (9½ inches)

Pierced foot rim

Edition size unannounced

Numbered with certificate

22-K46-1.1
1979 *The Adoration*
Prices: Issue $29.50; 1983 High $140.00;
Low $75.00; Close $75.00; Down $65.00

22-K46-1.2
1980 *Flight into Egypt*
Prices: Issue $29.50; 1983 High $70.00;
Low $60.00; Close $60.00; Down $10.00

22-K46-1.3
1981 *Return into Galilee*
Prices: Issue $29.50; 1983 High $40.00;
Low $38.00; Close $40.00; Up $2.00

22-K46-1.4
1982 *Following the Star*
Prices: Issue $29.50; 1983 High $50.00;
Low $29.50; Close $50.00; Up $20.50

22-K46-1.5
1983 *Rest on the Flight*
Prices: Issue $29.50; 1983 High $29.50;
Low $29.50; Close $29.50; No Change

22-K46-1.6
1984 *The Nativity*
Issue price: $29.50

Grimm's Fairy Tale Series

Artist: Charles Gehm. Artist's signature appears on front

Overglaze-decorated porcelain

Diameter: 19 centimeters (7½ inches)

Pierced foot rim

Edition size undisclosed, limited by period of issue

Numbered with certificate

22-K46-2.1
1981 *Rumpelstilzchen*
Prices: Issue $23.00; 1983 High $25.00;
Low $23.00; Close $25.00; Up $2.00

22-K46-2.2
1982 *Rapunzel*
Prices: Issue $25.00; 1983 High $35.00;
Low $25.00; Close $35.00; Up $10.00

22-K46-2.3
1982 *Hänsel and Gretel*
Prices: Issue $25.00; 1983 High $25.00;
Low $25.00; Close $25.00; No Change

22-K46-2.4
1983 *The Shoemaker and the Elves*
Prices: Issue $25.00; 1983 High $25.00;
Low $25.00; Close $25.00; No Change

Sulamith's Love Song Series

Artist: Sulamith Wülfing. Artist's signature appears on front

Overglaze-decorated porcelain

Diameter: 19 centimeters (7½ inches)

Pierced foot rim

Edition size undisclosed, limited by announced period of issue

Numbered with certificate

22-K46-3.1
1982 *The Music*
Prices: Issue $29.00; 1983 High $50.00;
Low $29.00; Close $50.00; Up $21.00

22-K46-3.2
1983 *The Pledge*
Prices: Issue $29.00; 1983 High $29.00;
Low $29.00; Close $29.00; No Change

GERMANY
KÖNIGSZELT BAYERN
Waldsassen

22-K46-3.3
1983 *The Vision*
Prices: Issue $29.00; 1983 High $29.00;
Low $29.00; Close $29.00; No Change

22-K46-3.4
1983 *The Gift*
Prices: Issue $29.00; 1983 High $29.00;
Low $29.00; Close $29.00; No Change

22-K46-3.5
1984 *The Circle*
Issue price: $29.00

Philipp Rosenthal, Sr. began his business in 1879 in the town of Selb in Bavaria. He initially purchased "white ware" from various porcelain manufacturers in Selb (including Hutschenreuther) and painted it with his own designs.

In 1895 he established his own factory in Kronach where he produced fine porcelain signed *Rosenthal* on the back, making him one of the first porcelain makers to use his name rather than a symbol. Philipp died in 1937 and the business was taken over by his son, Philipp, Jr., who still heads the firm.

Rosenthal's *Traditional Classic Rose Christmas* series began in 1910 and continues through 1984. In 1974, Rosenthal changed its backstamp to reflect their Classic Rose Collection. From 1969 to 1971 some of the earlier plates were reissued in small quantities (no more than 500 per reissue). Reissued plates, regardless of the year depicted, have a post-1957 backstamp and their foot rims are not pierced. After 1971, the firm discontinued the practice of reissuing plates from previous years, and each Rosenthal collector's plate is now produced only during its current year. The *Traditional Classic Rose Christmas* plates now qualify as limited editions.

In 1971 Rosenthal began the first of its Studio-Linie collections with the *Wiinblad Christmas* series. These plates carry intricate modern designs partially hand-painted in as many as eighteen colors and are embellished with platinum and 18k gold. The *Nobility of Children* series and the *Oriental Gold* series also began in 1976 and carried Rosenthal's Classic Rose Collection backstamp. Both series ended in 1979.

Danish artist Bjørn Wiinblad graduated from the Royal Academy of Art in 1944 and worked for Nymølle Art Fajance Factory from 1946 to 1956. His creations attracted the attention of Philipp Rosenthal, Jr., who after extensive negotiation, persuaded Wiinblad to design works for the German maker. He was assigned to create products for the Studio-Linie, a high-quality/high-price line of Rosenthal ware. His distinctive collector's plates are world renowned, and the "Lotus" pattern of dinnerware he designed won the 1965 American Interior Design Award. Wiinblad today divides his time among his Rosenthal studio at Selb, his private workshop in Kongens Lyngby near Copenhagen, and the Nymølle Art Fajance Factory, which he now owns. His works now hang in the Museum of Decorative Art in Copenhagen, the Museum of Decorative Art in Bergen, Norway, the Faenza Museum in Italy, and the National Museum of Sweden in Stockholm. Edna Hibel, at twenty-two, became the youngest living artist to have a painting in a major American museum when the Boston Museum purchased one of her canvases in 1939. She is an elected member of the Royal Society of Arts in London, and is one of the only living female artists with a U.S. museum devoted to her works. In 1979, she gave a one-woman show at the Monaco Fine Arts Gallery under the patronage of Prince Rainier and Princess Grace and won the "International Year of the Child" award in the United States. She held an internationally acclaimed show in 1980 at Castle Mainau in Germany sponsored by Count and Countess Lennart Bernadotte.

GERMANY
ROSENTHAL

Selb, Rothbühl, Kronach, Amberg, Bad Soden, Landstuhl, Thomas Kulm, Waldershofen

Traditional Classic Rose Christmas Series

Artist: as indicated. Artist's name appears on back

Overglaze-decorated porcelain, many in series have gold inner rim and lettering

Diameter: 21.6 centimeters (8½ inches)

Pierced foot rim until 1971, attached back hanger thereafter

Edition size undisclosed

Not numbered, without certificate

22-R55-1.1
1910 *Winter Peace*
Artist: Jul V. Guldbrandson
Issue price: $1.34

22-R55-1.2
1911 *The Three Wise Men*
Artist: Heinrich Vogoler
Issue price: $1.95

22-R55-1.3
1912 *Shooting Stars*
Artist: Paul Rieth
Issue price: $1.03

22-R55-1.4
1913 *Christmas Lights*
Artist: Julius Dietz
Issue price: $1.47

22-R55-1.5
1914 *Christmas Song*
Artist: Prof. Ludwig von Zumbusch
Issue price: $1.47

22-R55-1.6
1915 *Walking to Church*
Artist: Jul V. Guldbrandson
Issue price: $1.47

22-R55-1.7
1916 *Christmas During War*
Artist: Jul V. Guldbrandson
Issue price: $1.47

22-R55-1.8
1917 *Angel of Peace*
Artist: Prof. Mermagen
Issue price: $1.47

22-R55-1.9
1918 *Peace on Earth*
Artist: K. Pfeiffer
Issue price: $1.47

22-R55-1.10
1919 *St. Christopher with the Christ
Child*
Artist: Dr. W. Schertel
Issue price: $5.96

22-R55-1.11
1920 *The Manger in Bethlehem*
Artist: Dr. W. Schertel
Issue price: $5.96

22-R55-1.12
1921 *Christmas in the Mountains*
Artist: Jupp Wiertz
Issue price: $5.96

22-R55-1.13
1922 *Advent Branch*
Artist: Friedrich Nicolai
Issue price: $5.96

22-R55-1.14
1923 *Children in the Winter Wood*
Artist: Ernst Hofer
Issue price: $5.96

22-R55-1.15
1924 *Deer in the Woods*
Artist: Theo Karner
Issue price: $2.98

22-R55-1.16
1925 *The Three Wise Men*
Artist: Otto Tauscheck
Issue price: $2.98

22-R55-1.17
1926 *Christmas in the Mountains*
Artist: Theo Schmutz-Baudiss
Issue price: $2.98

GERMANY
ROSENTHAL
Selb, Rothbühl, Kronach, Amberg, Bad Soden,
Landstuhl, Thomas Kulm, Waldershofen

22-R55-1.18
1927 *Station on the Way*
Artist: Theo Schmutz-Baudiss
Issue price: $2.98

22-R55-1.19
1928 *Chalet Christmas*
Artist: Heinrich Fink
Issue price: $2.98

22-R55-1.20
1929 *Christmas in the Alps*
Artist: Heinrich Fink
Issue price: $2.98

22-R55-1.21
1930 *Group of Deer under the Pines*
Artist: Theo Karner
Issue price: $2.98

22-R55-1.22
1931 *Path of the Magi*
Artist: Heinrich Fink
Issue price: $3.09

22-R55-1.23
1932 *Christ Child*
Artist: Otto Koch
Issue price: $3.09

22-R55-1.24
1933 *Through the Night to Light*
Artist: Hans Schiffner
Issue price: $3.09

22-R55-1.25
1934 *Christmas Peace*
Artist: Heinrich Fink
Issue price: $3.09

22-R55-1.26
1935 *Christmas by the Sea*
Artist: Heinrich Fink
Issue price: $3.09

22-R55-1.27
1936 *Nurnberg Angel*
Artist: Heinrich Fink
Issue price: $3.09

22-R55-1.28
1937 *Berchtesgaden*
Artist: Heinrich Fink
Issue price: $3.09

22-R55-1.29
1938 *Christmas in the Alps*
Artist: Heinrich Fink
Issue price: $3.09

22-R55-1.30
1939 *Schneekoppe Mountain*
Artist: Heinrich Fink
Issue price: $3.09

22-R55-1.31
1940 *Marien Church in Danzig*
Artist: Walter Mutze
Issue price: $3.09

22-R55-1.32
1941 *Strassburg Cathedral*
Artist: Walter Mutze
Issue price: $3.09

22-R55-1.33
1942 *Marianburg Castle*
Artist: Walter Mutze
Issue price: $3.09

22-R55-1.34
1943 *Winter Idyll*
Artist: Amadeus Dier
Issue price: $3.09

22-R55-1.35
1944 *Wood Scape*
Artist: Willi Hein
Issue price: $3.09

22-R55-1.36
1945 Christmas Peace
Artist: Alfred Mundel
Issue price: $3.09

22-R55-1.37
1946 Christmas in an Alpine Valley
Artist: Willi Hein
Issue price: $3.09

22-R55-1.38
1947 The Dillingen Madonna
Artist: Louis Hagen
Issue price: $6.00

22-R55-1.39
1948 Message to the Shepherds
Artist: Richard Hoffman
Issue price: $6.00

22-R55-1.40
1949 The Holy Family
Artist: Prof. Karl
Issue price: $6.00

22-R55-1.41
1950 Christmas in the Forest
Artist: Willi Hein
Issue price: $5.25

22-R55-1.42
1951 Star of Bethlehem
Artist: Anne V. Groote
Issue price: $5.75

22-R55-1.43
1952 Christmas in the Alps
Artist: Willi Hein
Issue price: $5.75

22-R55-1.44
1953 The Holy Light
Artist: Willi Hein
Issue price: $5.75

22-R55-1.45
1954 *Christmas Eve*
Artist: Willi Hein
Issue price: $6.25

22-R55-1.46
1955 *Christmas in a Village*
Artist: Willi Hein
Issue price: $6.25

22-R55-1.47
1956 *Christmas in the Alps*
Artist: Willi Hein
Issue price: $6.25

22-R55-1.48
1957 *Christmas by the Sea*
Artist: Willi Hein
Issue price: $6.25

22-R55-1.49
1958 *Christmas Eve*
Artist: Willi Hein
Issue price: $6.50

22-R55-1.50
1959 *Midnight Mass*
Artist: Willi Hein
Issue price: $6.75

22-R55-1.51
1960 *Christmas in Small Village*
Artist: Willi Hein
Issue price: $7.25

22-R55-1.52
1961 *Solitary Christmas*
Artist: Willi Hein
Issue price: $7.75

22-R55-1.53
1962 *Christmas Eve*
Artist: Willi Hein
Issue price: $8.75

GERMANY
ROSENTHAL
Selb, Rothbühl, Kronach, Amberg, Bad Soden,
Landstuhl, Thomas Kulm, Waldershofen

22-R55-1.54
1963 *Silent Night*
Artist: Willi Hein
Issue price: $8.75

22-R55-1.55
1964 *Christmas Market in Nurnberg*
Artist: Georg Küspert
Issue price: $8.75

22-R55-1.56
1965 *Christmas in Munich*
Artist: Georg Küspert
Issue price: $11.00

22-R55-1.57
1966 *Christmas in Ulm*
Artist: Georg Küspert
Issue price: $11.00

22-R55-1.58
1967 *Christmas in Regensburg*
Artist: Georg Küspert
Issue price: $11.00

22-R55-1.59
1968 *Christmas in Bremen*
Artist: Georg Küspert
Issue price: $11.00

22-R55-1.60
1969 *Christmas in Rothenburg*
Artist: Georg Küspert
Issue price: $15.75

22-R55-1.61
1970 *Christmas in Cologne*
Artist: Georg Küspert
Issue price: $16.00

22-R55-1.62
1971 *Christmas in Garmisch*
Artist: Georg Küspert
Prices: Issue $66.00; 1983 High $96.00;
Low $90.00; Close $90.00; Down $4.00

22-R55-1.63
1972 *Christmas Celebration in Franconia*
Artist: Georg Küspert
Prices: Issue $66.00; 1983 High $99.00;
Low $97.00; Close $99.00; Up $2.00

22-R55-1.64
1973 *Christmas in Lübeck-Holstein*
Artist: Georg Küspert
Prices: Issue $84.00; 1983 High $105.00;
Low $105.00; Close $105.00; No Change

22-R55-1.65
1974 *Christmas in Wurzburg*
Artist: Georg Küspert
Prices: Issue $85.00; 1983 High $100.00;
Low $98.00; Close $100.00; Up $2.00

22-R55-1.66
1974 *Memorial Church in Berlin*
Artist: Helmut Drexler
Prices: Issue $84.00; 1983 High $200.00;
Low $175.00; Close $200.00; Up $25.00

22-R55-1.67
1975 *Freiburg Cathedral*
Artist: Helmut Drexler
Prices: Issue $75.00; 1983 High $100.00;
Low $80.00; Close $100.00; Up $20.00

22-R55-1.68
1976 *The Castle Cochem*
Artist: Helmut Drexler
Prices: Issue $95.00; 1983 High $80.00;
Low $80.00; Close $80.00; No Change

22-R55-1.69
1977 *Hannover Town Hall*
Artist: Helmut Drexler
Prices: Issue $125.00; 1983 High $110.00;
Low $110.00; Close $110.00; No Change

22-R55-1.70
1978 *Cathedral at Aachen*
Artist: Helmut Drexler
Prices: Issue $150.00; 1983 High $140.00;
Low $116.00; Close $140.00; Up $24.00

22-R55-1.71
1979 *Cathedral in Luxemburg*
Artist: Helmut Drexler
Prices: Issue $165.00; 1983 High $135.00;
Low $130.00; Close $135.00; Up $1.00

GERMANY
ROSENTHAL

Selb, Rothbühl, Kronach, Amberg, Bad Soden,
Landstuhl, Thomas Kulm, Waldershofen

22-R55-1.72
1980 *Christmas in Brussels*
Artist: Helmut Drexler
Prices: Issue $190.00; 1983 High $175.00;
Low $170.00; Close $175.00; Up $5.00

22-R55-1.73
1981 *Christmas in Trier*
Artist: Helmut Drexler
Prices: Issue $190.00; 1983 High $190.00;
Low $190.00; Close $190.00; No Change

22-R55-1.74
1982 *Milan Cathedral*
Artist: Helmut Drexler
Prices: Issue $190.00; 1983 High $190.00;
Low $190.00; Close $190.00; No Change

22-R55-1.75
1983 *Church at Castle Wittenberg*
Artist: Helmut Drexler
Prices: Issue $195.00; 1983 High $195.00;
Low $195.00; Close $195.00; No Change

Wiinblad Christmas Series

Artist: Bjørn Wiinblad. Artist's
signature appears on front

Overglaze-decorated porcelain
partially hand-painted in 18 colors
with 18k gold design on border

Diameter: 29.2 centimeters
(11½ inches)

Attached back hanger

Edition size undisclosed

Not numbered, without certificate

22-R55-2.1
1971 *Maria and Child*
Prices: Issue $100.00; 1983 High $1560.00;
Low $1300.00; Close $1300.00;
Down $260.00

22-R55-2.2
1972 *Caspar*
Prices: Issue $100.00; 1983 High $690.00;
Low $550.00; Close $550.00; Down $140.00

22-R55-2.3
1973 *Melchior*
Prices: Issue $125.00; 1983 High $566.00;
Low $490.00; Close $490.00; Down $76.00

22-R55-2.4
1974 *Balthazar*
Prices: Issue $125.00; 1983 High $572.00;
Low $500.00; Close $500.00; Down $72.00

22-R55-2.5
1975 *The Annunciation*
Prices: Issue $195.00; 1983 High $236.00;
Low $200.00; Close $200.00; Down $36.00

22-R55-2.6
1976 *Angel with Trumpet*
Prices: Issue $195.00; 1983 High $250.00;
Low $180.00; Close $180.00; Down $70.00

22-R55-2.7
1977 *Adoration of the Shepherds*
Prices: Issue $225.00; 1983 High $270.00;
Low $235.00; Close $235.00; Down $35.00

22-R55-2.8
1978 *Angel with Harp*
Prices: Issue $275.00; 1983 High $280.00;
Low $275.00; Close $275.00; Down $5.00

22-R55-2.9
1979 *Exodus from Egypt*
Prices: Issue $310.00; 1983 High $310.00;
Low $310.00; Close $310.00; No Change

22-R55-2.10
1980 *Angel with a Glockenspiel*
Prices: Issue $360.00; 1983 High $360.00;
Low $330.00; Close $360.00; No Change

22-R55-2.11
1981 *Christ Child Visits Temple*
Prices: Issue $375.00; 1983 High $375.00;
Low $375.00; Close $375.00; No Change

GERMANY
ROSENTHAL

Selb, Rothbühl, Kronach, Amberg, Bad Soden,
Landstuhl, Thomas Kulm, Waldershofen

22-R55-2.12
1982 *Christening of Christ*
Prices: Issue $375.00; 1983 High $375.00;
Low $375.00; Close $375.00; No Change
Series Closed

The Nobility of Children Series

Artist: Edna Hibel. Artist's signature appears on front

Overglaze-decorated porcelain banded in gold

Diameter: 25.4 centimeters (10 inches)

Attached back hanger

Edition size limited to 12,750

Numbered with certificate

22-R55-6.1
1976 *La Contessa Isabella*
Prices: Issue $120.00; 1983 High $188.00;
Low $165.00; Close $165.00; Down $23.00

22-R55-6.2
1977 *Le Marquis Maurice-Pierre*
Prices: Issue $120.00; 1983 High $120.00;
Low $110.00; Close $110.00; Down $10.00

22-R55-6.3
1978 *Baronesse Johanna-Maryke Van
Vollendam Tot Marken*
Prices: Issue $130.00; 1983 High $137.00;
Low $135.00; Close $135.00; Down $2.00

22-R55-6.4
1979 *Chief Red Feather*
Prices: Issue $140.00; 1983 High $140.00;
Low $140.00; Close $140.00; No Change
Series Closed

22-R55-8.1

Oriental Gold Series

Artist: Edna Hibel. Artist's signature appears on front

Overglaze-decorated porcelain highlighted in gold

Diameter: 25.4 centimeters (10 inches)

Attached back hanger

Edition size limited to 2,000

Numbered with certificate

22-R55-8.1
1976 Yasuko
Prices: Issue $275.00; 1983 High $1120.00;
Low $1100.00; Close $1100.00; No Change

22-R55-8.2
1977 Mr. Obata
Prices: Issue $275.00; 1983 High $560.00;
Low $560.00; Close $560.00; No Change

22-R55-8.3
1978 Sakura
Prices: Issue $295.00; 1983 High $500.00;
Low $400.00; Close $400.00; Down $75.00

22-R55-8.4
1979 Michio
Prices: Issue $325.00; 1983 High $510.00;
Low $450.00; Close $450.00; Down $56.00
Series Closed

22-R55-2.1 "Maria and Child"
1971 Rosenthal *Wiinblad Christmas*
The Rosenthal/Wiinblad collaboration required an unprecedented 18 colors for the main design, and featured a lavish use of platinum and 18k gold design in the border.

The pottery now known as Royal Bayreuth began in 1794 in the mountain village of Tettau as the Koniglich Privilegierter Porzellanfabrik Tettau, the first porcelain manufacturer in Bavaria. Now a subsidiary of Royal Tettau, Royal Bayreuth began its *Mother's Day* series in 1973 with art by contemporary artists. The series ended in 1982.

Brazilian Ozz Franca, a specialist in the art of children's portraiture, began the *Mother's Day* series in 1973. In 1974 Leo Jansen succeeded him as the series artist. Born in The Hague, The Netherlands, Jansen spent his youth in Indonesia, where he developed his skills as a portrait-painter by sketching the bronze-skinned Malay children. He returned to the Netherlands to study at the Academy of Fine Arts, and later refined his work in the famous "Pigalle" section of Paris. His "Young Americans VI" was 1979 Plate of the Year on the Canadian plate market.

GERMANY
ROYAL BAYREUTH
Tettau

Mother's Day Series

Artist: as indicated. Artist's signature appears on back until 1975, on front thereafter

Overglaze-decorated porcelain

Diameter: 19.7 centimeters (7¾ inches)

Attached back hanger

Edition size: as indicated

Numbered without certificate

22-R58-2.1
1973 *Consolation*
Artist: Ozz Franca/Edition: 4,000
Prices: Issue $16.50; 1983 High $44.00;
Low $40.00; Close $44.00; Up $4.00

22-R58-2.2
1974 *Young Americans*
Artist: Leo Jansen/Edition: 4,000
Prices: Issue $25.00; 1983 High $160.00;
Low $126.00; Close $160.00; Up $34.00

22-R58-2.3
1975 *Young Americans II*
Artist: Leo Jansen/Edition: 5,000
Prices: Issue $25.00; 1983 High $110.00;
Low $108.00; Close $110.00; Up $2.00

22-R58-2.4
1976 *Young Americans III*
Artist: Leo Jansen/Edition: 5,000
Prices: Issue $30.00; 1983 High $63.00;
Low $60.00; Close $63.00; Up $3.00

22-R58-2.5
1977 *Young Americans IV*
Artist: Leo Jansen/Edition: 5,000
Prices: Issue $40.00; 1983 High $55.00;
Low $52.00; Close $55.00; Up $3.00

22-R58-2.6
1978 *Young Americans V*
Artist: Leo Jansen/Edition: 5,000
Prices: Issue $45.00; 1983 High $40.00;
Low $28.00; Close $28.00; Down $12.00

22-R58-2.7
1979 *Young Americans VI*
Artist: Leo Jansen/Edition: 5,000
Prices: Issue $60.00; 1983 High $75.00;
Low $71.00; Close $75.00; Up $1.00

22-R58-2.8
1980 *Young Americans VII*
Artist: Leo Jansen/Edition: 5,000
Prices: Issue $65.00; 1983 High $63.00;
Low $50.00; Close $50.00; Down $13.00

22-R58-2.9
1981 *Young Americans VIII*
Artist: Leo Jansen/Edition: 5,000
Prices: Issue $65.00; 1983 High $73.00;
Low $50.00; Close $50.00; Down $23.00

22-R58-2.10
1982 *Young Americans IX*
Artist: Leo Jansen/Edition: 5,000
Prices: Issue $65.00; 1983 High $65.00;
Low $65.00; Close $65.00; No Change
Series Closed

22-R58-2.7 "Young Americans VI"
1979 Royal Bayreuth *Mother's Day*
Luminous eyes and realistic flesh tones
characterized the artwork of the late Leo
Jansen.

Schmid

Schmid was established in Boston in the 1930s. Since then the firm has been a specialized importer of porcelain bells and mugs as well as plates. Schmid limited-edition plates are produced by the Porzellanfabrik Johann Seltmann Vohenstrauss GmbH factory in Germany.

Both the *Christmas* series, which began in 1971, and the *Mother's Day* series, which started the following year, feature art created by the late Berta Hummel. The Hummel plates bear her signature depending on whether Berta Hummel had signed the original artwork.

Both Hummel series feature art created by Berta Hummel before she entered the Franciscan order at Siessen in 1934 and took the name Sister Maria Innocentia Hummel (see Germany, GOEBEL). Prior to taking her vows, she had received extensive training at art academies in Simbach and Munich, where she evolved the distinctive style that instantly identifies her work to collectors worldwide.

Christmas Series

Artist: Berta Hummel. Artist's signature or initials appear on front except 1975, 1977, 1981, 1982, 1983, and 1984

Overglaze-decorated porcelain

Diameter: 19.7 centimeters (7¾ inches)

Attached back hanger

Edition size undisclosed, limited by year of issue

Not numbered, without certificate

22-S12-1.1
1971 *Angel in a Christmas Setting*
Prices: Issue $15.00; 1983 High $70.00;
Low $60.00; Close $60.00; Down $10.00

22-S12-1.2
1972 *Angel with Flute*
Prices: Issue $15.00; 1983 High $32.00;
Low $32.00; Close $32.00; No Change

22-S12-1.3
1973 *The Nativity*
Prices: Issue $15.00; 1983 High $218.00;
Low $200.00; Close $200.00; Down $18.00

22-S12-1.4
1974 *The Guardian Angel*
Prices: Issue $18.50; 1983 High $35.00;
Low $35.00; Close $35.00; No Change

22-S12-1.5
1975 *Christmas Child*
Prices: Issue $25.00; 1983 High $30.00;
Low $30.00, Close $30.00; No Change

22-S12-1.6
1976 *Sacred Journey*
Prices: Issue $27.50; 1983 High $57.00;
Low $40.00; Close $40.00; Down $17.00

22-S12-1.7
1977 *Herald Angel*
Prices: Issue $27.50; 1983 High $41.00;
Low $33.00; Close $33.00; Down $6.00

22-S12-1.8
1978 *Heavenly Trio*
Prices: Issue $32.50; 1983 High $30.00;
Low $30.00; Close $30.00; No Change

22-S12-1.9
1979 *Starlight Angel*
Prices: Issue $38.00; 1983 High $43.00;
Low $28.00; Close $28.00; Down $15.00

22-S12-1.10
1980 *Parade into Toyland*
Prices: Issue $45.00; 1983 High $72.00;
Low $50.00; Close $50.00; Down $22.00

22-S12-1.11
1981 *A Time to Remember*
Prices: Issue $45.00; 1983 High $45.00;
Low $45.00; Close $45.00; No Change

22-S12-1.12
1982 *Angelic Procession*
Prices: Issue $45.00; 1983 High $52.00;
Low $45.00; Close $52.00; Up $7.00

22-S12-1.13
1983 *Angelic Messenger*
Prices: Issue $45.00; 1983 High $45.00;
Low $45.00; Close $45.00; No Change

22-S12-1.14
1984 *A Gift from Heaven*
Issue price: $45.00

Mother's Day Series

Artist: Berta Hummel. Artist's
signature or initials appear on front
from 1972 thru 1975, and 1977

Overglaze-decorated porcelain

Diameter: 19.7 centimeters
(7¾ inches)

Attached back hanger

Edition size undisclosed, limited
by year of issue

Not numbered, without certificate

22-S12-2.1
1972 *Playing Hooky*
Prices: Issue $15.00; 1983 High $32.00;
Low $30.00; Close $30.00; Down $2.00

22-S12-2.2
1973 *The Little Fisherman*
Prices: Issue $15.00; 1983 High $84.00;
Low $65.00; Close $65.00; Down $19.00

SCHMID
Selb

22-S12-2.3
1974 *The Bumblebee*
Prices: Issue $18.50; 1983 High $36.00;
Low $30.00; Close $30.00; Down $6.00

22-S12-2.4
1975 *Message of Love*
Prices: Issue $25.00; 1983 High $36.00;
Low $31.00; Close $31.00; Down $5.00

22-S12-2.5
1976 *Devotion for Mother*
Prices: Issue $27.50; 1983 High $30.00;
Low $25.00; Close $25.00; Down $5.00

22-S12-2.6
1977 *Moonlight Return*
Prices: Issue $27.50; 1983 High $37.00;
Low $30.00; Close $30.00; Down $7.00

22-S12-2.7
1978 *Afternoon Stroll*
Prices: Issue $32.50; 1983 High $34.00;
Low $20.00; Close $20.00; Down $14.00

22-S12-2.8
1979 *Cherub's Gift*
Prices: Issue $38.00; 1983 High $38.00;
Low $18.00; Close $18.00; Down $17.00

22-S12-2.9
1980 *Mother's Little Helpers*
Prices: Issue $45.00; 1983 High $45.00;
Low $30.00; Close $30.00; Down $14.00

22-S12-2.10
1981 *Playtime*
Prices: Issue $45.00; 1983 High $45.00;
Low $45.00; Close $45.00; No Change

22-S12-2.11
1982 *The Flower Basket*
Prices: Issue $45.00; 1983 High $45.00;
Low $45.00; Close $45.00; No Change

22-S12-2.12
1983 *Spring Bouquet*
Prices: Issue $45.00; 1983 High $45.00;
Low $45.00; Close $45.00; No Change

22-S12-2.13
1984 *A Joy to Share*
Issue price: $45.00

Belleek Pottery Ltd., maker of thin, translucent parian china, was established in 1857 by David McBirney and Robert W. Armstrong on the banks of the River Erne near the small village of Belleek in County Fermanagh, Northern Ireland. The site is near deposits of clay discovered when the owner of Castle Caldwell in Fermanagh became interested in the brilliant whitewash used on local cottages and found that his entire estate lay on a bed of feldspar clay.

When combined with metallic washes, this clay produces the unique iridescent effect for which Belleek is known—a mother-of-pearl luster that is used on tea sets, figurines, and tableware. Queen Victoria and her son, the Prince of Wales, are among those who commissioned elaborate table services from the firm. Belleek ware is still made today much as it was a century ago.

Belleek's *Christmas* series, based on Irish subjects, began in 1970 and ended in 1977. The *Irish Wildlife Christmas* series began in 1978.

Artists for Belleek plates are not disclosed.

BELLEEK

Belleek, County Fermanagh

Christmas Series

Artist: undisclosed

Parian china

Diameter: 21.6 centimeters
(8½ inches)

No hanger

Edition size limited to announced
quantity of 7,500

Not numbered, without certificate

26-B18-1.1
1970 *Castle Caldwell*
Prices: Issue $25.00; 1983 High $125.00;
Low $125.00; Close $125.00; No Change

26-B18-1.2
1971 *Celtic Cross*
Prices: Issue $25.00; 1983 High $53.00;
Low $45.00; Close $45.00; Down $8.00

26-B18-1.3
1972 *Flight of the Earls*
Prices: Issue $30.00; 1983 High $53.00;
Low $50.00, Close $50.00; Down $2.00

26-B18-1.4
1973 *Tribute to W. B. Yeats*
Prices: Issue $38.50; 1983 High $72.00;
Low $69.00; Close $70.00; No Change

26-B18-1.5
1974 *Devenish Island*
Prices: Issue $45.00; 1983 High $250.00;
Low $215.00; Close $250.00; Up $35.00

26-B18-1.6
1975 *The Celtic Cross*
Prices: Issue $48.00; 1983 High $65.00;
Low $58.00; Close $65.00; Up $7.00

26-B18-1.7
1976 *Dove of Peace*
Prices: Issue $55.00; 1983 High $78.00;
Low $73.00; Close $78.00; Up $3.00

26-B18-1.8
1977 *Wren*
Prices: Issue $55.00; 1983 High $59.00;
Low $59.00; Close $59.00; No Change
Series Closed

Irish Wildlife Christmas Series

Artist: undisclosed

Parian china

Diameter: 22.9 centimeters (9 inches)

No hanger

Edition size undisclosed

Not numbered, without certificate

26-B18-2.1
1978 A Leaping Salmon
Prices: Issue $55.00; 1983 High $73.00;
Low $70.00; Close $70.00; Down $3.00

26-B18-2.2
1979 Hare at Rest
Prices: Issue $58.50; 1983 High $70.00;
Low $70.00; Close $70.00; No Change

26-B18-2.3
1980 Hedgehog
Prices: Issue $66.50; 1983 High $90.00;
Low $67.00; Close $90.00; Up $22.00

26-B18-2.4
1981 Red Squirrel
Prices: Issue $78.00; 1983 High $78.00;
Low $78.00; Close $78.00; No Change

26-B18-2.5
1982 Irish Seal
Prices: Issue $78.00; 1983 High $78.00;
Low $78.00; Close $78.00; No Change

26-B18-2.6
1983 Red Fox
Issue price: $85.00
Series Closed

26-B18-1.1 "Castle Caldwell"
1970 Belleek *Christmas*
Translucent parian china in Belleek's
renowned white relief design.

The Davenport Pottery was founded by Arthur Wood and Son, descendants of esteemed potters who made their name and fortune by crafting Toby jugs at the close of the eighteenth century. Davenport is committed to preserving the tradition of fine British pottery, still relying on techniques that have been carefully handed down through generations of craftsmen.

With its move into the medium of limited-edition plates, The Davenport Pottery introduced, in 1983, the first collector's plate series based on the 200-year-old Toby tradition with "Toby Fillpot," the first issue in the Toby Plate Collection. Each plate in this edition is hand-cast and hand-painted by artisans using techniques that date back to the eighteenth century.

W. A. Blandford was commissioned as master modeller to design the "Toby Fillpot" plate. Mr. Blandford's distinguished career in ceramics began in the 1930s with an apprenticeship to Wood & Sons, the Staffordshire ceramics house which has long been associated with Toby jugs.

His entire career has been spent in the Staffordshire area, and he has modelled literally hundreds of fine and intricately detailed ceramic pieces.

DAVENPORT POTTERY
Staffordshire

Toby Plate Collection

Artist: as indicated. Artist's signature appears on front

Earthenware

Diameter: 21.6 centimeters (8½ inches)

No hanger

Edition size undisclosed, limited by period of issue

Numbered with certificate

26-D8-1.1
1983 *Toby Fillpot*
Artist: Wilfred Blandford
Issue price: $35.00

Longton Crown Pottery maintains a long tradition of quality English bone china manufacture. Josiah Spode perfected the process by which animal bone ash is added to china clay to produce bone china, which is creamy white and translucent. His formula came to be known as English bone china and remains the standard today.

Longton Crown Pottery began its first Baronet bone china collector's plate series in 1981 with *The Canterbury Tales* collection, interpreting Geoffrey Chaucer's literary classic of the same name, and with the sponsorship of the Centre for Medieval & Renaissance Studies of Oxford, England.

The artist for the series, G. A. Hoover, carries on a family tradition of artists which began with his grandfather. He earned a Master of Fine Arts degree and is considered a master of the style known as Romantic Realism. His paintings are in permanent collections of the Museums of Art in Medellín, Colombia, and St. Paul, Minnesota, and are also in the Tulane University Museum.

LONGTON CROWN POTTERY

Longton, Stoke-on-Trent, Staffordshire

The Canterbury Tales Collection

Artist: G. A. Hoover. Artist's signature appears on front

Baronet bone china

Diameter: 21.6 centimeters (8½ inches)

No hanger

Edition size undisclosed, limited by period of issue

Numbered with certificate

26-L46-1.1
1981 *The Man of Law's Tale*
Prices: Issue $29.80; 1983 High $30.00;
Low $29.80; Close $30.00; Up $.20

26-L46-1.2
1982 *The Franklin's Tale*
Prices: Issue $29.80; 1983 High $30.00;
Low $29.80; Close $30.00; Up $.20

26-L46-1.3
1982 *The Knight's Tale*
Prices: Issue $31.80; 1983 High $35.00;
Low $31.80; Close $35.00; Up $3.20

26-L46-1.4
1982 *The Wife of Bath's Tale*
Prices: Issue $31.80; 1983 High $34.00;
Low $31.80; Close $34.00; Up $2.20
Series Closed

Royal Doulton dates to 1815, when a potter named John Doulton invested his life savings of £100 in a one-kiln pottery in the Lambeth section of London.

At the International Exhibition of 1871, John's son Henry Doulton exhibited many of his experimental art pieces. Their favorable reception led to the development of decorative ceramics whose extensive range of colors and decorative techniques ultimately established Doulton Lambethware as an art form.

In 1877, Henry Doulton turned his attention to the development of tableware. At a small earthenware factory in Burslem, Staffordshire, table services for everyday use were produced along with more costly services with raised gold and acid-etched decorations, often combined with the finest of hand painting. Queen Victoria conferred knighthood upon Henry Doulton in 1887 for his accomplishments in the area of ceramic techniques, thus making him the first potter in England to receive such an honor. In 1901 the company received the Royal warrant, giving it authority to use *Royal* with its name.

The *Beswick Christmas* series, sponsored by Royal Doulton's Beswick Potteries from 1972 to 1978, depicted Christmas traditions from around the world. The Collector's International Gallery of "Fine Art on Fine China" began with the *Mother and Child* series in 1973. These plates show mothers and children of various countries. Other series in the Collector's International group are by contemporary artists and include the *Commedia Dell' Arte* series begun in 1974 and ended in 1978, and *The Log of the "Dashing Wave"* series which began in 1976. The *Valentine's Day* series also began in 1976 with artwork from Victorian prints. In 1980 Royal Doulton began the *Portraits of Innocence* series.

Royal Doulton has recruited several important artists to design its collector's plates. John Stobart grew up in the English shipping town of Liverpool. He attended Derby College of Arts and won a scholarship to the Royal Academy of Art in London. He has traveled extensively by sea and some of the most exotic ports in the world have served as settings for his paintings. His works hang in such prestigious collections as the Marine Museum of Upper Canada in Toronto, the National Maritime Museum in Greenwich, England, and the Royal Naval College. His paintings have been featured as cover art for *American Heritage, American Artist, Reader's Digest, Oceans,* and *International Yachtsman.* The maker was the first to commission Edna Hibel to work in the limited-edition plate medium. She has since become one of the most successful plate artists (see Germany, HIBEL STUDIO, ROSENTHAL; United States, KNOWLES). Another famous Royal Doulton artist is LeRoy Neiman, recipient of the gold medal of the *Salon d'Art Moderne* in Paris. His work has appeared on the covers of *Time* and *Newsweek* magazines and is in the permanent collection of Oxford University. Francisco J.J.C. Masseria won his first gold medal at the age of fourteen in the *Salon Annuale de Entre Rios* in his native Argentina. He studied the works of the Italian and Spanish Renaissance masters while in Europe, and there developed his own distinctive style of porcelain-like, mysterious faces set against almost abstract backgrounds.

ROYAL DOULTON
Burslem, Stoke-on-Trent, Staffordshire

Beswick Christmas Series

Artist: as indicated

Earthenware in hand-cast bas-relief hand-painted in 15 colors

Diameter: 20.5 centimeters (8 inches square)

Pierced foot rim

Edition size limited to 15,000

Not numbered, without certificate

26-R62-1.1
1972 *Christmas in England*
Artist: Harry Sales
Prices: Issue $35.00; 1983 High $47.00;
Low $40.00; Close $40.00; Down $7.00

26-R62-1.2
1973 *Christmas in Mexico*
Artist: Chavela Castrejon
Prices: Issue $37.50; 1983 High $29.00;
Low $24.00; Close $25.00; Down $4.00

26-R62-1.3
1974 *Christmas in Bulgaria*
Artist: Dimitri Yordanov
Prices: Issue $37.50; 1983 High $45.00;
Low $40.00; Close $40.00; Down $5.00

26-R62-1.4
1975 *Christmas in Norway*
Artist: Alton Toby
Prices: Issue $45.00; 1983 High $54.00;
Low $54.00; Close $54.00; No Change

26-R62-1.5
1976 *Christmas in Holland*
Artist: Alton Toby
Prices: Issue $50.00; 1983 High $44.00;
Low $44.00; Close $44.00; No Change

26-R62-1.6
1977 *Christmas in Poland*
Artist: Alton Toby
Prices: Issue $50.00; 1983 High $90.00;
Low $73.00; Close $90.00; Up $17.00

26-R62-1.7
1978 *Christmas in America*
Artist: Alton Toby
Prices: Issue $55.00; 1983 High $52.00;
Low $52.00; Close $52.00; No Change
Series Closed

Mother and Child Series

Artist: Edna Hibel. Artist's signature appears on front

Bone china banded in gold

Diameter: 21 centimeters (8¼ inches)

No hanger

Edition size limited to 15,000

Numbered since 1974, without certificate

26-R62-2.1
1973 Colette and Child
Prices: Issue $40.00; 1983 High $485.00;
Low $465.00; Close $465.00; Down $20.00

26-R62-2.2
1974 Sayuri and Child
Prices: Issue $40.00; 1983 High $204.00;
Low $150.00; Close $150.00; Down $54.00

26-R62-2.3
1975 Kristina and Child
Prices: Issue $50.00; 1983 High $132.00;
Low $125.00; Close $125.00; Down $7.00

26-R62-2.4
1976 Marilyn and Child
Prices: Issue $55.00; 1983 High $125.00;
Low $120.00; Close $120.00; Down $5.00

26-R62-2.5
1977 Lucia and Child
Prices: Issue $60.00; 1983 High $100.00;
Low $92.00; Close $100.00; Up $4.00

26-R62-2.6
1978 Kathleen and Child
Prices: Issue $85.00; 1983 High $120.00;
Low $90.00; Close $90.00; Down $30.00
Series Closed

GREAT BRITAIN
ROYAL DOULTON
Burslem, Stoke-on-Trent, Staffordshire

Commedia Dell' Arte Series

Artist: LeRoy Neiman. Artist's signature appears on front

Bone china banded in gold

Diameter: 25.4 centimeters (10 inches)

No hanger

Edition size limited to 15,000

Numbered without certificate

26-R62-3.1
1974 Harlequin
Prices: Issue $50.00; 1983 High $96.00;
Low $70.00; Close $70.00; Down $26.00

26-R62-3.2
1975 Pierrot
Prices: Issue $60.00; 1983 High $84.00;
Low $65.00; Close $65.00; Down $19.00

26-R62-3.3
1977 Columbine
Prices: Issue $70.00; 1983 High $55.00;
Low $55.00; Close $55.00; No Change

26-R62-3.4
1978 Punchinello
Prices: Issue $70.00; 1983 High $52.00;
Low $52.00; Close $52.00; No Change
Series Closed

The Log of the "Dashing Wave" Series

Artist: John Stobart. Artist's signature appears on front

Bone china banded in gold

Diameter: 26.7 centimeters (10½ inches)

No hanger

Edition size limited to 15,000

Numbered without certificate

26-R62-6.1
1976 Sailing with the Tide
Prices: Issue $65.00; 1983 High $133.00;
Low $120.00; Close $120.00; Down $13.00

26-R62-6.2
1977 Running Free
Prices: Issue $70.00; 1983 High $148.00;
Low $135.00; Close $135.00; Down $10.00

26-R62-6.3
1978 *Rounding the Horn*
Prices: Issue $70.00; 1983 High $90.00;
Low $90.00; Close $90.00; No Change

26-R62-6.4
1979 *Hong Kong*
Prices: Issue $75.00; 1983 High $92.00;
Low $90.00; Close $92.00; Up $2.00

26-R62-6.5
1981 *Bora Bora*
Prices: Issue $95.00; 1983 High $95.00;
Low $95.00; Close $95.00; No Change

Maker had
no photo at
press time

26-R62-6.6
1982 *Journey's End*
Prices: Issue $95.00; 1983 High $99.00;
Low $95.00; Close $99.00; Up $4.00
Series Closed

Valentine's Day Series

Artist: Unknown. Reproduced
from nineteenth-century Victorian
prints

Bone china banded in gold

Diameter: 21 centimeters
(8¼ inches)

No hanger

Edition size undisclosed, limited
by period of issue

Not numbered, without certificate

26-R62-7.1
1976 *Victorian Boy and Girl*
Prices: Issue $25.00; 1983 High $52.00;
Low $40.00; Close $40.00; Down $12.00

26-R62-7.2
1977 *My Sweetest Friend*
Prices: Issue $25.00; 1983 High $23.00;
Low $13.00; Close $13.00; Down $10.00

ROYAL DOULTON

Burslem, Stoke-on-Trent, Staffordshire

26-R62-7.3
1978 *If I Loved You*
Prices: Issue $25.00; 1983 High $40.00;
Low $40.00; Close $40.00; No Change

26-R62-7.4
1979 *My Valentine*
Prices: Issue $29.95; 1983 High $38.00;
Low $30.00; Close $30.00; Down $8.00

26-R62-7.5
1980 *On a Swing*
Prices: Issue $32.95; 1983 High $38.00;
Low $30.00; Close $30.00; Down $6.00

26-R62-7.6
1981 *Sweet Music*
Prices: Issue $35.00; 1983 High $40.00;
Low $40.00; Close $40.00; No Change

26-R62-7.7
1982 *From My Heart*
Prices: Issue $35.00; 1983 High $42.00;
Low $40.00; Close $42.00; Up $2.00

26-R62-7.8
1983 *Cherub's Song*
Prices: Issue $40.00; 1983 High $45.00;
Low $40.00; Close $45.00; Up $5.00

26-R62-7.9
1984 *Love in Bloom*
Issue price: $40.00

Portraits of Innocence Series

Artist: Francisco Masseria. Artist's signature appears on front

Bone china banded in gold

Diameter: 20.3 centimeters (8 inches)

No hanger

Edition size limited to 15,000

Numbered without certificate

26-R62-11.1
1980 Panchito
Prices: Issue $75.00; 1983 High $190.00;
Low $175.00; Close $175.00; Down $15.00

26-R62-11.2
1981 Adrien
Prices: Issue $85.00; 1983 High $132.00;
Low $110.00; Close $110.00; Down $22.00

26-R62-11.3
1982 Angelica
Prices: Issue $95.00; 1983 High $118.00;
Low $95.00; Close $110.00; Up $15.00

26-R62-11.4
1983 Juliana
Prices: Issue $95.00; 1983 High $125.00;
Low $95.00; Close $125.00; Up $30.00
Series Closed

Spode

Josiah Spode I established the Spode Works at Stoke-on-Trent, England, in 1776 after spending nearly thirty years learning every facet of the pottery business. From the beginning, the Spode name was highly respected, and the firm has been awarded the Royal warrant by each English monarch since George III.

Josiah Spode perfected the process by which animal bone ash is added to china clay to produce bone china, which is creamy white and translucent. His formula came to be known as English bone china and remains the standard to this day.

Upon Spode's death in 1797, his son, Josiah Spode II, continued the trade, with William Copeland in charge of sales. Josiah Spode III in turn headed the business, but upon his death, Copeland became sole owner, and from 1827 his descendants operated the firm. Under their direction it was called W. T. Copeland & Sons, Ltd., but retained the Spode trademark. Between 1967 and 1976, the firm was owned by Carborundum Company, but in 1976 Spode merged with Royal Worcester of England. The Spode trademark has been retained, and the present factory is located on the site of the original pottery.

Spode's bone china *Christmas* series, which began in 1970 and ended in 1981, is based on old English carols. The plate body itself reproduces an original eighteenth-century Spode model; the designs are based on work by Gillian West, a prominent nineteenth-century British ceramics artist. The 1970 and 1971 plates are decorated in gold; thereafter, decorations are in gold plus a second color which is changed every two years.

SPODE

Stoke-on-Trent, Staffordshire

Christmas Series

Artist: Gillian West

Bone china decorated in gold

Diameter: 20.3 centimeters
(8 inches)

No hanger

Edition size undisclosed, limited
by year of issue

Not numbered, without certificate

26-S63-1.1
1970 *Partridge in a Pear Tree*
Prices: Issue $35.00; 1983 High $71.00;
Low $60.00; Close $60.00; Down $11.00

26-S63-1.2
1971 *In Heaven the Angels Singing*
Prices: Issue $35.00; 1983 High $40.00;
Low $37.00; Close $37.00; Down $3.00

26-S63-1.3
1972 *We Saw Three Ships A'Sailing*
Prices: Issue $35.00; 1983 High $46.00;
Low $46.00; Close $46.00; No Change

26-S63-1.4
1973 *We Three Kings of Orient Are*
Prices: Issue $35.00; 1983 High $71.00;
Low $50.00; Close $65.00; Down $6.00

26-S63-1.5
1974 *Deck the Halls*
Prices: Issue $35.00; 1983 High $54.00;
Low $45.00; Close $45.00; Down $9.00

26-S63-1.6
1975 *Christbaum*
Prices: Issue $45.00; 1983 High $50.00;
Low $50.00; Close $50.00; No Change

26-S63-1.7
1976 *Good King Wenceslas*
Prices: Issue $45.00; 1983 High $45.00;
Low $40.00; Close $40.00; Down $5.00

26-S63-1.8
1977 *The Holly and the Ivy*
Prices: Issue $45.00; 1983 High $47.00;
Low $43.00; Close $47.00; Up $4.00

26-S63-1.9
1978 *While Shepherds Watched*
Prices: Issue $45.00; 1983 High $50.00;
Low $50.00; Close $50.00; No Change

26-S63-1.10
1979 *Away in a Manger*
Prices: Issue $50.00; 1983 High $50.00;
Low $45.00; Close $45.00; Down $3.00

26-S63-1.11
1980 *Bringing in the Boar's Head*
Prices: Issue $60.00; 1983 High $65.00;
Low $55.00; Close $55.00; Down $5.00

26-S63-1.12
1981 *Make We Merry*
Prices: Issue $65.00; 1983 High $73.00;
Low $55.00; Close $55.00; Down $17.00
Series Closed

Josiah Wedgwood I, Fellow of the Royal Society, is known as the "father of English potters." He founded the firm that bears his name in 1759 and built a new factory which he called "Etruria" ten years later.

Wedgwood himself developed many of the processes and materials used by the firm to this day. He is perhaps best known for his "Jasper ware" which he perfected in 1774. A vitreous, unglazed stoneware, Jasper is pure white in its original form but can be stained to produce a wide variety of colored backgrounds—green, lilac, yellow, maroon, black, and most popular of all, classic "Wedgwood blue"—onto which white or colored bas-relief decorations are applied by hand.

Although potters in England and abroad tried to duplicate Jasper ware, none was successful, and the Wedgwood name is so firmly linked with Jasper to this day that many people mistakenly think it is the only ware Wedgwood produces, and that it is made only in blue.

In 1940, having outgrown the pottery at Etruria, the firm moved to what has been described as the most up-to-date pottery in the world, near the village of Barlaston, Stoke-on-Trent, Staffordshire, England. There, in 1969, the firm celebrated the two-hundredth anniversary of the Etruria pottery by introducing a *Christmas* series of classic Wedgwood blue-and-white Jasper collector's plates commemorating famous English monuments. In 1971 Wedgwood began a series of *Mothers* plates, issued annually, made in black basalt ware and Jasper wares, and bearing designs created for Wedgwood in the late eighteenth century. The *Bicentennial of American Independence* series, also in blue-and-white Jasper, is a six-plate series which began in 1972 and closed in 1976. It commemorates events which led to American Independence. *The Blossoming of Suzanne* series on Wedgwood bone china, with designs by Mary Vickers, started in 1977. The *Mary Vickers My Memories* series began in 1981.

Artists for Wedgwood over the past two centuries have included some of the most distinguished names in plate design. William Hackwood was a modeler for Wedgwood from 1769 to 1832, and his eighteenth-century designs have been used on Wedgwood Jasper ware for generations. Lady Elizabeth Templetown was a designer for Wedgwood from 1783 to 1787. Most of her designs were modeled by William Hackwood. Among the staff artists of the Wedgwood Design Studio over the past thirty years are Rex Whistler, Eric Ravilious, Edward Bawden, Arnold Machin, Richard Guyatt, and Eduardo Paolozzi. Mary Vickers is one of the leading contemporary Romantic painters, and is also accomplished in lithographs and etchings. She studied at England's St. Martin's School of Art, the New York Art Students League, and the Pratt Institute. Her works are exhibited in major galleries on both sides of the Atlantic, and in private collections such as that of the Duke and Duchess of Marlborough.

GREAT BRITAIN
WEDGWOOD
Barlaston, Stoke-on-Trent, Staffordshire

Christmas Series

Artist: Tom Harper until 1978; undisclosed thereafter

Jasper stoneware

Diameter: 20.3 centimeters (8 inches)

No hanger

Edition size undisclosed, limited by year of issue

Not numbered, with certificate

26-W90-1.1
1969 *Windsor Castle*
Prices: Issue $25.00; 1983 High $275.00;
Low $250.00; Close $250.00; Down $25.00

26-W90-1.2
1970 *Christmas in Trafalgar Square*
Prices: Issue $30.00; 1983 High $30.00;
Low $27.00; Close $27.00; Down $3.00

26-W90-1.3
1971 *Piccadilly Circus, London*
Prices: Issue $30.00; 1983 High $40.00;
Low $40.00; Close $40.00; No Change

26-W90-1.4
1972 *St. Paul's Cathedral*
Prices: Issue $35.00; 1983 High $41.00;
Low $36.00; Close $36.00; Down $5.00

26-W90-1.5
1973 *The Tower of London*
Prices: Issue $40.00; 1983 High $48.00;
Low $45.00; Close $45.00; Down $3.00

26-W90-1.6
1974 *The Houses of Parliament*
Prices: Issue $40.00; 1983 High $37.00;
Low $37.00; Close $37.00; No Change

26-W90-1.7
1975 *Tower Bridge*
Prices: Issue $45.00; 1983 High $36.00;
Low $34.00; Close $34.00; Down $2.00

26-W90-1.8
1976 *Hampton Court*
Prices: Issue $55.00; 1983 High $46.00;
Low $46.00; Close $46.00; No Change

26-W90-1.9
1977 *Westminster Abbey*
Prices: Issue $55.00; 1983 High $35.00;
Low $35.00; Close $35.00; No Change

26-W90-1.10
1978 *The Horse Guards*
Prices: Issue $60.00; 1983 High $41.00;
Low $37.00; Close $41.00; Up $4.00

26-W90-1.11
1979 *Buckingham Palace*
Prices: Issue $65.00; 1983 High $56.00;
Low $49.00; Close $49.00; Down $7.00

26-W90-1.12
1980 *St. James Palace*
Prices: Issue $70.00; 1983 High $72.00;
Low $65.00; Close $65.00; Down $5.00

26-W90-1.13
1981 *Marble Arch*
Prices: Issue $75.00; 1983 High $75.00;
Low $75.00; Close $75.00; No Change

26-W90-1.14
1982 *Lambeth Palace*
Prices: Issue $80.00; 1983 High $90.00;
Low $80.00; Close $90.00; Up $10.00

26-W90-1.15
1983 *All Souls, Langham Palace*
Prices: Issue $80.00; 1983 High $80.00;
Low $80.00; Close $80.00; No Change

Mothers Series

Artist: as indicated

Jasper stoneware in varying colors

Diameter: 16.5 centimeters
(6½ inches)

No hanger

Edition size undisclosed, limited
by year of issue

Not numbered, without certificate

26-W90-2.1
1971 *Sportive Love*
Artist: Lady Elizabeth Templetown
Prices: Issue $20.00; 1983 High $29.00;
Low $26.00; Close $26.00; Down $2.00

26-W90-2.2
1972 *The Sewing Lesson*
Artist: Emma Crewe
Prices: Issue $20.00; 1983 High $34.00;
Low $15.00; Close $15.00; Down $19.00

26-W90-2.3
1973 *The Baptism of Achilles*
Artist: Lady Elizabeth Templetown
Prices: Issue $25.00; 1983 High $16.00;
Low $16.00; Close $16.00; No Change

26-W90-2.4
1974 *Domestic Employment*
Artist: Lady Elizabeth Templetown
Prices: Issue $30.00; 1983 High $33.00;
Low $30.00; Close $33.00; Up $3.00

26-W90-2.5
1975 *Mother and Child*
Artist: Lady Elizabeth Templetown
Prices: Issue $35.00; 1983 High $37.00;
Low $34.00; Close $37.00; Up $3.00

26-W90-2.6
1976 *The Spinner*
Artist: William Hackwood
Prices: Issue $35.00; 1983 High $35.00;
Low $30.00; Close $33.00; Down $2.00

26-W90-2.7
1977 *Leisure Time*
Artist: William Hackwood
Prices: Issue $35.00; 1983 High $33.00;
Low $33.00; Close $33.00; No Change

26-W90-2.8
1978 *Swan and Cygnets*
Artist: Undisclosed
Prices: Issue $40.00; 1983 High $40.00;
Low $33.00; Close $38.00; Up $5.00

26-W90-2.9
1979 *Deer and Fawn*
Artist: Undisclosed
Prices: Issue $45.00; 1983 High $36.00;
Low $34.00; Close $36.00; Up $2.00

26-W90-2.10
1980 *Birds*
Artist: Undisclosed
Prices: Issue $47.50; 1983 High $50.00;
Low $48.00; Close $50.00; Up $2.00

26-W90-2.11
1981 *Mare and Foal*
Artist: Undisclosed
Prices: Issue $50.00; 1983 High $50.00;
Low $50.00; Close $50.00; No Change

26-W90-2.12
1982 *Cherubs with Swing*
Artist: Undisclosed
Prices: Issue $55.00; 1983 High $55.00;
Low $55.00; Close $55.00; No Change

26-W90-2.13
1983 *Cupid and Butterfly*
Artist: Undisclosed
Prices: Issue $55.00; 1983 High $55.00;
Low $55.00; Close $55.00; No Change

26-W90-2.14
1984 *Cupid and Music*
Artist: Undisclosed
Issue price: $55.00

Bicentennial of American Independence Series

Artist: Undisclosed

Jasper stoneware

Diameter: 20.3 centimeters
(8 inches)

No hanger

Edition size undisclosed, limited
by year of issue

Not numbered, without certificate

26-W90-3.1
1972 *Boston Tea Party*
Prices: Issue $30.00; 1983 High $38.00;
Low $35.00; Close $35.00; Down $3.00

26-W90-3.2
1973 *Paul Revere's Ride*
Prices: Issue $35.00; 1983 High $120.00;
Low $100.00; Close $100.00; Down $16.00

WEDGWOOD

Barlaston, Stoke-on-Trent, Staffordshire

26-W90-3.3
1974 Battle of Concord
Prices: Issue $40.00; 1983 High $60.00;
Low $45.00; Close $45.00; Down $14.00

26-W90-3.4
1975 Across the Delaware
Prices: Issue $45.00; 1983 High $90.00;
Low $82.00; Close $82.00; Down $4.00

26-W90-3.5
1975 Victory at Yorktown
Prices: Issue $45.00; 1983 High $55.00;
Low $42.00; Close $42.00; Down $13.00

26-W90-3.6
1976 Declaration Signed
Prices: Issue $45.00; 1983 High $45.00;
Low $40.00; Close $40.00; Down $5.00
Series Closed

Blossoming of Suzanne Series

Artist: Mary Vickers. Artist's signature appears on front

Bone china banded in gold

Diameter: 23.5 centimeters (9¼ inches)

No hanger

Edition size limited to 17,000 in 1977; 24,000 thereafter

Numbered with certificate

26-W90-4.1
1977 Innocence
Prices: Issue $60.00; 1983 High $105.00;
Low $85.00; Close $85.00; Down $20.00

26-W90-4.2
1978 Cherish
Prices: Issue $60.00; 1983 High $62.00;
Low $62.00; Close $62.00; No Change

26-W90-4.3
1979 Daydream
Prices: Issue $65.00; 1983 High $65.00;
Low $65.00; Close $65.00; No Change

26-W90-4.4
1980 Wistful
Prices: Issue $70.00; 1983 High $76.00;
Low $73.00; Close $76.00; Up $3.00
Series Closed

Mary Vickers My Memories Series

Artist: Mary Vickers. Artist's signature appears on front

Queensware banded in gold

Diameter: 20.3 centimeters (8 inches)

No hanger

Edition size undisclosed, limited by period of issue

Numbered with certificate

26-W90-5.1
1981 Be My Friend
Prices: Issue $27.00; 1983 High $27.00;
Low $27.00; Close $27.00; No Change

26-W90-5.2
1982 Playtime
Prices: Issue $27.00; 1983 High $35.00;
Low $27.00; Close $35.00; Up $8.00

26-W90-5.3
1983 Our Garden
Prices: Issue $27.00; 1983 High $32.00;
Low $27.00; Close $32.00; Up $5.00

26-W90-5.4
1984 The Recital
Issue price: $27.00

26-W90-1.1 ''Windsor Castle''
1969 Wedgwood *Christmas*
26-W90-2.1 ''Sportive Love'' and
26-W90-2.11 ''Mare and Foal''
1971 and 1981 Wedgwood *Mothers*
Three examples of the varied colors that
Wedgwood's vitreous, unglazed stoneware
known as Jasper ware comes in. The white
or colored bas-relief decorations are applied
by hand.

The House of Anri, which claims to be the world's largest wood-carving manufactory, is a family firm established in 1916 by Anton Riffeser, Sr. and is headed by his grandson, Ernst Riffeser. The factory is located in the Tyrolean Alps, an area with a long tradition of wood carving.

Anri's *Christmas* series began in 1971. Using a process known as "toriart," the plates are molded and carved in wood material and hand-painted to produce a three-dimensional effect. Each plate is mounted in a circular European maple frame.

A master woodcarver from Saint Ulrich, Italy, Joseph Malfertheiner studied at the Ortesi Academy of Art and became Master Carver for Anri in 1966. Best known for his portrayals of Tyrolean history and three-dimensional replication of Renoir, Van Eyck, and Rembrandt, he has works in private collections in Italy, Austria, Germany, and Australia.

ITALY
ANRI
Santa Christina

Christmas Series
Artist: Joseph Malfertheiner until 1978; undisclosed thereafter

Hand-painted molded wood material

Diameter: 30.5 centimeters (12 inches)

Attached back hanger

Edition size limited to 10,000 until 1976; 6,000 thereafter

Numbered since 1972, without certificate

38-A54-1.1
1971 *St. Jakob in Groden*
Prices: Issue $37.50; 1983 High $93.00;
Low $93.00; Close $93.00; No Change

38-A54-1.2
1972 *Pipers at Alberobello*
Prices: Issue $45.00; 1983 High $105.00;
Low $96.00; Close $100.00; Down $5.00

38-A54-1.3
1973 *Alpine Horn*
Prices: Issue $45.00; 1983 High $375.00;
Low $360.00; Close $375.00; Up $15.00

38-A54-1.4
1974 *Young Man and Girl*
Prices: Issue $50.00; 1983 High $100.00;
Low $90.00; Close $100.00; No Change

38-A54-1.5
1975 *Christmas in Ireland*
Prices: Issue $60.00; 1983 High $88.00;
Low $85.00; Close $85.00; Down $3.00

38-A54-1.6
1976 *Alpine Christmas*
Prices: Issue $65.00; 1983 High $205.00;
Low $185.00; Close $205.00; Up $20.00

38-A54-1.7
1977 *Legend of Heiligenblut*
Prices: Issue $65.00; 1983 High $135.00;
Low $125.00; Close $125.00; Down $10.00

38-A54-1.8
1978 *The Klöckler Singers*
Prices: Issue $80.00; 1983 High $110.00;
Low $75.00; Close $75.00; Down $28.00

38-A54-1.9
1979 *The Moss Gatherers of Villnoess*
Prices: Issue $135.00; 1983 High $110.00;
Low $101.00; Close $110.00; Up $9.00

38-A54-1.10
1980 *Wintry Church-going in Santa Christina*
Prices: Issue $165.00; 1983 High $165.00;
Low $160.00; Close $160.00; Down $5.00

38-A54-1.11
1981 *Santa Claus in Tyrol*
Prices: Issue $165.00; 1983 High $168.00;
Low $168.00; Close $168.00; No Change

38-A54-1.12
1982 *Star Singers*
Prices: Issue $165.00; 1983 High $165.00;
Low $165.00; Close $165.00; No Change

38-A54-1.13
1983 *Unto Us a Child Is Born*
Prices: Issue $165.00; 1983 High $165.00;
Low $165.00; Close $165.00; No Change

38-A54-1.14
1984 *Christmas in the Valley*
Issue price: $165.00

38-A54-1.3 "Alpine Horn"
1973 Anri *Christmas*
This carved and hand-painted "toriart"
plate mounted in a European maple frame
produces a three-dimensional effect.

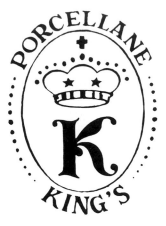

King's Porcelain was established
in the original Giuseppe Cappe
factory in the 1960s. The factory
had been known for its Cappe
figurines of which King's has
retained the original molds.

King's *Flowers of America*
series began in 1973 and ended
in 1977.

Chief sculptor for King's
Porcelain is the Italian artist
Aldo Falchi, who studied sculpture in Milan and later collabo-
rated with Bjørn Wiinblad on
works for Rosenthal of Germany.
Some of his pieces in terra cotta
can be found in Verona, Man-
tova, and Bozzolo, Italy.

KING'S

Usmate, Milan

Flowers of America Series

Artist: Aldo Falchi. Artist's signature appears on back since 1975

High relief, hand-painted porcelain banded in gold

Diameter: 22.3 centimeters (8¾ inches)

Attached back hanger

Edition size limited to 1,000

Numbered without certificate

38-K32-2.1
1973 *Pink Carnation*
Prices: Issue $85.00; 1983 High $120.00; Low $85.00; Close $85.00; Down $35.00

38-K32-2.2
1974 *Red Roses*
Prices: Issue $100.00; 1983 High $140.00; Low $136.00; Close $140.00; Up $4.00

38-K32-2.3
1975 *Yellow Dahlia*
Prices: Issue $110.00; 1983 High $175.00; Low $155.00; Close $175.00; Up $20.00

38-K32-2.4
1976 *Bluebells*
Prices: Issue $130.00; 1983 High $168.00; Low $164.00; Close $168.00; Up $4.00

38-K32-2.5
1977 *Anemones*
Prices: Issue $130.00; 1983 High $175.00; Low $170.00; Close $175.00; Up $5.00
Series Closed

Veneto Flair was established in 1946 by a consortium of potters and painters. Creative World of White Plains, New York, acts as importer and distributor of the Veneto Flair collector's plates.

A centuries-old technique is used to create the Veneto Flair plates. The resulting decorated and glazed earthenware is known as majolica or faience pottery. In this ancient process, terra cotta is hand-thrown on a potter's wheel and the design is incised with a scalpel on the baked clay. Colors are then hand-applied and the plates undergo a series of paintings and firings before a final firing with a secret-formula glaze which produces Veneto Flair's unique mosaic-effect finish.

In 1971, Veneto Flair entered the limited-edition plate market with a single issue, the Bellini "Madonna" plate. The *Last Supper* series, based on Leonardo da Vinci's painting, started in 1973. Their *St. Mark's of Venice* series began in 1984.

Born in Torgiano, Italy, Vincente Tiziano is credited with reviving ancient Etruscan techniques of ceramic production, and his classical style was greatly influenced by the ceramic tradi-tions of the sixteenth century. He is a recipient of the Amerigo Longhi Award from the International Ceramic Show of Deruta in the Italian province of Perugia. Many of his works are on display at the Deruta Ceramic Museum.

ITALY
VENETO FLAIR
Treviso

Bellini Plate

Artist: Vincente Tiziano (after Bellini's *Madonna)*

Terra cotta banded in gold

Diameter: 21.6 centimeters (8½ inches)

Pierced foot rim

Edition size limited to 500

Numbered with certificate

38-V22-1.1
1971 Madonna
Prices: Issue $45.00; 1983 High $440.00;
Low $400.00; Close $400.00; Down $40.00
Series Closed

Last Supper Series

Artist: Vincente Tiziano (after Leonardo da Vinci's *Last Supper).*
Artist's signature appears on front

Terra cotta banded in gold

Diameter: 21.6 centimeters (8½ inches)

Pierced foot rim

Edition size limited to 2,000

Numbered with certificate

38-V22-6.1
1973 Last Supper—Scene I
Prices: Issue $100.00; 1983 High $75.00;
Low $75.00; Close $75.00; No Change

38-V22-6.2
1973 Last Supper—Scene II
Prices: Issue $70.00; 1983 High $85.00;
Low $85.00; Close $85.00; No Change

38-V22-6.3
1974 Last Supper—Scene III
Prices: Issue $70.00; 1983 High $87.00;
Low $87.00; Close $87.00; No Change

38-V22-6.4
1975 Last Supper—Scene IV
Prices: Issue $70.00; 1983 High $125.00;
Low $90.00; Close $125.00; Up $35.00

38-V22-6.5
1976 Last Supper—Scene V
Prices: Issue $70.00; 1983 High $94.00;
Low $94.00; Close $94.00; No Change
Series Closed

St. Mark's of Venice Series

Artist: Franco Lamincia.
Artist's signature appears on front

Majolica-style earthenware, hand-painted and banded in gold

Diameter: 20.3 centimeters
(8 inches)

Pierced foot rim

Edition size undisclosed, limited by year of issue

Numbered with certificate

38-V22-15.1
1984 *Noah and the Dove*
Issue price: $60.00

38-V22-1.1 "Madonna"
1971 Veneto Flair *Bellini*
The mosaic and crackled effect on
terra cotta are the result of Veneto Flair's
secret-formula glaze.

Located in Tuscany, world center for the mining and carving of alabaster, the Studio Dante di Volteradici continues the Italian tradition of alabaster sculpturing.

Di Volteradici's *Grand Opera* series, commissioned by the Museo Teatrale alla Scala to commemorate the two-hundredth anniversary of La Scala Opera House, began in 1976, and ended in 1982. *Madonne Viventi (Living Madonnas),* its first proprietary series, began in 1978 and ended in 1984. Their *Ghiberti Doors* series began in 1983.

Gino Ruggeri, a sculptor in the neo-classic tradition, is best known for his work "The Crucifix," sculpted from the Casa Serena Institute of Cecina Mare, and his two sculptures, "Memorials to the Fallen," which pay tribute to World War I victims. Now in his late 70s, Ruggeri's last completed work was the "Aida" plate. His successor as designer of the *Grand Opera* series was Franco Ingargiola, whom Ruggeri personally tutored and who worked in onyx and ceramics as well as alabaster.

Alberto Santangela, current sculptor of the *Madonne Viventi* series, sculpts in the style of the Italian High Renaissance.

ITALY
STUDIO DANTE DI VOLTERADICI
Toscana

Grand Opera Series
Artist: as indicated. Artist's signature appears on front

Ivory alabaster

Diameter: 21.6 centimeters (8½ inches)

Attached back hanger

Edition size undisclosed, limited by period of issue

Numbered with certificate

38-V90-1.1
1976 Rigoletto
Artist: Gino Ruggeri
Prices: Issue $35.00; 1983 High $176.00;
Low $100.00; Close $100.00; Down $76.00

38-V90-1.2
1977 Madama Butterfly
Artist: Gino Ruggeri
Prices: Issue $35.00; 1983 High $56.00;
Low $50.00; Close $50.00; Down $6.00

38-V90-1.3
1978 Carmen
Artist: Gino Ruggeri
Prices: Issue $40.00; 1983 High $45.00;
Low $45.00; Close $45.00; No Change

38-V90-1.4
1979 Aida
Artist: Gino Ruggeri
Prices: Issue $40.00; 1983 High $47.00;
Low $46.00; Close $47.00; Up $1.00

38-V90-1.5
1980 The Barber of Seville
Artist: Franco Ingargiola
Prices: Issue $40.00; 1983 High $56.00;
Low $50.00; Close $55.00; Down $1.00

38-V90-1.6
1981 Tosca
Artist: Franco Ingargiola
Prices: Issue $40.00; 1983 High $40.00;
Low $40.00; Close $40.00; No Change

38-V90-1.7
1982 I Pagliacci
Artist: Franco Ingargiola
Prices: Issue $40.00; 1983 High $85.00;
Low $40.00; Close $85.00; Up $45.00
Series Closed

Madonne Viventi Series
(Living Madonnas Series)

Artist: Ado Santini in 1978;
Alberto Santangela thereafter.
Artist's signature appears on front

Ivory alabaster

Diameter: 21.6 centimeters
(8½ inches)

Attached back hanger

Edition size undisclosed, limited
by period of issue

Numbered with certificate

38-V90-2.1
1978 Madonna Pensosa
(The Pensive Madonna)
Prices: Issue $45.00; 1983 High $52.00;
Low $50.00; Close $50.00; Down $2.00

38-V90-2.2
1979 Madonna Serena
(The Serene Madonna)
Prices: Issue $45.00; 1983 High $45.00;
Low $45.00; Close $45.00; No Change

38-V90-2.3
1980 Madonna Beata
(The Beatific Madonna)
Prices: Issue $45.00; 1983 High $45.00;
Low $45.00; Close $45.00; No Change

38-V90-2.4
1981 Madonna Profetica
(The Prophetic Madonna)
Prices: Issue $45.00; 1983 High $70.00;
Low $52.00; Close $70.00; Up $18.00

38-V90-2.5
1982 Madonna Modesta
(The Demure Madonna)
Prices: Issue $45.00; 1983 High $70.00;
Low $45.00; Close $70.00; Up $25.00

38-V90-2.6
1983 Madonna Saggio
(The Wise Madonna)
Prices: Issue $45.00; 1983 High $45.00;
Low $45.00; Close $45.00; No Change

38-V90-2.7
1984 Madonna Tenera
(The Tender Madonna)
Issue price: $45.00
Series Closed

STUDIO DANTE DI VOLTERADICI
Toscana

Ghiberti Doors Series
Artist: Alberto Santangela.
Artist's signature appears on front

Ivory alabaster

Diameter: 21.6 centimeters
(8½ inches)

Attached back hanger

Edition size undisclosed, limited
by period of issue

Numbered with certificate

38-V90-3.1
1983 *Adoration of the Magi*
Prices: Issue $50.00; 1983 High $50.00;
Low $50.00; Close $50.00; No Change

38-V90-3.2
1984 *The Nativity*
Issue price: $50.00

Although the present Fukagawa Porcelain factory was organized in the 1880s in Arita by the Fukagawa family, the heritage of its Izumistone porcelain goes back some four centuries to the discovery of kaolin deposits on the island of Kyushu, Japan. It was there, on the slopes of Mount Izumi, that the Korean master potter Yi Samp'yŏng ended his twenty-year search for a pure white clay base to be used in the manufacture of fine porcelain. As the direct result of his discovery, a number of small porcelain workshops— the first in all Japan—sprang up in the nearby town of Arita, and delicate plates and saucers were being shipped to the West from the harbor city of Imari decades before porcelain manufacture began in Europe.

The establishment of Fukagawa Porcelain was actually a merger of a number of small workshops whose standards and techniques dated to the time of Yi Samp'yŏng. In 1913, Fukagawa was granted the title "Purveyor to the Imperial Household," which indicates patronage from the royal family of Japan. In recognition of this honor, all Fukagawa ceramics bear the imprint "Imperial." The factory, which is still in the hands of the Fukagawa family, continues to employ the original Izumiyama clay from Mount Izumi to give its porcelain a uniquely white body.

In 1977, Fukagawa began its first series of collector's plates—the *Warabe No Haiku (Haiku about Children)* series. The series ended in 1980.

Master of the traditional "Sea of Whiteness" style, Suetomi is the principal artist for Fukagawa and is the recipient of the Gold Prize from Japan's Ministry of International Trade and Industry.

Warabe No Haiku Series
(Haiku about Children)

Artist: Suetomi. Artist's signature
and seal appear on front

Overglaze-decorated porcelain

Diameter: 26 centimeters
(10¼ inches)

No hanger

Edition size undisclosed, limited
by period of issue

Numbered with certificate

Original Haiku poem appears on
front

42-F78-1.1
1977 Beneath the Plum Branch
Prices: Issue $38.00; 1983 High $47.00;
Low $44.00; Close $44.00; Down $3.00

42-F78-1.2
1978 Child of Straw
Prices: Issue $42.00; 1983 High $42.00;
Low $42.00; Close $42.00; No Change

42-F78-1.3
1979 Dragon Dance
Prices: Issue $42.00; 1983 High $42.00;
Low $42.00; Close $42.00; No Change

42-F78-1.4
1980 Mask Dancing
Prices: Issue $42.00; 1983 High $112.00;
Low $105.00; Close $112.00; Up $7.00
Series Closed

Schmid

A Japanese subsidiary of Schmid (see Germany, SCHMID) produces several series of plates based on contemporary cartoon characters.

The *Peanuts Christmas* series and the *Peanuts Mother's Day* series began in 1972 and ended in 1982. The *Peanuts Valentine's Day* series began in 1977. The *Disney Christmas* series was introduced in 1973 and the *Disney Mother's Day* series in 1974— both ended in 1982. The *Raggedy Ann Annual* series started in 1980.

Cartoonist Charles Schulz, creator of the widely-syndicated cartoon strip ''Peanuts,'' designed or approved all plates in the three *Peanuts* series. Walt Disney Productions staff artists designed both *Disney* series. Artists for the *Raggedy Ann* series are not disclosed.

JAPAN
SCHMID
Seto City

Peanuts Christmas Series

Artist: Charles Schulz. Artist's signature appears on front

Overglaze-decorated porcelain

Diameter: 19 centimeters (7½ inches)

Attached back hanger

Edition size undisclosed, limited by year of issue, except as indicated

Not numbered except as indicated, without certificate

42-S12-1.1
1972 *Snoopy Guides the Sleigh*
Prices: Issue $10.00; 1983 High $71.00; Low $65.00; Close $70.00; Up $5.00

42-S12-1.2
1973 *Christmas Eve at the Doghouse*
Prices: Issue $10.00; 1983 High $115.00; Low $98.00; Close $115.00; Up $17.00

42-S12-1.3
1974 *Christmas Eve at the Fireplace*
Prices: Issue $10.00; 1983 High $62.00; Low $56.00; Close $62.00; Up $6.00

42-S12-1.4
1975 *Woodstock, Santa Claus*
Prices: Issue $12.50; 1983 High $21.00; Low $16.00; Close $16.00; Down $5.00

42-S12-1.5
1976 *Woodstock's Christmas*
Prices: Issue $13.00; 1983 High $25.00; Low $25.00; Close $25.00; No Change

42-S12-1.6
1977 *Deck the Doghouse*
Prices: Issue $13.00; 1983 High $21.00; Low $15.00; Close $15.00; Down $6.00

42-S12-1.7
1978 *Filling the Stocking*
Prices: Issue $15.00; 1983 High $18.00; Low $15.00; Close $17.00; Down $1.00

42-S12-1.8
1979 *Christmas at Hand*
Edition: 15,000
Prices: Issue $17.50; 1983 High $20.00; Low $20.00; Close $20.00; No Change

42-S12-1.9
1980 *Waiting for Santa*
Edition: 15,000
Prices: Issue $17.50; 1983 High $55.00;
Low $45.00; Close $45.00; Down $5.00

42-S12-1.10
1981 *A Christmas Wish*
Edition: 15,000
Prices: Issue $17.50; 1983 High $20.00;
Low $20.00; Close $20.00; No Change

42-S12-1.11
1982 *Perfect Performance*
Edition: 15,000
Prices: Issue $18.50; 1983 High $22.00;
Low $18.50; Close $22.00; Up $3.50
Series Closed

Peanuts Mother's Day Series

Artist: Charles Schulz. Artist's
signature appears on front except
1975

Overglaze-decorated porcelain

Diameter: 19 centimeters
(7½ inches)

Attached back hanger

Edition size undisclosed, limited
by year of issue, except as
indicated

Not numbered except as indicated,
without certificate

42-S12-2.1
1972 *Linus*
Prices: Issue $10.00; 1983 High $15.00;
Low $13.00; Close $13.00; Down $1.00

42-S12-2.2
1973 *Mom?*
Prices: Issue $10.00; 1983 High $23.00;
Low $20.00; Close $20.00; Down $1.00

42-S12-2.3
1974 *Snoopy and Woodstock on Parade*
Prices: Issue $10.00; 1983 High $20.00;
Low $18.00; Close $20.00; No Change

42-S12-2.4
1975 *A Kiss for Lucy*
Prices: Issue $12.50; 1983 High $18.00;
Low $18.00; Close $18.00; No Change

42-S12-2.5
1976 *Linus and Snoopy*
Prices: Issue $13.00; 1983 High $17.00;
Low $15.00; Close $15.00; Down $2.00

42-S12-2.6
1977 Dear Mom
Prices: Issue $13.00; 1983 High $13.00;
Low $13.00; Close $13.00; No Change

42-S12-2.7
1978 Thoughts That Count
Prices: Issue $15.00; 1983 High $15.00;
Low $13.00; Close $13.00; Down $2.00

42-S12-2.8
1979 A Special Letter
Edition: 10,000
Prices: Issue $17.50; 1983 High $13.00;
Low $13.00; Close $13.00; No Change

42-S12-2.9
1980 A Tribute to Mom
Edition: 10,000
Prices: Issue $17.50; 1983 High $21.00;
Low $16.00; Close $16.00; Down $4.00

42-S12-2.10
1981 Mission for Mom
Edition: 10,000
Prices: Issue $17.50; 1983 High $22.00;
Low $18.00; Close $18.00; Down $4.00

42-S12-2.11
1982 Which Way to Mother?
Edition: 10,000
Prices: Issue $18.50; 1983 High $19.00;
Low $18.50; Close $19.00; Up $.50
Series Closed

Disney Christmas Series

Artist: Undisclosed

Overglaze-decorated porcelain

Diameter: 19 centimeters
(7½ inches)

Attached back hanger

Edition size undisclosed, limited
by year of issue, except as
indicated

Not numbered except as indicated,
without certificate

42-S12-3.1
1973 Sleigh Ride
Prices: Issue $10.00; 1983 High $320.00;
Low $300.00; Close $315.00; Up $15.00

42-S12-3.2
1974 Decorating the Tree
Prices: Issue $10.00; 1983 High $80.00;
Low $50.00; Close $80.00; Up $27.00

42-S12-3.3
1975 Caroling
Prices: Issue $12.50; 1983 High $20.00;
Low $17.00; Close $18.00; Down $2.00

42-S12-3.4
1976 Building a Snowman
Prices: Issue $13.00; 1983 High $18.00;
Low $15.00; Close $15.00; Down $3.00

42-S12-3.5
1977 Down the Chimney
Prices: Issue $13.00; 1983 High $18.00;
Low $16.00; Close $18.00; Up $2.00

42-S12-3.6
1978 Night Before Christmas
Prices: Issue $15.00; 1983 High $21.00;
Low $18.00; Close $18.00; Down $3.00

42-S12-3.7
1979 Santa's Surprise
Edition: 15,000
Prices: Issue $17.50; 1983 High $20.00;
Low $18.00; Close $20.00; Up $2.00

42-S12-3.8
1980 Sleigh Ride
Edition: 15,000
Prices: Issue $17.50; 1983 High $30.00;
Low $27.00; Close $30.00; Up $3.00

42-S12-3.9
1981 Happy Holidays
Edition: 15,000
Prices: Issue $17.50; 1983 High $19.00;
Low $18.00; Close $19.00; Up $1.00

42-S12-3.10
1982 Winter Games
Edition: 15,000
Prices: Issue $18.50; 1983 High $19.00;
Low $18.50; Close $19.00; Up $.50
Series Closed

JAPAN
SCHMID
Seto City

Disney Mother's Day Series

Artist: Undisclosed

Overglaze-decorated porcelain

Diameter: 19 centimeters
(7½ inches)

Attached back hanger

Edition size undisclosed, limited
by year of issue, except as
indicated

Not numbered except as indicated,
without certificate

42-S12-4.1
1974 *Flowers for Mother*
Prices: Issue $10.00; 1983 High $60.00;
Low $52.00; Close $52.00; Down $5.00

42-S12-4.2
1975 *Snow White and the Seven Dwarfs*
Prices: Issue $12.50; 1983 High $30.00;
Low $25.00; Close $25.00; Down $5.00

42-S12-4.3
1976 *Minnie Mouse and Friends*
Prices: Issue $13.00; 1983 High $25.00;
Low $23.00; Close $23.00; Down $2.00

42-S12-4.4
1977 *Pluto's Pals*
Prices: Issue $13.00; 1983 High $18.00;
Low $14.00; Close $14.00; Down $4.00

42-S12-4.5
1978 *Flowers for Bambi*
Prices: Issue $15.00; 1983 High $19.00;
Low $19.00; Close $19.00; No Change

42-S12-4.6
1979 *Happy Feet*
Edition: 10,000
Prices: Issue $17.50; 1983 High $17.00;
Low $16.00; Close $17.00; Up $1.00

42-S12-4.7
1980 *Minnie's Surprise*
Edition: 10,000
Prices: Issue $17.50; 1983 High $18.00;
Low $18.00; Close $18.00; No Change

42-S12-4.8
1981 *Playmates*
Edition: 10,000
Prices: Issue $17.50; 1983 High $24.00;
Low $23.00; Close $24.00; Up $1.00

42-S12-4.9
1982 *A Dream Come True*
Edition: 10,000
Prices: Issue $18.50; 1983 High $19.00;
Low $18.50; Close $19.00; Up $.50
Series Closed

Peanuts Valentine's Day Series

Artist: Charles Schulz. Artist's signature appears on front

Overglaze-decorated porcelain

Diameter: 19 centimeters
(7½ inches)

Attached back hanger

Edition size undisclosed, limited by year of issue

Not numbered, without certificate

42-S12-7.1
1977 *Home Is Where the Heart Is*
Prices: Issue $13.00; 1983 High $20.00;
Low $17.00; Close $17.00; Down $2.00

42-S12-7.2
1978 *Heavenly Bliss*
Prices: Issue $13.00; 1983 High $20.00;
Low $17.00; Close $17.00; Down $3.00

42-S12-7.3
1979 *Love Match*
Prices: Issue $17.50; 1983 High $18.00;
Low $17.00; Close $17.00; Down $1.00

42-S12-7.4
1980 *From Snoopy, with Love*
Prices: Issue $17.50; 1983 High $23.00;
Low $21.00; Close $23.00; Up $2.00

42-S12-7.5
1981 *Hearts-a-Flutter*
Prices: Issue $17.50; 1983 High $58.00;
Low $52.00; Close $55.00; Up $3.00

JAPAN
SCHMID
Seto City

42-S12-7.6
1982 *Love Patch*
Prices: Issue $17.50; 1983 High $18.00;
Low $17.50; Close $18.00; Up $.50
Series Closed

Raggedy Ann Annual Series
Artist: Undisclosed

Overglaze-decorated porcelain

Diameter: 19 centimeters
(7½ inches)

Attached back hanger

Edition size limited to 10,000

Numbered without certificate for
1980 plate; with certificate
thereafter

42-S12-9.1
1980 *The Sunshine Wagon*
Prices: Issue $17.50; 1983 High $64.00;
Low $60.00; Close $60.00; No Change

42-S12-9.2
1981 *The Raggedy Shuffle*
Prices: Issue $17.50; 1983 High $21.00;
Low $21.00; Close $21.00; No Change

42-S12-9.3
1982 *Flying High*
Prices: Issue $18.50; 1983 High $23.00;
Low $18.00; Close $18.00; Down $.50

42-S12-9.4
1983 *Winning Streak*
Prices: Issue $22.50; 1983 High $38.00;
Low $22.50; Close $38.00; Up $15.50

42-S12-9.5
1984 *Rocking Rodeo*
Issue price: $22.50
Series Closed

Johan Jeremiason established Porsgrund, Norway's only porcelain factory, in 1885. Jeremiason began his business by importing English clay which was modeled by ceramist Carl Bauer. Porcelain tableware and decorative wares have been produced since then. Porsgrund's first collector's plate was a 1909 Christmas issue entitled "Christmas Flowers" (OTC). The series was abandoned after a single issue.

A *Christmas* series based on religious themes was introduced in 1968 and ended with the 1977 issue. The *Mother's Day* series began in 1970. In 1978 Porsgrund began a nostalgic Christmas series entitled the *Traditional Norwegian Christmas* series. The series closed in 1982.

Born in Fredrikstad, Norway, Gunnar Bratlie is a master of the traditional Norwegian folk art known as "rosemaling" and he has worked in such diverse styles as oil, tempera, aquarelle, and etching. Among his many awards are the Scandinavian book prize for illustration, a contest-winning city design for Fredrikstad's 400-year jubilee, and a special stipend from the Norwegian Design Organization. His work is represented in many museums around the world, most notably in the Commune of Oslo, the Art Society of Fredrikstad, the Museo del Arte in Pisoia, Italy, and at Oregon University in the United States. In 1967 Bratlie was commissioned as the sole artist for the Porsgrund Pottery. His works primarily depict Norwegian country scenes.

PORSGRUND
Porsgrunn, Telemark County

Christmas Series
Artist: Gunnar Bratlie

Porcelain decorated in cobalt blue underglaze

Diameter: 17.8 centimeters (7 inches)

Pierced foot rim

Edition size undisclosed, limited by year of issue

Not numbered, without certificate

54-P62-1.1
1968 *Church Scene*
Prices: Issue $12.00; 1983 High $204.00;
Low $135.00; Close $135.00; Down $69.00

54-P62-1.2
1969 *Three Kings*
Prices: Issue $12.00; 1983 High $23.00;
Low $21.00; Close $21.00; Down $2.00

54-P62-1.3
1970 *Road to Bethlehem*
Prices: Issue $12.00; 1983 High $14.00,
Low $12.00; Close $12.00; Down $2.00

54-P62-1.4
1971 *A Child Is Born in Bethlehem*
Prices: Issue $12.00; 1983 High $20.00;
Low $16.00; Close $16.00; Down $4.00

54-P62-1.5
1972 *Hark, the Herald Angels Sing*
Prices: Issue $12.00; 1983 High $24.00;
Low $24.00; Close $24.00; No Change

54-P62-1.6
1973 *Promise of the Savior*
Prices: Issue $15.00; 1983 High $35.00;
Low $28.00; Close $35.00; Up $7.00

54-P62-1.7
1974 *The Shepherds*
Prices: Issue $15.00; 1983 High $43.00;
Low $43.00; Close $43.00; No Change

54-P62-1.8
1975 *Jesus on the Road to the Temple*
Prices: Issue $19.50; 1983 High $24.00;
Low $24.00; Close $24.00; No Change

54-P62-1.9
1976 *Jesus and the Elders*
Prices: Issue $22.00; 1983 High $18.00;
Low $18.00; Close $18.00; No Change

54-P62-1.10
1977 *The Draught of Fish*
Prices: Issue $24.00; 1983 High $20.00;
Low $18.00; Close $20.00; Up $2.00
Series Closed

Mother's Day Series

Artist: Gunnar Bratlie until 1982;
Thorstein Rittun thereafter

Porcelain decorated in cobalt blue
underglaze

Diameter: 12.7 centimeters
(5 inches)

Pierced foot rim

Edition size undisclosed, limited
by year of issue

Not numbered, without certificate

54-P62-2.1
1970 *Mare and Foal*
Prices: Issue $7.50; 1983 High $15.00;
Low $15.00; Close $15.00; No Change

54-P62-2.2
1971 *Boy and Geese*
Prices: Issue $7.50; 1983 High $14.00;
Low $8.00; Close $8.00; Down $6.00

54-P62-2.3
1972 *Doe and Fawn*
Prices: Issue $10.00; 1983 High $10.00;
Low $9.00; Close $9.00; Down $1.00

54-P62-2.4
1973 *Cat and Kittens*
Prices: Issue $10.00; 1983 High $11.00;
Low $10.00; Close $11.00; Up $1.00

54-P62-2.5
1974 *Boy and Goats*
Prices: Issue $10.00; 1983 High $16.00;
Low $14.00; Close $14.00; Down $2.00

PORSGRUND
Porsgrunn, Telemark County

54-P62-2.6
1975 *Dog and Puppies*
Prices: Issue $12.50; 1983 High $23.00;
Low $21.00; Close $23.00; Up $2.00

54-P62-2.7
1976 *Girl and Calf*
Prices: Issue $15.00; 1983 High $22.00;
Low $19.00; Close $21.00; Down $1.00

54-P62-2.8
1977 *Boy and Chickens*
Prices: Issue $16.50; 1983 High $22.00;
Low $20.00; Close $22.00; Up $2.00

54-P62-2.9
1978 *Girl and Pigs*
Prices: Issue $17.50; 1983 High $25.00;
Low $23.00; Close $25.00; Up $2.00

54-P62-2.10
1979 *Boy and Reindeer*
Prices: Issue $19.50; 1983 High $24.00;
Low $21.00; Close $21.00; Down $3.00

54-P62-2.11
1980 *Girl and Lambs*
Prices: Issue $21.50; 1983 High $30.00;
Low $22.00; Close $22.00; Down $8.00

54-P62-2.12
1981 *Boy and Birds*
Prices: Issue $24.00; 1983 High $24.00;
Low $24.00; Close $24.00; No Change

54-P62-2.13
1982 *Girl and Rabbits*
Prices: Issue $26.00; 1983 High $27.00;
Low $26.00; Close $27.00; Up $1.00

54-P62-2.14
1983 *Mother and Kittens*
Prices: Issue $26.00; 1983 High $26.00;
Low $26.00; Close $26.00; No Change

54-P62-2.15
1984 *By the Pond*
Issue price: $25.00

Traditional Norwegian Christmas Series

Artist: Gunnar Bratlie. Artist's initials appear on back

Porcelain decorated in cobalt blue underglaze

Diameter: 17.8 centimeters (7 inches)

Pierced foot rim

Edition size undisclosed, limited by year of issue

Not numbered, without certificate

54-P62-5.1
1978 *Guests Are Coming for Christmas Eve*
Prices: Issue $27.00; 1983 High $30.00;
Low $30.00; Close $30.00; No Change

54-P62-5.2
1979 *Home for Christmas*
Prices: Issue $30.00; 1983 High $30.00;
Low $28.00; Close $30.00; Up $2.00

54-P62-5.3
1980 *Preparing for Christmas*
Prices: Issue $34.00; 1983 High $42.00;
Low $40.00; Close $40.00; Down $1.00

54-P62-5.4
1981 *Christmas Skating*
Prices: Issue $38.00; 1983 High $40.00;
Low $38.00; Close $39.00; Up $1.00

54-P62-5.5
1982 *White Christmas*
Prices: Issue $42.00; 1983 High $46.00;
Low $42.00; Close $44.00; Up $2.00
Series Closed

72-L41-0.0

SPAIN
LLADRÓ
Tabernes Blanques, Valencia

The Lladró Porcelain factory was established in the 1950s by three Lladró brothers—Juan, Jose, and Vicente, sons of a peasant. At night, they studied porcelain designing, modeling, and firing and built their first kiln while in their teens. By 1970 their factory was one of the best-equipped in Europe and had become known for its vases and figurines.

Lladró initiated its limited-edition *Mother's Day* series in 1971. The series closed in 1979.

Artists for Lladró plates are not disclosed.

LLADRÓ
Tabernes Blanques, Valencia

Mother's Day Series

Artist: Undisclosed

White bisque center in bas-relief with underglaze-decorated porcelain border and banded in gold

Diameter: 20.3 centimeters (8 inches)

No hanger

Edition size undisclosed, limited by year of issue

Not numbered, without certificate

72-L41-2.1
1971 *Kiss of the Child*
Prices: Issue $27.50; 1983 High $73.00;
Low $65.00; Close $65.00; Down $8.00

72-L41-2.2
1972 *Bird and Chicks*
Prices: Issue $27.50; 1983 High $31.00;
Low $20.00; Close $20.00; Down $11.00

72-L41-2.3
1973 *Mother and Children*
Prices: Issue $35.00; 1983 High $25.00;
Low $25.00; Close $25.00; No Change

72-L41-2.4
1974 *Mother Nursing*
Prices: Issue $45.00; 1983 High $133.00;
Low $133.00; Close $133.00; No Change

72-L41-2.5
1975 *Mother and Child*
Prices: Issue $60.00; 1983 High $53.00;
Low $50.00; Close $53.00; Up $3.00

72-L41-2.6
1976 *Tender Vigil*
Prices: Issue $60.00; 1983 High $53.00;
Low $48.00; Close $48.00; Down $5.00

72-L41-2.7
1977 *Mother and Daughter*
Prices: Issue $67.50; 1983 High $53.00;
Low $52.00; Close $53.00; Up $1.00

72-L41-2.8
1978 *The New Arrival*
Prices: Issue $80.00; 1983 High $55.00;
Low $55.00; Close $55.00; No Change

72-L41-2.9

SPAIN
LLADRÓ
Tabernes Blanques, Valencia

72-L41-2.9
1979 *Off to School*
Prices: Issue $90.00; 1983 High $80.00;
Low $74.00; Close $80.00; Up $1.00
Series Closed

72-L41-2.2 "Bird and Chicks"
1972 Lladró *Mother's Day*
Lladró's unique bas-relief plates feature
bisque-fired centers and highly-glazed
porcelain borders with a gold banded rim.

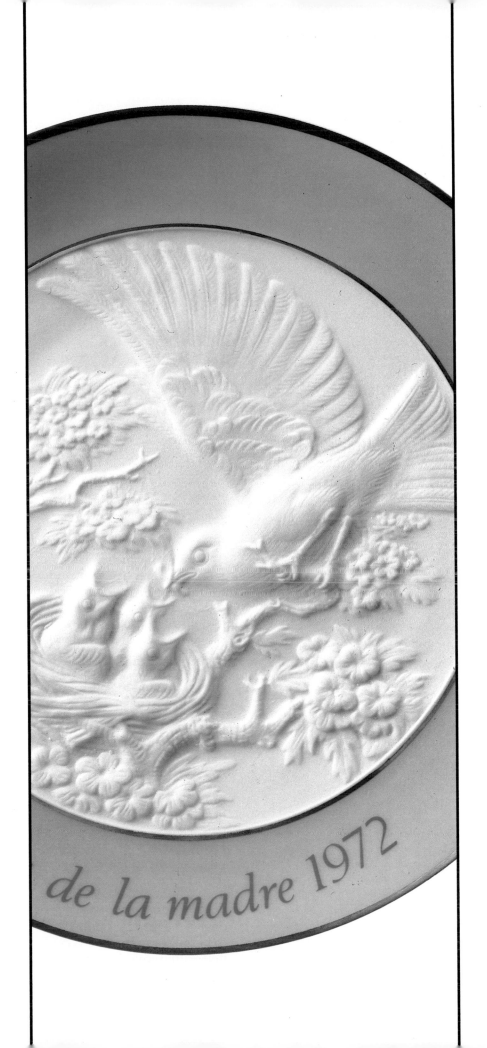

de la madre 1972

Orrefors was originally established in 1726 as an ironworks. In 1898 they began manufacturing glass ink bottles and window glass. Although the ironworks was no longer profitable, Johan Ekman purchased the property in 1913. He was interested in improving the facilities for glassmaking and recognized the importance of the valuable forest land of the area as fuel for glass furnaces. He eventually built an entire community around the glassworks.

Orrefors crystal is made from a mixture of seashore sand and potash, plus a heavy lead content. The ornamentation is created by master blowers who apply liquid molten glass in desired shapes.

In 1970 Orrefors began its *Annual Cathedral* series, made in untinted crystal, depicting famous places of worship. This series ended in 1978. These plates are handmade with the designs engraved in the crystal and filled with 24k gold.

John Selbing is regarded as one of the world's leading photographers of glass. He is credited with developing the technique which enabled production of inlaid-gold crystal plates. At the age of nineteen he joined Orrefors and for forty-six years handled their design, photography, and advertising projects. For the last several years he has been working independently in fine art.

Annual Cathedral Series

Artist: John Selbing

Leaded crystal with engraved designs inlaid in 24k gold

Diameter: 25.4 centimeters (10 inches)

No hanger

Edition size: as indicated

Numbered since 1975, without certificate

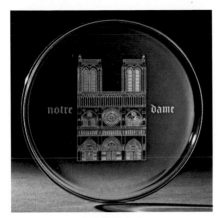

76-O74-1.1
1970 *Notre Dame Cathedral*
Edition: 5,000
Prices: Issue $50.00; 1983 High $68.00;
Low $40.00; Close $40.00; Down $28.00

76-O74-1.2
1971 *Westminster Abbey*
Edition: 5,000
Prices: Issue $50.00; 1983 High $42.00;
Low $42.00; Close $42.00; No Change

76-O74-1.3
1972 *Basilica di San Marco*
Edition: 5,000
Prices: Issue $50.00; 1983 High $60.00;
Low $60.00; Close $60.00; No Change

76-O74-1.4
1973 *Cologne Cathedral*
Edition: 5,000
Prices: Issue $50.00; 1983 High $70.00;
Low $70.00; Close $70.00; No Change

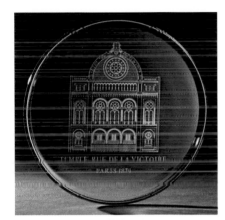

76-O74-1.5
1974 *Temple Rue de la Victoire, Paris*
Edition: 5,000
Prices: Issue $60.00; 1983 High $73.00;
Low $72.00; Close $72.00; Down $1.00

76-O74-1.6
1975 *Basilica di San Pietro, Rome*
Edition, 5,000
Prices: Issue $85.00; 1983 High $115.00;
Low $90.00; Close $90.00; Down $25.00

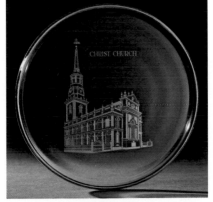

76-O74-1.7
1976 *Christ Church, Philadelphia*
Edition: 3,000
Prices: Issue $85.00; 1983 High $85.00;
Low $70.00; Close $70.00; Down $15.00

76-O74-1.8
1977 *Masjid-E-Shah*
Edition: 3,000
Prices: Issue $90.00; 1983 High $118.00;
Low $117.00; Close $118.00; Up $1.00

76-O74-1.9
1978 *Santiago de Compostela*
Edition: 3,000
Prices: Issue $95.00; 1983 High $100.00;
Low $100.00; Close $100.00; No Change
Series Closed

76-O74-1.1 "Notre Dame Cathedral"
1970 Orrefors *Annual Cathedral*
Orrefor's leaded crystal collector's plate features engraved designs inlaid in 24k gold.

76-R54-0.0

The Rörstrand Porcelain Factory is Sweden's oldest pottery and the second oldest in Europe. Originally founded in Stockholm in 1726 under government patronage, the plant was later moved inland to Lidkoping for safety during World War II.

Rörstrand is one of the few factories in the world that produces all three ceramic bodies—porcelain, stoneware, and high-fired earthenware. The output of the factory includes both dinnerware and decorative art, including collector's plates. Rörstrand's first collector's plate series was a *Christmas* series (OTC), started in 1904 and ended in 1926. In 1968 Rörstrand began its series of square *Christmas* plates with designs derived from Swedish folk tales and traditions.

Rörstrand artist Gunnar Nylund has exhibited at the Swedish National Museum and is widely known for his monumental ceramic reliefs.

SWEDEN
RÖRSTRAND
Lidkoping

Christmas Series

Artist: Gunnar Nylund

Porcelain decorated in Scandia blue underglaze

Diameter: 19 centimeters (7½ inches square)

Pierced foot rim

Edition size undisclosed, limited by year of issue

Not numbered, without certificate

76-R54-1.1
1968 Bringing Home the Tree
Prices: Issue $12.00; 1983 High $575.00;
Low $525.00; Close $550.00; Down $25.00

76-R54-1.2
1969 Fisherman Sailing Home
Prices: Issue $13.50; 1983 High $95.00;
Low $60.00; Close $60.00; Down $33.00

76-R54-1.3
1970 Nils with His Geese
Prices: Issue $13.50; 1983 High $32.00;
Low $29.00; Close $29.00; Down $3.00

76-R54-1.4
1971 Nils in Lapland
Prices: Issue $15.00; 1983 High $28.00;
Low $28.00; Close $28.00; No Change

76-R54-1.5
1972 Dalecarlian Fiddler
Prices: Issue $15.00; 1983 High $33.00;
Low $28.00; Close $28.00; Down $5.00

76-R54-1.6
1973 Farm in Smaland
Prices: Issue $16.00; 1983 High $104.00;
Low $100.00; Close $100.00; Down $4.00

76-R54-1.7
1974 Vadstena
Prices: Issue $19.00; 1983 High $60.00;
Low $58.00; Close $60.00; Up $2.00

76-R54-1.8
1975 Nils in Vastmanland
Prices: Issue $20.00, 1983 High $36.00;
Low $33.00; Close $36.00; Up $3.00

76-R54-1.9
1976 Nils in Uppland
Prices: Issue $20.00; 1983 High $30.00;
Low $28.00; Close $30.00; Up $2.00

76-R54-1.10
1977 Nils in Värmland
Prices: Issue $29.50; 1983 High $26.00;
Low $23.00; Close $23.00; Down $3.00

76-R54-1.11
1978 Nils in Fjallbacka
Prices: Issue $32.50; 1983 High $33.00;
Low $30.00; Close $30.00; Down $3.00

76-R54-1.12
1979 Nils in Vaestergoetland
Prices: Issue $38.50; 1983 High $35.00;
Low $30.00; Close $30.00; Down $5.00

76-R54-1.13
1980 Nils in Halland
Prices: Issue $55.00; 1983 High $51.00;
Low $51.00; Close $51.00; No Change

76-R54-1.14
1981 Nils in Gotland
Prices: Issue $55.00; 1983 High $58.00;
Low $55.00; Close $58.00; Up $3.00

76-R54-1.15
1982 Nils at Skansen in Stockholm
Prices: Issue $47.50; 1983 High $50.00;
Low $47.50; Close $50.00; Up $2.50

76-R54-1.16
1983 Nils in Oland
Issue price: $42.50

76-R54-1.1 "Bringing Home the Tree"
1968 Rörstrand *Christmas*
Detail from the world's first square collector's plate showing porcelain decorated in Scandia blue underglaze.

Artists of the World

Initially organized as DeGrazia of Scottsdale, the company was founded by James LaFond to represent Arizona artist Ted DeGrazia. The present name, Artists of the World, was adopted in 1977 when the company's scope was enlarged to include additional artists.

Children of Aberdeen, a proprietary series with artwork by Kee Fung Ng, began in 1979 and depicts the children who live on boats anchored at the fishing village of Aberdeen near Hong Kong.

Artist Kee Fung Ng was born in Canton, China, and educated at its Fu San Art School. His works have received critical acclaim for their subtle balancing of both Eastern and Western artistic concepts.

UNITED STATES
ARTISTS OF THE WORLD
Scottsdale, Arizona

Children of Aberdeen Series
Artist: Kee Fung Ng. Artist's signature appears on front

China banded in gold

Diameter: 25.4 centimeters (10 inches)

No hanger

Edition size unannounced

Numbered with certificate

84-A72-1.1
1979 Girl with Little Brother
Prices: Issue $50.00; 1983 High $60.00; Low $55.00; Close $55.00; Down $4.00

84-A72-1.2
1980 Sampan Girl
Prices: Issue $50.00; 1983 High $70.00; Low $58.00; Close $65.00; Up $7.00

84-A72-1.3
1981 Girl with Little Sister
Prices: Issue $55.00; 1983 High $60.00; Low $57.00; Close $60.00; Up $3.00

84-A72-1.4
1982 Girl with Seashells
Prices: Issue $60.00; 1983 High $70.00, Low $60.00; Close $70.00; Up $10.00

84-A72-1.5
1983 Girl with Seabirds
Prices: Issue $60.00; 1983 High $80.00; Low $60.00; Close $80.00; Up $20.00

84-A72-1.6
1984 Brother and Sister
Issue price: $60.00
Series Closed

perfection in porcelain

Crown Parian, Ltd. was incorporated in South El Monte, California in 1978 for the purpose of producing fine porcelain limited-edition plates and related products.

Crown Parian has introduced two series by well-known comedian Red Skelton: the *Freddie the Freeloader* series in 1979 and *Freddie's Adventures* series in 1982. The *American Folk Heroes* series began in 1983 with artwork by Gene Boyer.

Gene Boyer, born in 1948, is best known for over 45 covers and illustrations for *The Saturday Evening Post* from 1975 to 1978. He has done numerous private portrait commissions, including a portrait of Jack Oakie, and won the Marion de Sala Mendes Memorial Award in 1976 and 1977.

Freddie the Freeloader Series

Artist: Red Skelton. Artist's signature appears on front

Overglaze-decorated porcelain banded in gold

Diameter: 21.6 centimeters (8½ inches)

No hanger

Edition size limited to 10,000

Numbered without certificate

84-C72-1.1
1979 *Freddie in the Bathtub*
Prices: Issue $55.00; 1983 High $240.00;
Low $225.00; Close $225.00; Down $15.00

84-C72-1.2
1980 *Freddie's Shack*
Prices: Issue $55.00; 1983 High $118.00;
Low $95.00; Close $95.00; Down $23.00

84-C72-1.3
1981 *Freddie on the Green*
Prices: Issue $60.00; 1983 High $98.00;
Low $75.00; Close $75.00; Down $23.00

84-C72-1.4
1982 *Love That Freddie*
Prices: Issue $60.00; 1983 High $63.00;
Low $63.00; Close $63.00; No Change
Series Closed

American Folk Heroes Series

Artist: Gene Boyer. Artist's signature appears on front

Overglaze-decorated porcelain banded in gold

Diameter: 21.6 centimeters (8½ inches)

No hanger

Edition size undisclosed, limited by announced period of issue

Numbered with certificate

84-C72-2.1
1983 *Johnny Appleseed*
Prices: Issue $35.00; 1983 High $35.00;
Low $35.00; Close $35.00; No Change

84-C72-2.2
1984 *Davy Crockett*
Issue price: $35.00

84-C72-3.1

Freddie's Adventures Series

Artist: Red Skelton. Artist's signature appears on front

Overglaze-decorated porcelain banded in gold

Diameter: 21.6 centimeters (8½ inches)

No hanger

Edition size limited to 15,000

Numbered without certificate

84-C72-3.1
1981 *Captain Freddie*
Prices: Issue $60.00; 1983 High $64.00; Low $60.00; Close $64.00; Up $4.00

84-C72-3.2
1982 *Bronco Freddie*
Prices: Issue $60.00; 1983 High $60.00; Low $55.00; Close $55.00; Down $5.00

84-C72-3.3
1983 *Sir Freddie*
Prices: Issue $62.50; 1983 High $62.50; Low $62.50; Close $62.50; No Change

Maker had
no photo at
press time

84-C72-3.4
1984 *Gertrude and Heathcliffe*
Issue price: $62.50

84-C72-1.1 "Freddie in the Bathtub"
1979 Crown Parian *Freddie the Freeloader*
Multi-color decalcomania bears the signature of well-known comedian and plate artist Red Skelton.

R.J. Ernst Enterprises Inc.

R. J. Ernst Enterprises was founded in 1976 by Ray and Marilyn Ernst. Originally operating from a collectibles gallery in Escondido, California, the company now has expanded offices in San Marcos. Ernst Enterprises produces a variety of limited-edition collectibles as well as collector's plates.

In 1981, the Ernst plate series *Seems Like Yesterday* introduced artist Rusty Money to the collector's market. Ms. Money was born in Oak Park, Illinois and now lives and paints in Escondido, California. Her favorite subjects are children and turn-of-the-century period scenes; her work is characterized by the use of delicate pastels in a semi-Impressionistic style.

Seems Like Yesterday Series

Artist: Rusty Money. Artist's signature appears on front

Porcelain

Diameter: 21.6 centimeters (8½ inches)

No hanger

Edition size undisclosed, limited by announced period of issue

Numbered with certificate

84-E74-1.1
1981 *Stop and Smell the Roses*
Prices: Issue $24.50; 1983 High $27.00;
Low $24.50; Close $25.00; Up $.50

84-E74-1.2
1982 *Home by Lunch*
Prices: Issue $24.50; 1983 High $25.00;
Low $24.50; Close $25.00; Up $.50

84-E74-1.3
1982 *Lisa's Creek*
Prices: Issue $24.50; 1983 High $25.00;
Low $24.00; Close $24.00; Down $.50

84-E74-1.4
1983 *It's Got My Name on It*
Prices: Issue $24.50; 1983 High $24.50;
Low $24.50; Close $24.50; No Change

84-E74-1.5
1984 *My Magic Hat*
Issue price $24.50

84-E74-1.6
1984 *Little Prince*
Issue price: $24.50
Series Closed

Fairmont China was established in 1976 to produce limited-edition plates. Two series began that year: the *Holiday* series with artwork by Ted DeGrazia, and the *Famous Clowns* series by comedian Red Skelton. In 1978, Fairmont issued the third plate in the *DeGrazia Children* series, originally started by Gorham (see United States, GORHAM). In 1978 Fairmont started their *Classical American Beauties* series and, in 1981, began their *Playful Memories* series with artwork by Sue Etém.

Ted DeGrazia, one-time apprentice to the great Mexican muralist Diego Rivera, first came to international attention in 1960 when his work was featured on a UNICEF card. Since then, his stylized re-creations of Southwestern subjects and themes have made him one of the most instantly recognizable of American artists. DeGrazia died in 1982. Red Skelton, a comedian widely known for his film, stage, and television characterizations, has also earned a devoted following for his artwork. Sue Etém is a self-taught painter, and has held numerous shows in California, including such cities as Costa Mesa, Westminister, and Huntington Beach.

UNITED STATES
FAIRMONT
Pasadena, California

DeGrazia Holiday Series

Artist: Ted DeGrazia. Artist's signature appears on front; first 500 autographed on back

China banded in gold

Diameter: 26 centimeters (10¼ inches)

No hanger

Edition size limited to 10,000

Numbered since 1977, without certificate

84-F4-1.1
1976 *The Festival of Lights*
Prices: Issue $45.00; 1983 High $275.00; Low $256.00; Close $275.00; Up $19.00

84-F4-1.2
1977 *The Bell of Hope*
Prices: Issue $45.00; 1983 High $200.00; Low $172.00; Close $180.00; Up $8.00

84-F4-1.3
1978 *Little Madonna*
Prices: Issue $45.00; 1983 High $250.00; Low $210.00; Close $210.00; Down $17.00

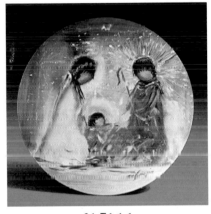

84-F4-1.4
1979 *The Nativity*
Prices: Issue $50.00; 1983 High $160.00; Low $133.00; Close $160.00; Up $27.00

84-F4-1.5
1980 *Little Pima Indian Drummer Boy*
Prices: Issue $50.00; 1983 High $145.00; Low $100.00; Close $145.00; Up $45.00

84-F4-1.6
1981 *Little Prayer—The Christmas Angel*
Prices: Issue $55.00; 1983 High $185.00; Low $118.00; Close $185.00; Up $67.00

84-F4-1.7
1982 *The Blue Boy*
Prices: Issue $60.00; 1983 High $150.00; Low $100.00; Close $150.00; Up $50.00

84-F4-1.8
1983 *Heavenly Blessings*
Prices: Issue $65.00; 1983 High $140.00; Low $65.00; Close $140.00; Up $75.00

84-F4-1.9
1984 *Navajo Madonna*
Issue price: $65.00

Famous Clowns Series

Artist: Red Skelton. Artist's signature appears on front

China banded in gold

Diameter: 21.6 centimeters (8½ inches)

No hanger

Edition size limited to 10,000

Numbered without certificate

84-F4-2.1
1976 *Freddie the Freeloader*
Prices: Issue $55.00; 1983 High $410.00;
Low $375.00; Close $410.00; Up $7.00

84-F4-2.2
1977 *W. C. Fields*
Prices: Issue $55.00; 1983 High $112.00;
Low $66.00; Close $66.00; Down $46.00

84-F4-2.3
1978 *Happy*
Prices: Issue $55.00; 1983 High $105.00;
Low $65.00; Close $65.00; Down $40.00

84-F4-2.4
1979 *The Pledge*
Prices: Issue $55.00; 1983 High $104.00;
Low $90.00; Close $90.00; Down $14.00
Series Closed

FAIRMONT

Pasadena, California

DeGrazia Children Series

Artist: Ted DeGrazia. Artist's signature appears on front; first 500 autographed on back

China banded in gold

Diameter: 26 centimeters (10¼ inches)

No hanger

Edition size limited to 10,000

Numbered without certificate

84-F4-4.1
1978 *Flower Girl*
Prices: Issue $45.00; 1983 High $220.00; Low $175.00; Close $175.00; Down $20.00

84-F4-4.2
1979 *Flower Boy*
Prices: Issue $45.00; 1983 High $165.00; Low $134.00; Close $165.00; Up $31.00

84-F4-4.3
1980 *Little Cocopah Indian Girl*
Prices: Issue $50.00; 1983 High $130.00; Low $96.00; Close $130.00; Up $34.00

84-F4-4.4
1981 *Beautiful Burden*
Prices: Issue $50.00; 1983 High $142.00; Low $82.00; Close $142.00; Up $60.00

84-F4-4.5
1982 *Merry Little Indian*
Prices: Issue $55.00; 1983 High $225.00; Low $97.00; Close $225.00; Up $128.00

84-F4-4.6
1983 *Wondering*
Prices: Issue $60.00; 1983 High $122.00; Low $92.00; Close $115.00; Up $23.00

84-F4-4.7
1984 *Pink Papoose*
Issue price: $65.00

Classical American Beauties

Artist: Vincent. Artist's signature appears on front

China banded in gold

Diameter: 26 centimeters (10¼ inches)

No hanger

Edition size limited to 7,500

Numbered without certificate

84-F4-8.1
1979 *Colleen*
Prices: Issue $60.00; 1983 High $86.00;
Low $75.00; Close $75.00; Down $10.00

84-F4-8.2
1979 *Heather*
Prices: Issue $60.00; 1983 High $72.00;
Low $65.00; Close $65.00; Down $7.00

84-F4-8.3
1980 *Dawn*
Prices: Issue $60.00; 1983 High $69.00;
Low $66.00; Close $66.00; No Change

84-F4-8.4
1981 *Eve*
Prices: Issue $60.00; 1983 High $60.00;
Low $60.00; Close $60.00; No Change
Series Closed

Playful Memories Series

Artist: Sue Etém. Artist's signature appears on front

China banded in gold

Diameter: 22.3 centimeters (8¾ inches)

No hanger

Edition size limited to 10,000

Numbered without certificate

84-F4-10.1
1981 *Renee*
Prices: Issue $39.50; 1983 High $145.00;
Low $132.00; Close $145.00; Up $13.00

84-F4-10.2
1982 *Jeremy*
Prices: Issue $42.50; 1983 High $90.00;
Low $67.00; Close $86.00; Up $19.00

UNITED STATES
FAIRMONT
Pasadena, California

84-F4-10.3
1983 *Jamie*
Prices: Issue $42.50; 1983 High $70.00;
Low $42.50; Close $70.00; Up $27.50

84-F4-10.4
1983 *Randy*
Prices: Issue $45.00; 1983 High $55.00;
Low $45.00; Close $55.00; Up $10.00
Series Closed

UNITED STATES
FRANKLIN MINT
Franklin Center, Pennsylvania

The Franklin Mint, the world's largest private mint, was established in the Philadelphia vicinity in 1965 by Joseph Segel. The firm specializes in porcelain collectibles, sculptures, fine art prints, jewelry, and has several international subsidiaries and branches.

The Franklin Mint entered the limited-edition plate field in 1970 with the six-plate *Rockwell Christmas* series, crafted in sterling silver.

The *Rockwell Christmas* series is the only one to be designed especially for the collector's plate market by the artist, Norman Rockwell. One of the most widely-known artists in the twentieth century, Norman Rockwell created well over 3,000 works including 323 *Saturday Evening Post* covers as well as numerous illustrations for *Life, Look, Boys Life,* and annual Boy Scout calendars. His works hang in a number of museums: from the Smithsonian Institution and the Metropolitan Museum of Art in New York, to the Corner House in the artist's adopted home of Stockbridge, Massachusetts.

UNITED STATES
FRANKLIN MINT
Franklin Center, Pennsylvania

Rockwell Christmas Series

Artist: Norman Rockwell. Artist's signature appears on front

Etched sterling silver

Diameter: 20.3 centimeters (8 inches)

No hanger

Edition size: as indicated

Numbered, with certificate since 1972

84-F64-1.1
1970 *Bringing Home the Tree*
Edition: 18,321
Prices: Issue $100.00; 1983 High $350.00;
Low $150.00; Close $150.00; Down $200.00

84-F64-1.2
1971 *Under the Mistletoe*
Edition: 24,792
Prices: Issue $100.00; 1983 High $172.00;
Low $100.00; Close $100.00; Down $72.00

84-F64-1.3
1972 *The Carolers*
Edition: 29,074
Prices: Issue $125.00; 1983 High $165.00;
Low $100.00; Close $100.00; Down $61.00

84-F64-1.4
1973 *Trimming the Tree*
Edition: 18,010
Prices: Issue $125.00; 1983 High $168.00;
Low $110.00; Close $110.00; Down $54.00

84-F64-1.5
1974 *Hanging the Wreath*
Edition: 12,822
Prices: Issue $175.00; 1983 High $171.00;
Low $110.00; Close $110.00; Down $61.00

84-F64-1.6
1975 *Home for Christmas*
Edition: 11,059
Prices: Issue $180.00; 1983 High $195.00;
Low $160.00; Close $160.00; Down $34.00
Series Closed

In 1831 Jabez Gorham, a silversmith, established the Gorham Corporation. Today a division of Textron, the firm is one of the world's largest producers of sterling and hollowware, figurines, and ornaments.

Gorham Corporation acquired crystal and china manufacturing companies in 1970, enabling it to produce limited-edition plates in china as well as silver.

Gorham's *Rockwell Four Seasons* series, which began in 1971 and ended in 1980, was comprised of four plates each year (spring, summer, fall, and winter). A *Christmas* series, also with artwork by Norman Rockwell, was started in 1974. The *DeGrazia Children* series and the *Sugar and Spice* series began in 1976 with the latter ending in 1979. The *Prince Tatters* series was started in 1977 and ended in 1980.

Since 1978, Fairmont China has made the *DeGrazia Children* plates (see United States, FAIRMONT). The *Sugar and Spice* and *Prince Tatters* series are produced for Kern Collectibles by Gorham (see United States, KERN COLLECTIBLES).

One of the most widely-known artists in the twentieth century, Norman Rockwell created well over 3,000 works including 323 *Saturday Evening Post* covers as well as numerous illustrations for *Life, Look, Boys Life,* and annual Boy Scout calendars. His works hang in a number of museums: from the Smithsonian Institution and the Metropolitan Museum of Art in New York, to the Corner House in the artist's adopted home of Stockbridge, Massachusetts. Ted DeGrazia, one-time apprentice to the great Mexican muralist Diego Rivera, first came to international attention in 1960 when his work was featured on a UNICEF card. Since then, his stylized recreations of Southwestern subjects and themes have made him one of the most instantly recognizable of American artists. DeGrazia died in 1982. Born in The Hague, The Netherlands, Leo Jansen spent his youth in Indonesia, where he developed his skills as a portrait painter by sketching the bronze-skinned Malay children. He returned to The Netherlands to study at the Academy of Fine Arts and later refined his work in the famous "Pigalle" section of Paris.

GORHAM
Providence, Rhode Island

Rockwell Four Seasons Series

Artist: Norman Rockwell. Artist's signature appears on front

China banded in 24k gold

Diameter: 26.7 centimeters (10½ inches)

No hanger

Edition size undisclosed, limited by year of issue

Not numbered, without certificate

Issued in sets of four

84-G58-1.1-1
1971 *A Boy and His Dog;*
A Boy Meets His Dog
Prices: Issue $50.00; 1983 High $418.00;
Low $325.00; Close $325.00; Down $93.00

84-G58-1.1-2
1971 *Adventurers Between Adventures*

84-G58-1.1-3
1971 *A Mysterious Malady*

84-G58-1.1-4
1971 *Pride of Parenthood*

84-G58-1.2-1
1972 *Young Love; Flying Colors*
Prices: Issue $60.00; 1983 High $176.00;
Low $110.00; Close $110.00; Down $66.00

84-G58-1.2-2
1972 *Beguiling Buttercup*

84-G58-1.2-3
1972 *A Scholarly Pace*

84-G58-1.2-4
1972 *Downhill Daring*

84-G58-1.3-1
1973 *The Ages of Love;*
Sweet Song So Young
Prices: Issue $60.00; 1983 High $315.00;
Low $175.00; Close $175.00; Down $140.00

84-G58-1.3-2
1973 *Flowers in Tender Bloom*

84-G58-1.3-3
1973 *Fondly Do We Remember*

84-G58-1.3-4
1973 *Gaily Sharing Vintage*

84-G58-1.4-1
1974 *Grandpa and Me; Day Dreamers*
Prices: Issue $60.00; 1983 High $158.00;
Low $115.00; Close $115.00; Down $43.00

84-G58-1.4-2
1974 *Goin' Fishin'*

84-G58-1.4-3
1974 *Pensive Pals*

84-G58-1.4-4
1974 *Gay Blades*

84-G58-1.5-1
1975 *Me and My Pal;*
Young Man's Fancy
Prices: Issue $70.00; 1983 High $206.00;
Low $140.00; Close $140.00; Down $63.00

84-G58-1.5-2
1975 *Fisherman's Paradise*

84-G58-1.5-3
1975 *Disastrous Daring*

84-G58-1.5-4
1975 *A Lickin' Good Bath*

84-G58-1.6-1
1976 *Grand Pals; Soaring Spirits*
Prices: Issue $70.00; 1983 High $250.00;
Low $180.00; Close $180.00; Down $70.00

84-G58-1.6-2
1976 *Fish Finders*

84-G58-1.6-3
1976 *Ghostly Gourds*

84-G58-1.6-4
1976 *Snow Sculpture*

84-G58-1.7-1
1977 *Going on Sixteen; Sweet Serenade*
Prices: Issue $75.00; 1983 High $248.00;
Low $175.00; Close $175.00; Down $73.00

84-G58-1.7-2
1977 *Sheer Agony*

84-G58-1.7-3
1977 Pilgrimage

84-G58-1.7-4
1977 Chilling Chore

84-G58-1.8-1
1978 The Tender Years; Spring Tonic
Prices: Issue $100.00; 1983 High $107.00;
Low $95.00; Close $95.00; Down $12.00

84-G58-1.8-2
1978 Cool Aid

84-G58-1.8-3
1978 Chilly Reception

84-G58-1.8-4
1978 New Year Look

84-G58-1.9-1
1979 A Helping Hand;
Closed for Business
Prices: Issue $100.00; 1983 High $100.00;
Low $90.00; Close $90.00; Down $10.00

84-G58-1.9-2
1979 Swatters Rights

84-G58-1.9-3
1979 The Coal Season's Coming

GORHAM
Providence, Rhode Island

84-G58-1.9-4
1979 *Year End Count*

84-G58-1.10-1
1980 *Dad's Boy; In His Spirit*
Prices: Issue $135.00; 1983 High $135.00;
Low $95.00; Close $110.00; Down $23.00
Series Closed

84-G58-1.10-2
1980 *Trout Dinner*

84-G58-1.10-3
1980 *Careful Aim*

84-G58-1.10-4
1980 *Ski Skills*

Rockwell Christmas Series

Artist: Norman Rockwell. Artist's
signature appears on front

China banded in 24k gold

Diameter: 21.6 centimeters
(8½ inches)

No hanger

Edition size undisclosed, limited
by year of issue

Not numbered, without certificate

84-G58-3.1
1974 *Tiny Tim*
Prices: Issue $12.50; 1983 High $65.00;
Low $45.00; Close $45.00; Down $20.00

84-G58-3.2
1975 *Good Deeds*
Prices: Issue $17.50; 1983 High $64.00;
Low $50.00; Close $50.00; Down $14.00

84-G58-3.3
1976 Christmas Trio
Prices: Issue $19.50; 1983 High $50.00;
Low $38.00; Close $38.00; Down $12.00

84-G58-3.4
1977 Yuletide Reckoning
Prices: Issue $19.50; 1983 High $45.00;
Low $45.00; Close $45.00; No Change

84-G58-3.5
1978 Planning Christmas Visits
Prices: Issue $24.50; 1983 High $25.00;
Low $25.00; Close $25.00; No Change

84-G58-3.6
1979 Santa's Helpers
Prices: Issue $24.50; 1983 High $21.00;
Low $20.00; Close $20.00; Down $1.00

84-G58-3.7
1980 Letter to Santa
Prices: Issue $27.50; 1983 High $28.00;
Low $25.00; Close $25.00; Down $2.00

84-G58-3.8
1981 Santa Plans His Visit
Prices: Issue $29.50; 1983 High $30.00;
Low $30.00; Close $30.00; No Change

84-G58-3.9
1982 The Jolly Coachman
Prices: Issue $29.50; 1983 High $30.00;
Low $29.50; Close $30.00; Up $.50

84-G58-3.10
1983 Christmas Dancers
Prices: Issue $29.50; 1983 High $29.50;
Low $29.50; Close $29.50; No Change

84-G58-3.11
1984 Christmas Medley
Issue price: $29.50

UNITED STATES

GORHAM
Providence, Rhode Island

DeGrazia Children Series
Artist: Ted DeGrazia. Artist's
signature appears on front

China banded in 24k gold

Diameter: 26.7 centimeters
(10½ inches)

No hanger

Edition size: as indicated

Not numbered, without certificate

84-G58-5.1
1976 *Los Niños*
Edition: 5,000
Prices: Issue $35.00; 1983 High $1400.00;
Low $875.00; Close $1400.00; Up $525.00

84-G58-5.2
1977 *The White Dove*
Edition: 10,000
Prices: Issue $40.00; 1983 High $185.00;
Low $158.00; Close $160.00; Up $2.00
Series Closed

Sugar and Spice Series
Artist: Leo Jansen. Artist's
signature appears on front

China banded in 24k gold

Diameter: 21.6 centimeters
(8½ inches)

No hanger

Edition size limited to 7,500

Numbered without certificate

84-G58-6.1
1976 *Dana and Debbie*
Prices: Issue $40.00; 1983 High $140.00;
Low $130.00; Close $130.00; Down $8.00

84-G58-6.2
1977 *Becky and Baby*
Prices: Issue $42.50; 1983 High $75.00,
Low $60.00; Close $60.00; Down $13.00

84-G58-6.3
1978 *Jeanette and Julie*
Prices: Issue $47.50; 1983 High $61.00;
Low $50.00; Close $50.00; Down $9.00

84-G58-6.4
1979 *Ramona and Rachel*
Prices: Issue $50.00; 1983 High $105.00;
Low $93.00; Close $105.00; Up $12.00
Series Closed

Prince Tatters Series

Artist: Leo Jansen. Artist's signature appears on front

China banded in 24k gold

Diameter: 21.6 centimeters (8½ inches)

No hanger

Edition size limited to 7,500

Numbered without certificate

84-G58-8.1
1977 Johnny and Duke
Prices: Issue $40.00; 1983 High $53.00;
Low $50.00; Close $50.00; Down $3.00

84-G58-8.2
1978 Randy and Rex
Prices: Issue $42.50; 1983 High $68.00;
Low $68.00; Close $68.00; No Change

84-G58-8.3
1979 Furry Friends
Prices: Issue $47.50; 1983 High $48.00;
Low $40.00; Close $40.00; Down $8.00

84-G58-8.4
1980 Benji's Burro
Prices: Issue $50.00; 1983 High $125.00;
Low $106.00; Close $125.00; Up $19.00
Series Closed

**Incolay Studios
of California**

Incolay Studios has been creating cameo *objets d'art* in Incolay stone since 1965. The manufacturing process by which Incolay stone is created is a closely guarded secret, but it is acknowledged that the process includes the addition of a range of quartz-based minerals to replicate the coloring and weight of semi-precious stone cameos of the past.

Incolay Studios began its first series of collector's plates, the *Romantic Poets Collection,* in 1977. The series is inspired by the poetry of early nineteenth-century poets. In 1979, a second series of cameo plates, the *Great Romances of History Collection,* began. Their *Voyages of Ulysses* series began in 1984.

Gayle Bright Appleby, designer of the first four issues in the *Romantic Poets Collection,* is widely-known for the intricate detail of her sculptures in Incolay stone and in bronze, silver, and gold. Roger Akers, the present sculptor, was schooled at the Cooper School of Art and the Art Institute of Chicago. His work has been selected by the Illinois Arts Council for permanent museum display. Carl Romanelli, sculptor of the *Great*

Romances of History Collection, has works on display throughout the world. One of the most famous is his bust of John Henry Cardinal Newman, which is on permanent display at the Vatican.

INCOLAY

San Fernando, California

Romantic Poets Collection

Artist: as indicated. Artist's signature appears on front

Incolay stone with high relief cameos

Diameter: 26 centimeters (10¼ inches)

Attached back hanger

Edition size undisclosed, limited by announced period of issue

Numbered with certificate

84-I31-1.1
1977 She Walks in Beauty
Artist: Gayle Bright Appleby
Prices: Issue $60.00; 1983 High $248.00;
Low $190.00; Close $190.00; Down $58.00

84-I31-1.2
1978 A Thing of Beauty Is a Joy Forever
Artist: Gayle Bright Appleby
Prices: Issue $60.00; 1983 High $82.00;
Low $68.00; Close $68.00; Down $14.00

84-I31-1.3
1979 To a Skylark
Artist: Gayle Bright Appleby
Prices: Issue $65.00; 1983 High $65.00;
Low $65.00; Close $65.00; No Change

84-I31-1.4
1980 She Was a Phantom of Delight
Artist: Gayle Bright Appleby
Prices: Issue $65.00; 1983 High $76.00;
Low $70.00; Close $70.00; Down $6.00

84-I31-1.5
1981 The Kiss
Artist: Roger Akers
Prices: Issue $65.00; 1983 High $66.00;
Low $65.00; Close $66.00; Up $1.00

84-I31-1.6
1982 My Heart Leaps Up When I Behold
Artist: Roger Akers
Prices: Issue $70.00; 1983 High $100.00;
Low $70.00; Close $100.00; Up $30.00

84-I31-1.7
1983 I Stood Tiptoe
Artist: Roger Akers
Prices: Issue $70.00; 1983 High $70.00;
Low $70.00; Close $70.00; No Change

Great Romances of History Collection

Artist: Carl Romanelli. Artist's signature appears on front

Incolay stone with high relief cameos

Diameter: 26 centimeters (10¼ inches)

Attached back hanger

Edition size undisclosed, limited by announced period of issue

Numbered with certificate

84-I31-3.1
1979 Antony and Cleopatra
Prices: Issue $65.00; 1983 High $67.00;
Low $67.00; Close $67.00; No Change

84-I31-3.2
1980 The Taj Mahal Lovers
Prices: Issue $65.00; 1983 High $69.00;
Low $67.00; Close $67.00; Down $2.00

84-I31-3.3
1981 Lancelot and Guinevere
Prices: Issue $65.00; 1983 High $65.00;
Low $65.00; Close $65.00; No Change

84-I31-3.4
1982 Lord Nelson and Lady Hamilton
Prices: Issue $70.00; 1983 High $70.00;
Low $70.00; Close $70.00; No Change
Series Closed

Voyage of Ulysses Series

Artist: Alan Brunettin. Artist's signature appears on front

Incolay stone with high relief cameos

Diameter: 21.6 centimeters (8½ inches)

Pierced foot rim

Edition size undisclosed, limited by year of issue

Numbered with certificate

84-I31-4.1
1984 Isle of Circe
Issue price: undetermined
at press time

84-I31-1.1 "She Walks in Beauty"
1977 Incolay *Romantic Poets*
The first incolay stone collector's plate; the sculptural technique closely resembles high-relief cameo.

The story of Kern Collectibles dates to 1969 when Oscar L. Kern founded Commemorative Imports, a distributor of limited-edition collectibles. Mr. Kern expanded his business one step further in 1972 with the establishment of Kern Collectibles. Kern Collectibles issues limited-edition plates produced especially for the company by several of the world's fine china manufacturers.

Leaders of Tomorrow began in 1980 and comprised four issues by the late Leo Jansen.

Born in The Hague, The Netherlands, Leo Jansen spent his youth in Indonesia, where he developed his skills as a portrait painter by sketching the bronze-skinned Malay children. He returned to The Netherlands to study at the Academy of Fine Arts and later refined his work in the famous "Pigalle" section of Paris.

UNITED STATES
KERN COLLECTIBLES
Stillwater, Minnesota

Leaders of Tomorrow Series

Artist: Leo Jansen. Artist's signature appears on front

China banded in gold

Diameter: 21.6 centimeters (8½ inches)

No hanger

Edition size limited to 9,800

Numbered without certificate

84-K20-7.1
1980 *Future Physician*
Prices: Issue $50.00; 1983 High $68.00;
Low $60.00; Close $60.00; Down $8.00

84-K20-7.2
1981 *Future Farmer*
Prices: Issue $50.00; 1983 High $50.00;
Low $42.00; Close $42.00; Down $8.00

84-K20-7.3
1982 *Future Florist*
Prices: Issue $50.00; 1983 High $50.00;
Low $45.00; Close $45.00; Down $5.00

84-K20-7.4
1983 *Future Teacher*
Prices: Issue $50.00; 1983 High $50.00;
Low $50.00; Close $50.00; No Change
Series Closed

The Edwin M. Knowles heritage of fine china can be traced to the early nineteenth century when Isaac Knowles, father of Edwin, established the family firm—Knowles, Taylor and Knowles—in East Liverpool, Ohio. The site was chosen for its proximity to deposits of high-quality kaolin clay. The firm became well known for its production of Lotus ware.

After apprenticing with Knowles, Taylor and Knowles, Edwin established his own company in Newell, West Virginia, and became a pre-eminent force in American china. He was honored by election to the presidency of the United States Potters Association.

After his death, the company ceased operations for a period of time until entering into an affiliation with The Bradford Exchange in order to preserve its time-honored name.

Since 1975 the Edwin M. Knowles name has appeared on issues certified by the Rockwell Society of America (see United States, ROCKWELL SOCIETY). The *Wizard of Oz*, first proprietary series to bear the name of Knowles, began in 1977 and ended in 1980. The *Americana* *Holidays* series and the *Gone With the Wind* series, which is endorsed by Metro-Goldwyn-Mayer, began in 1978. Knowles began the *Csatari Grandparent Plate* series in 1980, and the *Annie Collector's Plate* series in 1983. The *Biblical Mothers* series began in 1983 with artwork by Eve Licea. The *Jeanne Down's Friends I Remember* series began in 1983 and their *Four Ancient Elements, Edna Hibel Mother's Day,* and *A Father's Love* series' began in 1984.

Knowles has commissioned a number of important contemporary artists to create its plates, including: James Auckland, whose stylistic blend of fantasy and realism is uniquely suited to the *Wizard of Oz* series; Raymond Kursár, twice recipient of the Award of Merit from the Society of Illustrators and well-known for his prize-winning Broadway show posters; Don Spaulding, Norman Rockwell protégé and a leading exponent of authentic historical detail in painting; Joseph Csatari, winner of the Gold Medal from the Society of Illustrators of New York and designer of a commemorative stamp which took his work to an audience of more than one hundred countries; William Chambers, whose numerous honors include top awards in the American Society of Illustrators' annual show for several consecutive years, and first prize in the John Howard Sanden portrait competition; Eve Licea, a painter, sculptor, and lithographer, who is best known for her dimensional, embossed lithographs. Her sculptured metal pieces have also won wide acclaim and are exhibited in such prominent art galleries as the Pindar Galleries, Lever House, and Les Moriches in New York City; and Edna Hibel, an elected member of the Royal Society of Arts in London, and one of the only living female artists with a U.S. museum devoted to her works.

UNITED STATES
EDWIN M. KNOWLES
Newell, West Virginia

Wizard of Oz Series

Artist: James Auckland. Artist's signature appears on front

China

Diameter: 21.6 centimeters (8½ inches) through 1979; 25.4 centimeters (10 inches) for 1980 plate

No hanger

Edition size undisclosed, limited by announced period of issue

Numbered with certificate

84-K41-1.1
1977 *Over the Rainbow*
Prices: Issue $19.00; 1983 High $204.00; Low $130.00; Close $130.00; Down $74.00

84-K41-1.2
1978 *If I Only Had a Brain*
Prices: Issue $19.00; 1983 High $41.00; Low $36.00; Close $36.00; Down $5.00

84-K41-1.3
1978 *If I Only Had a Heart*
Prices: Issue $19.00; 1983 High $43.00; Low $40.00; Close $40.00; Down $3.00

84-K41-1.4
1978 *If I Were King of the Forest*
Prices: Issue $19.00; 1983 High $34.00; Low $34.00; Close $34.00; No Change

84-K41-1.5
1979 *The Wicked Witch of the West*
Prices: Issue $19.00; 1983 High $35.00; Low $32.00; Close $35.00; Up $3.00

84-K41-1.6
1979 *Follow the Yellow Brick Road*
Prices: Issue $19.00; 1983 High $30.00; Low $25.00; Close $30.00; Up $4.00

84-K41-1.7
1979 *Wonderful Wizard of Oz*
Prices: Issue $19.00; 1983 High $50.00; Low $25.00; Close $50.00; Up $25.00

84-K41-1.8
1980 *The Grand Finale
(We're Off to See the Wizard)*
Prices: Issue $24.00; 1983 High $50.00; Low $24.00; Close $50.00; Up $26.00
Series Closed

84-K41-2.1

Americana Holidays Series

Artist: Don Spaulding. Artist's signature appears on front

China

Diameter: 21.6 centimeters, (8½ inches)

No hanger

Edition size undisclosed, limited by period of issue

Numbered with certificate

84-K41-2.1
1978 *Fourth of July*
Prices: Issue $26.00; 1983 High $45.00; Low $39.00; Close $39.00; Down $3.00

84-K41-2.2
1979 *Thanksgiving*
Prices: Issue $26.00; 1983 High $87.00; Low $70.00; Close $70.00; Down $17.00

84-K41-2.3
1980 *Easter*
Prices: Issue $26.00; 1983 High $62.00; Low $53.00; Close $53.00; Down $9.00

84-K41-2.4
1981 *Valentine's Day*
Prices: Issue $26.00; 1983 High $26.00; Low $26.00; Close $26.00; No Change

84-K41-2.5
1982 *Father's Day*
Prices: Issue $26.00; 1983 High $28.00; Low $26.00; Close $28.00; Up $2.00

84-K41-2.6
1983 *Christmas*
Prices: Issue $26.00; 1983 High $26.00; Low $26.00; Close $26.00; No Change

84-K41-2.7
1984 *Mother's Day*
Issue price: $26.00
Series Closed

UNITED STATES
EDWIN M. KNOWLES
Newell, West Virginia

Gone With the Wind Series
Artist: Raymond Kursár. Artist's signature appears on front

China

Diameter: 21.6 centimeters (8½ inches)

No hanger

Edition size undisclosed, limited by period of issue

Numbered with certificate

84-K41-3.1
1978 *Scarlett*
Prices: Issue $21.50; 1983 High $250.00; Low $225.00; Close $225.00; Down $25.00

84-K41-3.2
1979 *Ashley*
Prices: Issue $21.50; 1983 High $150.00; Low $112.00; Close $150.00; Up $38.00

84-K41-3.3
1980 *Melanie*
Prices: Issue $21.50; 1983 High $60.00; Low $48.00; Close $60.00; Up $12.00

84-K41-3.4
1981 *Rhett*
Prices: Issue $23.50; 1983 High $32.00; Low $24.00; Close $32.00; Up $8.00

84-K41-3.5
1982 *Mammy Lacing Scarlett*
Prices: Issue $23.50; 1983 High $42.00; Low $23.50; Close $42.00; Up $18.50

84-K41-3.6
1983 *Melanie Gives Birth*
Prices: Issue $23.50; 1983 High $23.50; Low $23.50; Close $23.50; No Change

Maker had
no photo at
press time

84-K41-3.7
1984 *Scarlett's Green Dress*
Issue price: $25.50

84-K41-4.1

Csatari Grandparent Plate Series

Artist: Joseph Csatari. Artist's signature appears on front

China

Diameter: 21.6 centimeters (8½ inches)

No hanger

Edition size undisclosed, limited by period of issue

Numbered with certificate

84-K41-4.1
1980 *Bedtime Story*
Prices: Issue $18.00; 1983 High $67.00;
Low $60.00; Close $60.00; Down $7.00

84-K41-4.2
1981 *The Skating Lesson*
Prices: Issue $20.00; 1983 High $22.00;
Low $22.00; Close $22.00; No Change

84-K41-4.3
1982 *The Cookie Tasting*
Prices: Issue $20.00; 1983 High $50.00;
Low $20.00; Close $50.00; Up $30.00

84-K41-4.4
1983 *The Swinger*
Prices: Issue $20.00; 1983 High $20.00;
Low $20.00; Close $20.00; No Change

Annie Collector's Plate Series

Artist: William Chambers. Artist's signature appears on front

China

Diameter: 21.6 centimeters (8½ inches)

No hanger

Edition size undisclosed, limited by announced period of issue

Numbered with certificate

84-K41-5.1
1983 *Annie and Sandy*
Prices: Issue $19.00; 1983 High $60.00;
Low $19.00; Close $60.00; Up $41.00

84-K41-5.2
1983 *Daddy Warbucks*
Prices: Issue $19.00; 1983 High $19.00;
Low $19.00; Close $19.00; No Change

84-K41-5.3
1983 *Annie and Grace*
Prices: Issue $19.00; 1983 High $19.00; Low $19.00; Close $19.00; No Change

Biblical Mothers Series

Artist: Eve Licea. Artist's signature appears on front

China banded in 24k gold

Diameter: 26 centimeters (10¼ inches)

No hanger

Edition size undisclosed, limited by announced period of issue

Numbered with certificate

84-K41-6.1
1983 *Bathsheba and Solomon*
Prices: Issue $39.50; 1983 High $110.00; Low $39.50; Close $110.00; Up $70.50

84-K41-6.2
1984 *The Judgment of Solomon*
Issue price: $39.50

Jeanne Down's Friends I Remember Series

Artist: Jeanne Down. Artist's signature appears on front

China

Diameter: 21.6 centimeters (8½ inches)

No hanger

Edition size undisclosed, limited by announced period of issue

Numbered with certificate

84-K41-7.1
1983 *Fish Story*
Prices: Issue $17.50; 1983 High $17.50; Low $17.50; Close $17.50; No Change

Maker had no photo at press time

84-K41-7.2
1984 *Office Hours*
Issue price: $17.50

Four Ancient Elements Series

Artist: Georgia Lambert. Artist's signature appears on front

China

Diameter: 23.5 centimeters (9¼ inches)

No hanger

Edition size undisclosed, limited by year of issue

Numbered with certificate

84-K41-8.1
1984 *Earth*
Issue price: $27.50

84-K41-8.2
1984 *Water*
Issue price: $27.50

Hibel Mother's Day Series

Artist: Edna Hibel. Artist's signature appears on front

China banded in burnished gold

Diameter: 21.6 centimeters (8½ inches)

No hanger

Edition size undisclosed, limited by year of issue

Numbered with certificate

84-K41-9.1
1984 *Abby and Lisa*
Issue price: $29.50

A Father's Love Series

Artist: Betsey Bradley. Artist's signature appears on front

China

Diameter: 21.6 centimeters (8½ inches)

No hanger

Edition size undisclosed, limited by period of issue

Numbered with certificate

84-K41-10.1
1984 *Open Wide*
Issue price: undeterminted
at press time

84-K41-6.1 "Bathsheba and Solomon"
1983 Edwin M. Knowles *Biblical Mothers*
Art deco and art nouveau styles are balanced against the pure white plate body in a most unusual design.

LENOX

Walter Scott Lenox and his partner, Jonathan Coxon, Sr., established the Ceramic Art Company in Trenton, New Jersey, in 1889. In 1895 Lenox bought out Coxon and operated the business alone until it was reorganized in 1906 as Lenox, Inc. The plant later moved to Pomona. The firm's early products were bowls, vases, figurines, and later, tableware. All were made in "American Belleek," named for the town in Ireland where this creamy, ivory-tinted ware was first produced.

During World World I, Lenox was commissioned to supply President Wilson with a complete 1,700-piece dinner service, the first wholly American china ever used in the White House. Later, both Presidents Franklin Roosevelt and Harry Truman commissioned Lenox to make sets of dinnerware. In 1981, the Reagan administration commissioned Lenox to create a 4,372-piece dinnerware set for the White House.

In 1970 Lenox introduced its *Boehm Bird* series using paintings by artist Edward Marshall Boehm. The series ended in 1981. The *Boehm Woodland Wildlife* series began in 1973 with artwork adapted from original Boehm sculptures. The series ended in 1982.

From a background as farmer and veterinarian, Edward Marshall Boehm became a full-time sculptor in 1949, and at his death in 1969 was recognized as one of America's greatest wildlife artists. His faithful replication of nature scenes won a substantial following and his work has appeared in the collections of Dwight D. Eisenhower, John F. Kennedy, Lyndon B. Johnson, Queen Elizabeth II, and Pope John XXIII, as well as in many prestigious museums, including the Smithsonian Institution.

LENOX
Lawrenceville, New Jersey

Boehm Bird Series
Artist: Edward Marshall Boehm.
Artist's name appears on back

China with 24k gold design on border

Diameter: 26.7 centimeters (10½ inches)

No hanger

Edition size undisclosed

Not numbered, without certificate

84-L18-1.1
1970 *Wood Thrush*
Prices: Issue $35.00; 1983 High $272.00;
Low $230.00; Close $230.00; Down $42.00

84-L18-1.2
1971 *Goldfinch*
Prices: Issue $35.00; 1983 High $100.00;
Low $65.00; Close $65.00; Down $35.00

84-L18-1.3
1972 *Mountain Bluebird*
Prices: Issue $37.50; 1983 High $73.00;
Low $58.00; Close $58.00; Down $15.00

84-L18-1.4
1973 *Meadowlark*
Prices: Issue $41.00; 1983 High $72.00;
Low $50.00; Close $50.00; Down $22.00

84-L18-1.5
1974 *Rufous Hummingbird*
Prices: Issue $45.00; 1983 High $75.00;
Low $60.00; Close $60.00; Down $15.00

84-L18-1.6
1975 *American Redstart*
Prices: Issue $50.00; 1983 High $57.00;
Low $53.00; Close $53.00; Down $4.00

84-L18-1.7
1976 *Cardinal*
Prices: Issue $53.00; 1983 High $58.00;
Low $50.00; Close $50.00; Down $8.00

84-L18-1.8
1977 *Robins*
Prices: Issue $55.00; 1983 High $66.00;
Low $40.00; Close $40.00; Down $18.00

84-L18-1.9
1978 *Mockingbirds*
Prices: Issue $58.00; 1983 High $65.00;
Low $50.00; Close $50.00; Down $15.00

84-L18-1.10
1979 *Golden-Crowned Kinglets*
Prices: Issue $65.00; 1983 High $62.00;
Low $50.00; Close $50.00; Down $12.00

84-L18-1.11
1980 *Black-Throated Blue Warblers*
Prices: Issue $80.00; 1983 High $85.00;
Low $74.00; Close $85.00; Up $11.00

84-L18-1.12
1981 *Eastern Phoebes*
Prices: Issue $90.00; 1983 High $95.00;
Low $95.00; Close $95.00; No Change
Series Closed

Boehm Woodland Wildlife Series

Artist: Edward Marshall Boehm.
Artist's name appears on back

China with 24k gold design on border

Diameter: 26.7 centimeters
(10½ inches)

No hanger

Edition size undisclosed

Not numbered, without certificate

84-L18-3.1
1973 *Raccoons*
Prices: Issue $50.00; 1983 High $82.00;
Low $70.00; Close $70.00; Down $10.00

84-L18-3.2
1974 *Red Foxes*
Prices: Issue $52.50; 1983 High $48.00;
Low $40.00; Close $45.00; No Change

84-L18-3.3
1975 *Cottontail Rabbits*
Prices: Issue $58.50; 1983 High $76.00;
Low $70.00; Close $70.00; Down $6.00

84-L18-3.4
1976 *Eastern Chipmunks*
Prices: Issue $62.50; 1983 High $60.00;
Low $60.00; Close $60.00; No Change

84-L18-3.5
1977 *Beaver*
Prices: Issue $67.50; 1983 High $71.00;
Low $62.00; Close $62.00; Down $9.00

84-L18-3.6
1978 *Whitetail Deer*
Prices: Issue $70.00; 1983 High $65.00;
Low $62.00; Close $65.00; Up $3.00

84-L18-3.7
1979 *Squirrels*
Prices: Issue $76.00; 1983 High $75.00;
Low $69.00; Close $72.00; Down $2.00

84-L18-3.8
1980 *Bobcats*
Prices: Issue $92.50; 1983 High $95.00;
Low $80.00; Close $80.00; Down $15.00

84-L18-3.9
1981 *Martens*
Prices: Issue $100.00; 1983 High $104.00;
Low $90.00; Close $90.00; Down $14.00

84-L18-3.10
1982 *Otters*
Prices: Issue $100.00; 1983 High $120.00;
Low $100.00; Close $120.00; Up $20.00
Series Closed

UNITED STATES
MODERN MASTERS/GBS
Frankfort, Illinois

CLASSICS IN THEIR TIME

Modern Masters, Ltd. was founded in 1980 by limited-edition collectibles dealer Richard J. Sitarski. The firm is located in Frankfort, Illinois, and produces not only limited-edition plates, but also limited-edition graphics. Although Modern Masters has produced several series under its own name, the *Family Treasures Collection*, first offered in 1982, was co-produced with Chicago-based Graphics Buying Service.

Richard Zolan, the creator of the *Family Treasures Collection*, is descended from four generations of artists—and is the brother of prominent collector's plate artist Donald Zolan. He was born in Chicago, Illinois and now works in the Palm Desert area of California. His works are exhibited in numerous corporate art collections and owned by a number of celebrities. Additionally, he has exhibited in one-man shows, at major art museums and galleries including the Art Institute of Chicago.

UNITED STATES
MODERN MASTERS/GBS
Frankfort, Illinois

Family Treasures Collection

Artist: Richard Zolan. Artist's
signature appears on front

China

Diameter: 21.6 centimeters
(8½ inches)

No hanger

Edition size limited to 18,500

Numbered with certificate

84-M54-1.1
1981 *Cora's Recital*
Prices: Issue $39.50; 1983 High $48.00;
Low $35.00; Close $35.00; Down $4.50

84-M54-1.2
1982 *Cora's Tea Party*
Prices: Issue $39.50; 1983 High $39.50;
Low $38.00; Close $38.00; Down $1.50

84-M54-1.3
1983 *Cora's Garden Party*
Prices: Issue $39.50; 1983 High $40.00;
Low $39.50; Close $40.00; Up $.50

𝒪ℳ *Morgantown Crystal*

Floyd Jones and his father founded the Monongahela Valley Cut Glass Company in 1912 at Morgantown, West Virginia. Their most famous design was an elegant pattern known as "Morgantown Rose." The company flourished under the direction of the Jones family for four generations. In 1977 John Heiner purchased the firm and renamed it Morgantown Crystal, recently expanding operations to include glass etching and engraving as well as cutting.

The first limited-edition collector's plates series to bear the Morgantown Crystal hallmark, *Yates' Country Ladies*, began in 1981.

Designs for issues in the series are by Michael Yates. Born in Pennsylvania, Yates studied at the Art Institute of Pittsburgh. His works appear in numerous public buildings and churches throughout America as well as in many private collections. Prominent figures who have commissioned his work include Gerald Ford, the late Golda Meir, Johnny Cash, and former First Lady Pat Nixon.

MORGANTOWN CRYSTAL
Morgantown, West Virginia

*Michael Yates' Country
Ladies Series*

Artist: Michael Yates. Artist's
signature appears on front

Full-lead crystal

Diameter: 22.6 centimeters
(8⅞ inches)

No hanger

Edition size limited to 30,000

Numbered with certificate

84-M58-1.1
1981 *Angelica*
Prices: Issue $75.00; 1983 High $75.00;
Low $75.00; Close $75.00; No Change

84-M58-1.2
1982 *Violet*
Prices: Issue $75.00; 1983 High $75.00;
Low $75.00; Close $75.00; No Change

84-M58-1.3
1983 *Heather*
Prices: Issue $75.00; 1983 High $75.00;
Low $75.00; Close $75.00; No Change

Maker had
no photo at
press time

84-M58-1.4
1984 *Genevieve*
Issue Price: $75.00
Series Closed

The Newell Pottery Company is a division of the Edwin M. Knowles China Company. The firm is best known for its Newellware, a variety of earthenware.

In 1984, the Newell Pottery Company entered the limited-edition plate market with its Sarah Stilwell Weber Calendar series.

Sarah Stilwell Weber was born near Philadelphia, Pennsylvania, in 1878. She studied art at the Drexel Institute in Philadelphia under the tutelage of American illustrator Howard Pyle, and was one of the founders of the American realist movement. Between the years 1900 and 1930, Weber's work graced the pages of children's books and the covers of such magazines as *Collier's* and the *Saturday Evening Post.*

UNITED STATES
NEWELL POTTERY
Newell, West Virginia

Sarah Stilwell Weber's Calendar Series

Artist: Sarah Stilwell Weber

Newellware

Diameter: 18.4 centimeters (7¼ inches)

No hanger

Edition size undisclosed, limited by announced period of issue

Numbered with certificate

© 1984 SEPCO

84-N18-1.1
1984 *June*
Issue price: undetermined
at press time

UNITED STATES
PEMBERTON & OAKES
Santa Barbara, California

Pemberton & Oakes was founded in 1977. Originally located in Evanston, Illinois, the firm moved to Santa Barbara, California in 1979 and opened a gallery for the display of original art works from its proprietary plate series.

The first two Bradex-listed series produced by the company, *Zolan's Children* and the *Nutcracker Ballet Plate Collection,* were both introduced in 1978; they are listed under the maker's name, Viletta China Co. (see United States, VILETTA). The two most-recent Bradex-listed series from the company are listed under the Pemberton & Oakes name. The *Children at Christmas Collection*, introduced in 1981, and *Wonder of Childhood Collection*, introduced in 1982, both feature the work of Donald Zolan, already well-known to collectors for his earlier *Zolan's Children* series.

Donald Zolan also studied at the Art Institute of Chicago and won a scholarship to the American Academy of Art. His works hang in numerous galleries throughout the United States and in private collections in Mexico, Australia, France, Italy, South Korea, and Colombia.

UNITED STATES
PEMBERTON & OAKES
Santa Barbara, California

Wonder of Childhood Collection

Artist: Donald Zolan. Artist's signature appears on front

China

Diameter: 21.6 centimeters (8½ inches)

No hanger

Edition size undisclosed, limited by announced period of issue

Numbered with certificate

84-P19-1.1
1982 *Touching the Sky*
Prices: Issue $19.00; 1983 High $70.00;
Low $19.00; Close $40.00; Up $21.00

84-P19-1.2
1983 *Spring Innocence*
Prices: Issue $19.00; 1983 High $45.00;
Low $19.00; Close $35.00; Up $16.00

84-P19-1.3
1984 *Winter Angel*
Issue price: $22.00

Children at Christmas Collection

Artist: Donald Zolan. Artist's signature appears on front

China banded in gold

Diameter: 26 centimeters (10¼ inches)

No hanger

Edition size limited to 15,000

Numbered with certificate

84-P19-2.1
1981 *A Gift for Laurie*
Prices: Issue $48.00; 1983 High $87.00;
Low $75.00; Close $87.00; Down $10.00

84-P19-2.2
1982 *A Christmas Prayer*
Prices: Issue $48.00; 1983 High $50.00;
Low $48.00; Close $50.00; Up $2.00

84-P19-2.3
1983 *Erik's Delight*
Prices: Issue $48.00; 1983 High $48.00;
Low $48.00; Close $48.00; No Change

84-P19-2.4
1984 *Christmas Secret*
Issue price: $48.00

Pickard was established in Edgerton, Wisconsin, in 1894 by Wilder Austin Pickard, then moved to Chicago in 1897. For some forty years the Pickard China Studio, as the firm was then known, was a decorating company employing artists to hand-paint white blanks of bowls, pitchers, and other items obtained from factories in Europe.

In 1920 Pickard was incorporated and in 1938 moved to Antioch, Illinois, the site of the present pottery. Here the firm began making its own fine china. Today Pickard, Inc. is headed by Henry A. Pickard, a third generation descendant of the founder, making it the only American china company in the hands of the founding family.

In 1970 Pickard introduced its *Lockhart Wildlife* series. These plates were issued in pairs during the first four years of the series, but from 1974 individual plates were issued. The series ended in 1980. The *Christmas* series began in 1976, and in 1978 Pickard began the *Children of Renoir* series which ended in 1980. Pickard began its *Mother's Love* series in 1980 with artwork by Irene Spencer and in 1981 introduced

Oleg Cassini's Most Beautiful Women of All Time Collection. The *Children of Mexico* series began in 1981 with artwork by Jorge Sanchez. In 1982, the *Symphony of Roses* series began with artwork by Irene Spencer.

James Lockhart, an ardent naturalist and conservationist, is widely-known for his realistic portrayals of wild animals in their natural habitats. The designs for Pickard's *Christmas* and *Children of Renoir* series are reproductions of works by the Masters. Irene Spencer received her training at the Academy of Art and the Chicago Art Institute, where she developed her distinctive style, reminiscent of the Old Masters. In addition to her accomplishments as a fine artist, she has written and illustrated children's books and worked as a newspaper cartoonist. Oleg Cassini, the best known name in contemporary fashion, is also an accomplished artist. Born in Paris in 1913, Cassini is the son of Count and Countess Loiewski Cassini. As an adult, he renounced his right to the title of Count to become an American citizen. He received a law degree from the University of Florence and also graduated

from Florence's prestigious Academia delle Belle Artis. During the 1940s he worked as a fashion designer in Hollywood for such celebrities as Gene Tierney and Grace Kelly. Former First Lady Jacqueline Kennedy named Cassini her official couturier. Mexican artist Jorge Sanchez studied at the Art Academy of San Carlos and has held numerous one-man shows throughout Mexico. In 1978 the Museum of Mexico City exhibited his series of twenty-one paintings depicting the life of Sor Juana Ines de la Cruz.

PICKARD
Antioch, Illinois

Lockhart Wildlife Series
Artist: James Lockhart. Artist's signature appears on front

China banded in 24k gold

Diameter: as indicated

No hanger

Edition size: as indicated

Numbered with certificate

84-P29-1.1-1
1970 Woodcock
Edition: 2,000
Diameter: 26.7 cm. (10½ in.)
Pair Prices: Issue $150.00; 1983 High $350.00;
Low $290.00; Close $290.00; Down $60.00

84-P29-1.1-2
1970 Ruffed Grouse

84-P29-1.2-1
1971 Green-Winged Teal
Edition: 2,000
Diameter: 26.7 cm. (10½ in.)
Pair Prices: Issue $150.00; 1983 High $225.00;
Low $200.00; Close $200.00; Down $25.00

84-P29-1.2-2
1971 Mallard

84-P29-1.3-1
1972 Mockingbird
Edition: 2,000
Diameter: 26.7 cm. (10½ in.)
Pair Prices: Issue $162.50; 1983 High $220.00;
Low $185.00; Close $185.00; Down $35.00

84-P29-1.3-2
1972 Cardinal

84-P29-1.4-1
1973 Wild Turkey
Edition: 2,000
Diameter: 26.7 cm. (10½ in.)
Pair Prices: Issue $162.50; 1983 High $240.00;
Low $175.00; Close $175.00; Down $65.00

84-P29-1.4-2
1973 Ring-Necked Pheasant

84-P29-1.5
1974 *American Bald Eagle*
Edition: 2,000
Diameter: 33 cm. (13 in.)
Prices: Issue $150.00; 1983 High $750.00;
Low $630.00; Close $750.00; Up $120.00

84-P29-1.6
1975 *White-Tailed Deer*
Edition: 2,500
Diameter: 27.9 cm. (11 in.)
Prices: Issue $100.00; 1983 High $130.00;
Low $100.00; Close $100.00; Down $30.00

84-P29-1.7
1976 *American Buffalo*
Edition: 2,500
Diameter: 33 cm. (13 in.)
Prices: Issue $165.00; 1983 High $195.00;
Low $170.00; Close $170.00; Down $25.00

84-P29-1.8
1977 *Great Horned Owl*
Edition: 2,500
Diameter: 27.9 cm. (11 in.)
Prices: Issue $100.00; 1983 High $137.00;
Low $100.00; Close $100.00; Down $33.00

84-P29-1.9
1978 *American Panther*
Edition: 2,000
Diameter: 33 cm. (13 in.)
Prices: Issue $175.00; 1983 High $220.00;
Low $175.00; Close $175.00; Down $20.00

84-P29-1.10
1979 *The Red Fox*
Edition: 2,500
Diameter: 27.9 cm. (11 in.)
Prices: Issue $120.00; 1983 High $124.00;
Low $95.00; Close $95.00; Down $29.00

84-P29-1.11
1980 *Trumpeter Swan*
Edition: 2,000
Diameter: 33 cm. (13 in.)
Prices: Issue $200.00; 1983 High $200.00;
Low $150.00; Close $150.00; Down $50.00
Series Closed

PICKARD

Antioch, Illinois

Christmas Series

Artist: as indicated

China with 24k gold design on border

Diameter: 21 centimeters
(8¼ inches)

No hanger

Edition size: as indicated

Numbered without certificate

84-P29-2.1
1976 *The Alba Madonna*
Artist: Raphael/Edition: 7,500
Prices: Issue $60.00; 1983 High $236.00;
Low $130.00; Close $130.00; Down $106.00

84-P29-2.2
1977 *The Nativity*
Artist: Lorenzo Lotto/Edition: 7,500
Prices: Issue $65.00; 1983 High $135.00;
Low $92.00; Close $92.00; Down $43.00

84-P29-2.3
1978 *The Rest on the Flight into Egypt*
Artist: Gerard David/Edition: 10,000
Prices: Issue $65.00, 1983 High $100.00;
Low $65.00, Close $65.00, Down $35.00

84-P29-2.4
1979 *Adoration of the Magi*
Artist: Botticelli/Edition: 10,000
Prices: Issue $70.00; 1983 High $70.00;
Low $45.00; Close $45.00; Down $23.00

84-P29-2.5
1980 *Madonna and Child with the Infant Saint John*
Artist: Sodoma/Edition: 10,000
Prices: Issue $80.00; 1983 High $73.00;
Low $65.00; Close $65.00; Down $8.00

84-P29-2.6
1981 *Madonna and Child with Angels*
Artist: Hans Memling/Edition: 10,000
Prices: Issue $90.00; 1983 High $90.00;
Low $50.00; Close $50.00; Down $40.00
Series Closed

Children of Renoir Series

Artist: Pierre Auguste Renoir.
Artist's signature appears on front

China banded in 24k gold

Diameter: 21 centimeters
(8¼ inches)

No hanger

Edition size limited to 5,000. Two annual issues

Numbered without certificate

84-P29-4.1
1978 *A Girl with a Watering Can*
Prices: Issue $50.00; 1983 High $214.00;
Low $150.00; Close $150.00; Down $64.00

84-P29-4.2
1978 *Child in White*
Prices: Issue $50.00; 1983 High $110.00;
Low $70.00; Close $70.00; Down $40.00

84-P29-4.3
1979 *Girl with Hoop*
Prices: Issue $55.00; 1983 High $110.00;
Low $65.00; Close $65.00; Down $45.00

84-P29-4.4
1979 *At the Piano*
Prices: Issue $55.00; 1983 High $118.00;
Low $65.00; Close $65.00; Down $50.00

84-P29-4.5
1980 *Two Little Circus Girls*
Prices: Issue $60.00; 1983 High $90.00;
Low $50.00; Close $50.00; Down $40.00

84-P29-4.6
1980 *The Artist's Son Jean*
Prices: Issue $60.00; 1983 High $86.00;
Low $45.00; Close $45.00; Down $41.00
Series Closed

Oleg Cassini's Most Beautiful Women of All Time Collection

Artist: Oleg Cassini. Artist's signature appears on front

China banded in 24k gold

Diameter: 26.7 centimeters (10½ inches)

No hanger

Edition size undisclosed, limited by year of issue

Numbered with certificate

84-P29-5.1
1981 Helen of Troy
Prices: Issue $75.00; 1983 High $75.00;
Low $75.00; Close $75.00; No Change

84-P29-5.2
1982 Marie Antoinette
Prices: Issue $75.00; 1983 High $80.00;
Low $75.00; Close $80.00; Up $5.00

84-P29-5.3
1983 Lillie Langtry
Prices: Issue $75.00; 1983 High $75.00;
Low $75.00; Close $75.00; No Change

84-P29-5.4
1984 Salomé
Issue price: $75.00
Series Closed

Mother's Love Series

Artist: Irene Spencer. Artist's signature appears on front

China banded in 24k gold

Diameter: 23.8 centimeters (9⅜ inches)

No hanger

Edition size limited to 7,500

Numbered without certificate

84-P29-6.1
1980 Miracle
Prices: Issue $95.00; 1983 High $215.00;
Low $150.00; Close $150.00; Down $65.00

84-P29-6.2
1981 Story Time
Prices: Issue $110.00; 1983 High $133.00;
Low $100.00; Close $100.00; Down $33.00

84-P29-6.3
1982 *First Edition*
Prices: Issue $115.00; 1983 High $115.00;
Low $110.00; Close $110.00; Down $5.00

84-P29-6.4
1983 *Precious Moment*
Prices: Issue $120.00; 1983 High $140.00;
Low $120.00; Close $140.00; Up $20.00
Series Closed

Children of Mexico Series

Artist: Jorge Sanchez. Artist's
signature appears on front

China banded in 24k gold

Diameter: 26.7 centimeters
(10½ inches)

No hanger

Edition size limited to 5,000

Numbered without certificate

84-P29-7.1
1981 *Maria*
Prices: Issue $85.00; 1983 High $210.00;
Low $130.00; Close $130.00; Down $76.00

84-P29-7.2
1981 *Miguel*
Prices: Issue $85.00; 1983 High $135.00;
Low $100.00; Close $100.00; Down $35.00

84-P29-7.3
1982 *Regina*
Prices: Issue $90.00; 1983 High $110.00;
Low $85.00; Close $85.00; Down $9.00

84-P29-7.4
1983 *Raphael*
Prices: Issue $90.00; 1983 High $95.00;
Low $90.00; Close $95.00; Up $5.00
Series Closed

PICKARD
Antioch, Illinois

Symphony of Roses Series
Artist: Irene Spencer. Artist's signature appears on front

China with scalloped, gold-rimmed border

Diameter: 23.8 centimeters (9⅜ inches)

No hanger

Edition size limited to 10,000

Numbered without certificate

84-P29-8.1
1982 *Wild Irish Rose*
Prices: Issue $85.00; 1983 High $110.00;
Low $85.00; Close $100.00; Up $15.00

84-P29-8.2
1983 *Yellow Rose of Texas*
Prices: Issue $90.00; 1983 High $110.00;
Low $90.00; Close $110.00; Up $20.00

84-R60-0.0

UNITED STATES
RECO INTERNATIONAL
Port Washington, New York

Reco International was founded in 1967 by Heio W. Reich who continues as its president. From the beginning the firm has been an importer and maker of limited-edition plates.

World of Children, Reco International's first U.S. proprietary series, was introduced in 1977, with designs by John McClelland. The series ended in 1980. A second series with designs by the same artist, *McClelland's Mother Goose* series, was introduced in 1979. In 1981, Reco International began a third series, the *McClelland Children's Circus Collection.* The *Days Gone By* series, with artwork by Sandra Kuck, began in 1983.

John McClelland is an author of books on flower and portrait painting and is particularly noted for his portraiture of personages in politics and the arts.

UNITED STATES
RECO INTERNATIONAL
Port Washington, New York

World of Children Series

Artist: John McClelland. Artist's signature appears on front

China banded in 24k gold

Diameter: 26.7 centimeters (10½ inches)

No hanger

Edition size limited to 10,000 in 1977; 15,000 thereafter

Numbered with certificate since 1978

84-R60-1.1
1977 *Rainy Day Fun*
Prices: Issue $50.00; 1983 High $232.00; Low $150.00; Close $150.00; Down $82.00

84-R60-1.2
1978 *When I Grow Up*
Prices: Issue $50.00; 1983 High $103.00; Low $85.00; Close $85.00; Down $16.00

84-R60-1.3
1979 *You're Invited*
Prices: Issue $50.00; 1983 High $80.00; Low $80.00, Close $80.00; No Change

84-R60-1.4
1980 *Kittens for Sale*
Prices: Issue $50.00; 1983 High $65.00; Low $55.00; Close $55.00; Down $10.00
Series Closed

McClelland's Mother Goose Series

Artist: John McClelland. Artist's signature appears on front

China

Diameter: 21.6 centimeters (8½ inches)

No hanger

Edition size undisclosed, limited by year of issue

Numbered with certificate

84-R60-2.1
1979 *Mary, Mary*
Prices: Issue $22.50; 1983 High $273.00; Low $230.00; Close $230.00; Down $43.00

84-R60-2.2
1980 *Little Boy Blue*
Prices: Issue $22.50; 1983 High $105.00; Low $100.00; Close $100.00; No Change

84-R60-2.3
1981 Little Miss Muffet
Prices: Issue $24.50; 1983 High $32.00;
Low $24.50; Close $32.00; Up $7.50

84-R60-2.4
1982 Little Jack Horner
Prices: Issue $24.50; 1983 High $45.00;
Low $24.50; Close $45.00; Up $20.50

84-R60-2.5
1983 Little Bo Peep
Prices: Issue $24.50; 1983 High $24.50;
Low $24.50; Close $24.50; No Change

84-R60-2.6
1984 Diddle, Diddle, Dumpling
Issue price: undetermined
at press time

McClelland Children's Circus Collection

Artist: John McClelland. Artist's signature appears on front

China

Diameter: 23.5 centimeters
(9¼ inches)

No hanger

Edition size undisclosed, limited by year of issue

Numbered with certificate

84-R60-3.1
1981 Tommy the Clown
Prices: Issue $29.50; 1983 High $30.00;
Low $29.50; Close $30.00; Up $.50

84-R60-3.2
1982 Katie the Tightrope Walker
Prices: Issue $29.50; 1983 High $31.00;
Low $29.50; Close $31.00; Up $1.50

UNITED STATES
RECO INTERNATIONAL
Port Washington, New York

84-R60-3.3
1983 *Johnny the Strongman*
Prices: Issue $29.50; 1983 High $29.50;
Low $29.50; Close $29.50; No Change

84-R60-3.4
1983 *Maggie the Animal Trainer*
Prices: Issue $29.50; 1983 High $29.50;
Low $29.50; Close $29.50; No Change
Series Closed

Days Gone By Series

Artist: Sandra Kuck. Artist's
signature appears on front

China banded in 23K gold

Diameter: 23.5 centimeters
(9¼ inches)

No hanger

Edition size undisclosed, limited
by announced period of issue

Numbered with certificate

84-R60-8.1
1983 *Sunday Best*
Issue price: $29.50

84-R60-8.2
1983 *Amy's Magic Horse*
Issue price: $29.50

84-R60-8.3
1984 *Little Anglers*
Issue price: $29.50

Reed & Barton Silversmiths traces its origin to a factory established by Isaac Babbitt in the early nineteenth century. In 1824 Babbitt developed an alloy, harder and more lustrous than pewter, which he named Britannia metal. Henry G. Reed and Charles E. Barton, artists working for Babbitt, acquired the firm in the 1830s and continued to manufacture Brittania ware. In the late 1840s, the factory began to produce plated silverware. Reed & Barton was incorporated in 1888 and started producing solid silver services. Sterling flatware and hollowware soon replaced plated ware as their largest line. In 1903 the firm began reproducing colonial pewter ware.

In 1970 Reed & Barton began their *Christmas* series which changes theme every three years. The first three plates are based on Christmas carols; the second three are based on fifteenth-century altar art; the next are based on American Christmas scenes; and the next depict nineteenth-century American illustrations. The series ended in 1981.

Artist Robert Johnson, whose works are in private collections throughout the United States, Europe, and the Far East, developed the patented electroplating process used in the creation of the Reed & Barton *Christmas* series. The medium, known as Damascene silver, combines silver, gold, copper, and bronze, and the electroplating process is derived from a hand-craft method perfected at Damascus in the middle ages. Maxwell Mays specializes in Americana, and his art has appeared in such magazines as *Collier's, Yankee, Cosmopolitan,* and *New England.*

REED & BARTON
Taunton, Massachusetts

Christmas Series

Artist: as indicated

Damascene silver

Diameter: 27.9 centimeters (11 inches) through 1978; thereafter, 20.3 centimeters (8 inches)

No hanger

Edition size: as indicated

Numbered without certificate through 1978; thereafter not numbered, accompanied with numbered certificate

84-R18-2.1
1970 *A Partridge in a Pear Tree*
Artist: Robert Johnson/Edition: 2,500
Prices: Issue $55.00; 1983 High $214.00;
Low $175.00; Close $200.00; Down $14.00

84-R18-2.2
1971 *We Three Kings of Orient Are*
Artist: Robert Johnson/Edition: 7,500
Prices: Issue $60.00; 1983 High $75.00;
Low $65.00; Close $65.00; Down $5.00

84-R18-2.3
1972 *Hark! The Herald Angels Sing*
Artist: Robert Johnson/Edition: 7,500
Prices: Issue $60.00; 1983 High $60.00;
Low $60.00; Close $60.00; No Change

84-R18-2.4
1973 *Adoration of the Kings*
Artist: Rogier van der Weyden
Edition: 7,500
Prices: Issue $60.00; 1983 High $75.00;
Low $70.00; Close $75.00; Up $5.00

84-R18-2.5
1974 *The Adoration of the Magi*
Artist: Fra Angelico and Fra Lippi
Edition: 7,500
Prices: Issue $65.00; 1983 High $69.00;
Low $65.00; Close $65.00; Down $4.00

84-R18-2.6
1975 *Adoration of the Kings*
Artist: Steven Lochner/Edition: 7,500
Prices: Issue $65.00; 1983 High $65.00;
Low $65.00; Close $65.00; No Change

84-R18-2.7
1976 *Morning Train*
Artist: Maxwell Mays/Edition: 7,500
Prices: Issue $65.00; 1983 High $68.00;
Low $60.00; Close $60.00; Down $5.00

84-R18-2.8
1977 *Decorating the Church*
Artist: Maxwell Mays/Edition: 7,500
Prices: Issue $65.00; 1983 High $62.00;
Low $60.00; Close $60.00; Down $2.00

84-R18-2.9
1978 *The General Store at Christmas Time*
Artist: Maxwell Mays/Edition: 7,500
Prices: Issue $65.00; 1983 High $70.00;
Low $67.00; Close $70.00; Up $3.00

84-R18-2.10
1979 *Merry Old Santa Claus*
Artist: Thomas Nast/Edition: 2,500
Prices: Issue $55.00; 1983 High $63.00;
Low $63.00; Close $63.00; No Change

84-R18-2.11
1980 *Gathering Christmas Greens*
Artist: Unknown/Edition: 2,500
Prices: Issue $65.00; 1983 High $75.00;
Low $65.00; Close $75.00; Up $10.00

84-R18-2.12
1981 *The Shopkeeper at Christmas*
Artist: W. L. Sheppard/Edition: 2,500
Prices: Issue $75.00; 1983 High $75.00;
Low $75.00; Close $75.00; No Change
Series Closed

84-R18-2.1 "A Partridge in a Pear Tree"
1970 Reed & Barton *Christmas*
Damascene silver—an electroplating process that combines copper, silver, bronze, and gold.

River Shore, Ltd.®
Creators of Museum Quality Limited Editions

River Shore, Ltd. was established in 1975 to market limited-edition collectibles.

In 1976 River Shore began its *Famous Americans* series, the first collector's plates crafted in copper, based on artwork by Norman Rockwell and sculpted by Roger Brown. The series ended in 1979. River Shore introduced its *Signs of Love* series in 1981 with artwork by Yin-Rei Hicks.

Roger Brown, who sculpted the *Famous Americans* series, studied at the New York Sculpture Center and is a member of the National Sculpture Society. His works appear in museums throughout the United States, including the Lyndon Baines Johnson Memorial Library and the Teterboro Aviation Museum. Yin-Rei Hicks, a native of mainland China, was born during the Maoist takeover. Her family later fled to Taiwan, where her artistic ability first gained recognition. She won two scholarships from the University of Louisville in Kentucky, and graduated with a Master's Degree in Creative Art. Hicks has since become a prominent illustrator and designer of limited-edition collectibles.

Famous Americans Series

Artist: Roger Brown (after works by Norman Rockwell). Artist's signature appears on front along with name of Norman Rockwell

Copper

Diameter: 20.3 centimeters (8 inches)

No hanger

Edition size limited to 9,500

Numbered with certificate

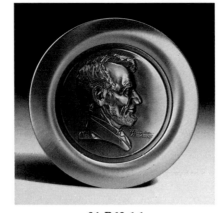

84-R69-1.1
1976 Lincoln
Prices: Issue $40.00; 1983 High $220.00;
Low $90.00; Close $90.00; Down $130.00

84-R69-1.2
1977 Rockwell
Prices: Issue $45.00; 1983 High $130.00;
Low $50.00; Close $50.00; Down $80.00

84-R69-1.3
1978 Peace Corps
Prices: Issue $45.00; 1983 High $70.00;
Low $30.00; Close $30.00; Down $40.00

84-R69-1.4
1979 Spirit of Lindbergh
Prices: Issue $50.00; 1983 High $58.00;
Low $40.00; Close $40.00; Down $18.00
Series Closed

Signs of Love Series

Artist: Yin-Rei Hicks. Artist's signature appears on front

China

Diameter: 21.6 centimeters (8½ inches)

No hanger

Edition size undisclosed, limited by announced period of issue

Numbered with certificate

84-R69-2.1
1981 A Kiss for Mother
Prices: Issue $18.50; 1983 High $22.00;
Low $20.00; Close $22.00; Up $2.00

84-R69-2.2
1981 A Watchful Eye
Prices: Issue $21.50; 1983 High $22.00;
Low $21.50; Close $22.00; Up $.50

84-R69-2.3
1982 *A Gentle Persuasion*
Prices: Issue $21.50; 1983 High $22.00;
Low $21.50; Close $22.00; Up $.50

84-R69-2.4
1983 *A Protective Embrace*
Prices: Issue $23.50; 1983 High $30.00;
Low $23.50; Close $30.00; Up $6.50

84-R69-2.5
1983 *A Tender Coaxing*
Prices: Issue $23.50; 1983 High $38.00;
Low $23.50; Close $38.00; Up $14.50

84-R69-1.1 "Lincoln"
1976 River Shore *Famous Americans*
The world's first copper collector's plate was based on artwork by Norman Rockwell and sculpted by Roger Brown.

84-R70-0.0

The Rockwell Society of America is a chartered non-profit organization devoted to the study and appreciation of the works of Norman Rockwell. The Society's *Christmas* series began in 1974, with the first issue manufactured by Ridgewood. Subsequent issues have been made by the Edwin M. Knowles China Company (see United States, KNOWLES). The *Mother's Day* series started in 1976, the *Rockwell Heritage* series began in 1977, and *Rockwell's Rediscovered Women* series was introduced in 1981. The *Rockwell on Tour Collection* and *Rockwell's Light Campaign* series started in 1983.

One of the most widely-known artists in the twentieth century, Norman Rockwell created well over 3,000 works including 323 *Saturday Evening Post* covers as well as numerous illustrations for *Life, Look, Boys Life,* and annual Boy Scout calendars. His works hang in a number of museums: from the Smithsonian Institution and the Metropolitan Museum of Art in New York, to the Corner House in the artist's adopted home of Stockbridge, Massachusetts.

UNITED STATES
ROCKWELL SOCIETY
Stony Brook, New York

Christmas Series

Artist: Norman Rockwell. Artist's signature appears on front

China

Diameter: 21 centimeters (8¼ inches)

No hanger

Edition size undisclosed, limited by announced period of issue

Numbered with certificate

84-R70-1.1
1974 Scotty Gets His Tree
Prices: Issue $24.50; 1983 High $160.00;
Low $120.00; Close $120.00; Down $40.00

84-R70-1.2
1975 Angel with a Black Eye
Prices: Issue $24.50; 1983 High $99.00;
Low $90.00; Close $90.00; Down $9.00

84-R70-1.3
1976 Golden Christmas
Prices: Issue $24.50; 1983 High $58.00;
Low $58.00; Close $58.00; No Change

84-R70-1.4
1977 Toy Shop Window
Prices: Issue $24.50; 1983 High $50.00;
Low $45.00; Close $45.00; Down $5.00

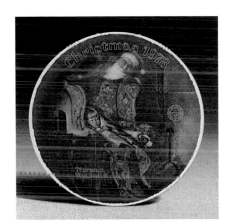

84-R70-1.5
1978 Christmas Dream
Prices: Issue $24.50; 1983 High $62.00;
Low $50.00; Close $50.00; Down $12.00

84-R70-1.6
1979 Somebody's Up There
Prices: Issue $24.50; 1983 High $30.00;
Low $27.00; Close $27.00; Down $3.00

84-R70-1.7
1980 Scotty Plays Santa
Prices: Issue $24.50; 1983 High $42.00;
Low $33.00; Close $33.00; Down $9.00

84-R70-1.8
1981 Wrapped Up in Christmas
Prices: Issue $25.50; 1983 High $30.00;
Low $28.00; Close $30.00; Up $2.00

84-R70-1.9
1982 *Christmas Courtship*
Prices: Issue $25.50; 1983 High $36.00;
Low $25.50; Close $36.00; Up $10.50

84-R70-1.10
1983 *Santa in the Subway*
Prices: Issue $25.50; 1983 High $25.50;
Low $25.50; Close $25.50; No Change

Mother's Day Series

Artist: Norman Rockwell. Artist's
signature appears on front

China

Diameter: 21.6 centimeters
(8½ inches)

No hanger

Edition size undisclosed, limited
by announced period of issue

Numbered with certificate

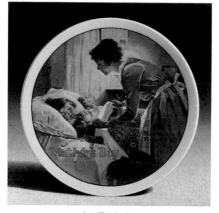

84-R70-2.1
1976 *A Mother's Love*
Prices: Issue $24.50; 1983 High $120.00;
Low $90.00; Close $90.00; Down $30.00

84-R70-2.2
1977 *Faith*
Prices: Issue $24.50; 1983 High $76.00;
Low $65.00; Close $65.00; Down $11.00

84-R70-2.3
1978 *Bedtime*
Prices: Issue $24.50; 1983 High $104.00;
Low $90.00; Close $90.00; Down $14.00

84-R70-2.4
1979 *Reflections*
Prices: Issue $24.50; 1983 High $38.00;
Low $36.00; Close $36.00; Down $2.00

84-R70-2.5
1980 *A Mother's Pride*
Prices: Issue $24.50; 1983 High $32.00;
Low $27.00; Close $32.00; Up $5.00

84-R70-2.6
1981 *After the Party*
Prices: Issue $24.50; 1983 High $32.00;
Low $29.00; Close $32.00; Up $3.00

84-R70-2.7
1982 *The Cooking Lesson*
Prices: Issue $25.50; 1983 High $30.00;
Low $25.50; Close $30.00; Up $4.50

84-R70-2.8
1983 *Add Two Cups and a Measure of Love*
Prices: Issue $25.50; 1983 High $58.00;
Low $25.50; Close $58.00; Up $32.50

84-R70-2.9
1984 *Grandma's Courting Dress*
Issue price: $25.50

Rockwell Heritage Series

Artist: Norman Rockwell. Artist's signature appears on front

China

Diameter: 21.6 centimeters (8½ inches)

No hanger

Edition size undisclosed, limited by announced period of issue

Numbered with certificate

84-R70-3.1
1977 *The Toy Maker*
Prices: Issue $14.50; 1983 High $262.00;
Low $213.00; Close $213.00; Down $49.00

84-R70-3.2
1978 *The Cobbler*
Prices: Issue $19.50; 1983 High $155.00;
Low $140.00; Close $140.00; Down $15.00

84-R70-3.3
1979 *The Lighthouse Keeper's Daughter*
Prices: Issue $19.50; 1983 High $105.00;
Low $85.00; Close $85.00; Down $20.00

84-R70-3.4
1980 *The Ship Builder*
Prices: Issue $19.50; 1983 High $63.00;
Low $55.00; Close $55.00; Down $5.00

84-R70-3.5
1981 *The Music Maker*
Prices: Issue $19.50; 1983 High $30.00;
Low $28.00; Close $30.00; Up $2.00

84-R70-3.6
1982 *The Tycoon*
Prices: Issue $19.50; 1983 High $32.00;
Low $19.50; Close $32.00; Up $12.50

84-R70-3.7
1983 *The Painter*
Prices: Issue $19.50; 1983 High $25.00;
Low $19.50; Close $25.00; Up $5.50

84-R70-3.8
1984 *The Storyteller*
Issue price: $19.50

Rockwell's Rediscovered Women Series

Artist: Norman Rockwell. Artist's signature appears on front

China

Diameter: 21.6 centimeters (8½ inches)

No hanger

Edition size undisclosed, limited by announced period of issue

Numbered with certificate

84-R70-4.1
1981 *Dreaming in the Attic*
Prices: Issue $19.50; 1983 High $34.00;
Low $25.00; Close $34.00; Up $9.00

84-R70-4.2
1982 *Waiting on the Shore*
Prices: Issue $22.50; 1983 High $30.00;
Low $22.50; Close $30.00; Up $7.50

UNITED STATES
ROCKWELL SOCIETY
Stony Brook, New York

84-R70-4.3
1983 *Pondering on the Porch*
Prices: Issue $22.50; 1983 High $30.00;
Low $22.50; Close $30.00; Up $7.50

84-R70-4.4
1983 *Making Believe at the Mirror*
Prices: Issue $22.50; 1983 High $22.50;
Low $22.50; Close $22.50; No Change

84-R70-4.5
1983 *Waiting at the Dance*
Prices: Issue $22.50; 1983 High $22.50;
Low $22.50; Close $22.50; No Change

84-R70-4.6
1983 *Gossiping in the Alcove*
Prices: Issue $22.50; 1983 High $22.50;
Low $22.50; Close $22.50; No Change

84-R70-4.7
1983 *Standing in the Doorway*
Prices: Issue $22.50; 1983 High $22.50;
Low $22.50; Close $22.50; No Change

84-R70-4.8
1983 *Flirting in the Parlor*
Prices: Issue $22.50; 1983 High $22.50;
Low $22.50; Close $22.50; No Change

84-R70-4.9
1984 *Working in the Kitchen*
Issue price: $22.50

84-R70-4.10
1984 *Meeting on the Path*
Issue price: $22.50

84-R70-4.11
1984 *Confiding in the Den*
Issue price: $22.50

84-R70-4.12
1984 *Reminiscing Neath the Eaves*
Issue price: $22.50

Rockwell on Tour Collection

Artist: Norman Rockwell. Artist's
signature appears on front

Newellware with raised border

Diameter: 19.7 centimeters
(7¾ inches)

No hanger

Edition size undisclosed, limited
by announced period of issue

Numbered with certificate

84-R70-5.1
1983 *Walking through Merrie Englande*
Prices: Issue $16.00; 1983 High $44.00;
Low $16.00; Close $44.00; Up $28.00

84-R70-5.2
1983 *Promenade à Paris*
Prices: Issue $16.00; 1983 High $16.00;
Low $16.00; Close $16.00; No Change

84-R70-5.3
1983 *When in Rome—*
Prices: Issue $16.00; 1983 High $16.00;
Low $16.00; Close $16.00; No Change

84-R70-5.4
1984 *Die Walk am Rhein*
Issue price: $16.00
Series Closed

Rockwell's Light Campaign Series

Artist: Norman Rockwell. Artist's signature appears on front

China banded in 14k gold

Diameter: 21.6 centimeters (8½ inches)

No hanger

Edition size undisclosed, limited by announced period of issue

Numbered with certificate

84-R70-6.1
1983 *This Is the Room That Light Made*
Prices: Issue $19.50; 1983 High $19.50;
Low $19.50; Close $19.50; No Change

84-R70-6.2
1984 *Grandpa's Treasure Chest*
Issue price: $19.50

84-R70-6.3
1984 *Father's Help*
Issue price: $19.50

84-R70-6.4
1984 *Evening's Ease*
Issue price: $19.50

Royal Devon plates are manufactured by the Gorham Company (see United States, GORHAM). Both the *Christmas* series and *Mother's Day* series, bearing artwork by Norman Rockwell, began in 1975. Both series ended in 1980.

One of the most widely-known artists in the twentieth century, Norman Rockwell created well over 3,000 works including 323 *Saturday Evening Post* covers as well as numerous illustrations for *Life, Look, Boys Life,* and annual Boy Scout calendars. His works hang in a number of museums: from the Smithsonian Institution and the Metropolitan Museum of Art in New York, to the Corner House in the artist's adopted home of Stockbridge, Massachusetts.

UNITED STATES
ROYAL DEVON
Providence, Rhode Island

Christmas Series

Artist: Norman Rockwell. Artist's signature appears on front

China banded in gold

Diameter: 21.6 centimeters (8½ inches)

No hanger

Edition size undisclosed, limited by year of issue

Not numbered, without certificate

84-R61-1.1
1975 *Downhill Daring*
Prices: Issue $24.50; 1983 High $49.00;
Low $35.00; Close $35.00; Down $14.00

84-R61-1.2
1976 *The Christmas Gift*
Prices: Issue $24.50; 1983 High $92.00;
Low $60.00; Close $60.00; Down $32.00

84-R61-1.3
1977 *The Big Moment*
Prices: Issue $27.50; 1983 High $102.00;
Low $90.00; Close $90.00; Down $12.00

84-R61-1.4
1978 *Puppets for Christmas*
Prices: Issue $27.50; 1983 High $45.00;
Low $40.00; Close $40.00; Down $4.00

84-R61-1.5
1979 *One Present Too Many*
Prices: Issue $31.50; 1983 High $35.00;
Low $33.00; Close $33.00; Down $2.00

84-R61-1.6
1980 *Gramps Meets Gramps*
Prices: Issue $33.00; 1983 High $33.00;
Low $33.00; Close $33.00; No Change
Series Closed

Mother's Day Series

Artist: Norman Rockwell. Artist's signature appears on front

China banded in gold

Diameter: 21.6 centimeters
(8½ inches)

No hanger

Edition size undisclosed, limited by year of issue

Not numbered, without certificate

84-R61-2.1
1975 Doctor and the Doll
Prices: Issue $23.50; 1983 High $85.00;
Low $65.00; Close $65.00; Down $20.00

84-R61-2.2
1976 Puppy Love
Prices: Issue $24.50; 1983 High $83.00;
Low $75.00; Close $75.00; Down $8.00

84-R61-2.3
1977 The Family
Prices: Issue $24.50; 1983 High $122.00;
Low $112.00; Close $112.00; Down $10.00

84-R61-2.4
1978 Mother's Day Off
Prices: Issue $27.00; 1983 High $72.00;
Low $60.00; Close $60.00; Down $12.00

84-R61-2.5
1979 Mother's Evening Out
Prices: Issue $30.00; 1983 High $34.00;
Low $30.00; Close $30.00; Down $4.00

84-R61-2.6
1980 Mother's Treat
Prices: Issue $32.50; 1983 High $33.00;
Low $30.00; Close $30.00; Down $3.00
Series Closed

VAGUE SHADOWS LTD.

Vague Shadows, Ltd. was established in 1977 to produce limited-edition works by Gregory Perillo. His *The Chieftains I* series was introduced in 1979.

Gregory Perillo studied at the Pratt Institute, the Art Students League, and the School of Visual Arts, all in New York City. He is the only living artist to have studied under renowned western painter William R. Leigh. Perillo has painted under commission for Funk & Wagnall's Encyclopedia, and his works appeared in numerous one-man shows in California, New York, and Paris.

UNITED STATES
VAGUE SHADOWS
Staten Island, New York

The Chieftains I Series
Artist: Gregory Perillo. Artist's signature appears on front

Overglaze-decorated porcelain banded in 24k gold

Diameter: 26 centimeters (10¼ inches)

No hanger

Edition size limited to 7,500

Numbered with certificate

84-V3-2.1
1979 *Chief Sitting Bull*
Issue price: $65.00

84-V3-2.2
1979 *Chief Joseph*
Issue price: $65.00

84-V3-2.3
1980 *Chief Red Cloud*
Issue price: $65.00

84-V3-2.4
1980 *Chief Geronimo*
Issue price: $65.00

84-V3-2.5
1981 *Chief Crazy Horse*
Issue price: $65.00
Series Closed

Viletta China Company was started in 1959 in Roseberg, Oregon, by Viletta West, who hand-painted china and sold it through stores in the Pacific Northwest. The firm is involved in many areas of the giftware and fine china field, including commemorative china items and limited-edition collector's plates.

In 1979 Viletta China moved from Roseberg to Houston, Texas.

The *Zolan's Children* series began in 1978 and was completed in 1981. The *Nutcracker Ballet Plate Collection* began in 1978 and ended in 1980.

Shell Fisher's work represents some of the finest examples of contemporary realism. Fisher studied at the Art Institute of Chicago and at the American Academy of Art. One of his oil paintings won first prize at the 1977 Artist's Guild Annual Chicago Artist's Show, and Fisher's works are on display at the Art Institute of Chicago and at the Chicago Wildlife Museum. Fisher has also done commissioned work for Queen Elizabeth II and Sammy Davis, Jr. Donald Zolan also studied at the Art Institute of Chicago and won a scholarship to the American Academy of Art. His works, created in the representational style, hang in numerous galleries throughout the United States and in private collections in Mexico, Australia, France, Italy, South Korea, and Colombia.

UNITED STATES
VILETTA
Houston, Texas

Zolan's Children Series

Artist: Donald Zolan. Artist's signature appears on front

China

Diameter: 21.6 centimeters (8½ inches)

No hanger

Edition size undisclosed, limited by period of issue

Numbered with certificate

84-V36-1.1
1978 *Erik and Dandelion*
Prices: Issue $19.00; 1983 High $201.00; Low $120.00; Close $120.00; Down $81.00

84-V36-1.2
1979 *Sabina in the Grass*
Prices: Issue $22.00; 1983 High $195.00; Low $125.00; Close $125.00; Down $70.00

84-V36-1.3
1980 *By Myself*
Prices: Issue $24.00; 1983 High $45.00; Low $35.00, Close $35.00; Down $10.00

84-V36-1.4
1981 *For You*
Prices: Issue $24.00; 1983 High $27.00; Low $27.00; Close $27.00; No Change
Series Closed

Nutcracker Ballet Plate Collection

Artist: Shell Fisher. Artist's signature appears on front

China

Diameter: 21.6 centimeters (8½ inches)

No hanger

Edition size undisclosed, limited by year of issue

Numbered with certificate

84-V36-2.1
1978 *Clara and Nutcracker*
Prices: Issue $19.50; 1983 High $62.00; Low $30.00; Close $30.00; Down $32.00

84-V36-2.2
1979 *A Gift from Godfather*
Prices: Issue $19.50; 1983 High $36.00; Low $25.00; Close $25.00; Down $11.00

84-V36-2.3
1979 *The Sugarplum Fairy*
Prices: Issue $19.50; 1983 High $35.00;
Low $30.00; Close $30.00; Down $5.00

84-V36-2.4
1979 *The Snow King and Queen*
Prices: Issue $19.50; 1983 High $47.00;
Low $30.00; Close $30.00; Down $17.00

84-V36-2.5
1980 *The Waltz of the Flowers*
Prices: Issue $19.50; 1983 High $24.00;
Low $24.00; Close $24.00; No Change

84-V36-2.6
1980 *Clara and the Prince*
Prices: Issue $19.50; 1983 High $33.00;
Low $30.00; Close $30.00; Down $3.00
Series Closed

BRADEX-LISTED
PLATE ARTIST INFORMATION

AKERS, Roger (1940-   ). *ARTIST FOR:* Incolay. *STUDIED AT:* Cooper School of Art (Cleveland, Ohio), Art Institute of Chicago and American Academy of Art (both in Chicago, Illinois). *AWARDS/HONORS/COMMISSIONS:* Best of Show at Excellence in Woodcarving Show (1981); commissioned 1974 by American Numismatic Association for "Coin of the Year." *EXHIBITS:* IDEA Exhibit of Chicago (1979), Illinois Arts Council (1979). *WORKS HANGING:* In midwestern galleries; permanent museum display by the Illinois Arts Council.

APPLEBY, Gayle Bright (1949-   ). *ARTIST FOR:* Incolay. *STUDIED AT:* San Fernando Valley State College (California), Otis Art School. *EXHIBITS:* Mari's of Hawaii in Lahaina, Alchemists Garden (Kihei, Hawaii).

BAHNSEN, Frode (1923-1983). *ARTIST FOR:* Grande Copenhagen. *STUDIED AT:* Copenhagen Royal Academy of Art (Denmark). *AWARDS/HONORS/COMMISSIONS:* Created Knight of Dannebrog by Queen of Denmark (1978); named Chief Sculpturer of Royal Mint, Denmark (1968). *EXHIBITS:* Charlottenborg Art Exhibition (Copenhagen), Federal International Danish Medal Exhibitions. *WORK HANGING:* In the Denmark National Museum.

BARRER, Gertrude (1940-   ). *ARTIST FOR:* Anna-Perenna. *STUDIED AT:* Art Student's League (New York City). *AWARDS/HONORS:* Who's Who of American Women, Who's Who in American Art, World's Who's Who of Women. *EXHIBITS:* One-woman shows in New York, Connecticut, and Pennsylvania (1947-72). Participant in annual local exhibitions and private gallery shows. *WORKS HANGING:* In the collections of the United Nations, the Vatican, Cologne Cathedral, the Art Institute of Chicago, the Whitney Museum, New York University, and the Brooklyn Museum, and the private collections of Cyrus Vance and Helmut Schmidt.

Photograph
not available
at press time

Photograph
not available
at press time

BOEHM, Edward Marshall (1914-1969). *ARTIST FOR:* Lenox. *STUDIED AT:* Self-taught. *AWARDS/HONORS:* Numerous awards from shows in the United States. *WORKS HANGING:* In the Houston Museum of Fine Arts (Texas), the Smithsonian Institution (Washington, D.C.), the Governor's Mansion (Richmond, Virginia), and the Metropolitan Museum of Art (New York City). Works have been included in the private collections of Dwight D. Eisenhower, John F. Kennedy, Queen Elizabeth II, and Pope John XXIII.

BOYER, Gene (1948-). *ARTIST FOR:* Crown Parian. *STUDIED AT:* Self-taught. *AWARDS/HONORS:* Show awards in Denver area; Marion de Sala Mendes Memorial Award (1976-1977). Placed second in a contest sponsored by *The Saturday Evening Post;* designed more than 45 covers and illustrations for the magazine between 1975 and 1978. *EXHIBITS:* Primarily in the Denver (Colorado) and Washington, D.C. areas. *WORKS HANGING:* In private collections throughout the United States, including that of Mrs. Jack Okee.

BRATLIE, Gunnar (1918-). *ARTIST FOR:* Porsgrund. *STUDIED AT:* Norwegian schools for drawing and painting; educated in graphic design and print. *AWARDS/HONORS:* Scandinavian Children's Book Prize for illustration; first prize in Fredrikstad's 400-year jubilee city-flag contest; member, the Norwegian Design Organization and the Norwegian Graphic Society. *EXHIBITS:* Several one-man shows in Norway and numerous group exhibitions both in Norway and abroad. *WORKS HANGING:* In the Commune of Oslo and the Art Society of Fredrikstad (both in Norway); *Museo del Arte* (Pisoia, Italy); Oregon University.

BROWN, Roger (1933-). *ARTIST FOR:* River Shore. *STUDIED AT:* The New York Sculpture Center under Dorothea Denslow. *AWARDS/HONORS:* Member of the New York Sculpture Center and the National Sculpture Center. *WORKS HANGING:* In the Studebaker Museum (South Bend, Indiana), the Remington Museum and the Whitney Museum of American Art (both of New York City), and the New Jersey Aviation Hall of Fame.

CAMBIER, Guy (1923-). *ARTIST FOR:* Henri d'Arceau & Fils. *STUDIED AT:* Self-taught. *AWARDS/HONORS: Laureate de la Médaille International des Arts* (1977), *Médaille d'Or au Prix de Léonardo da Vinci* (1972), *Prix de la Jeune Peinture de Paris* (1957), *Prix de la Critique* (Monte Carlo, 1955), *Prix de la Jeune Peinture Méditerranée* (1955). *EXHIBITS:* First one-man show at age 19; exhibited in Belgium and France (1942-1981); Zantman Art Galleries (Carmel, California, 1963, 1973, 1979). *WORKS HANGING:* In museums and private collections in Europe and the United States.

CASSINI, Oleg (1913-). *ARTIST FOR:* Pickard. *STUDIED AT:* University of Florence, *Acadamia delle Belle Artis. AWARDS/HONORS:* Official couturier for Mrs. John F. Kennedy.

CHAMBERS, William (1940-). *ARTIST FOR:* Edwin M. Knowles. *STUDIED AT:* Northeastern Illinois University and the Academy of Art (both in Chicago, Illinois). *AWARDS/HONORS:* Participant, American Society of Illustrators' annual show (New York City); first prize, John Howard Sanden portrait competition. *EXHIBITS:* The American Show at Marshall Field's and the Mongerson Galleries (both in Chicago). *WORKS HANGING:* In various private homes and businesses in the United States, and at Ron De Bouver Fine Arts, Inc. (Chicago).

CSATARI, Joseph (1929-). *ARTIST FOR:* Edwin M. Knowles. *STUDIED AT:* Newark Academy of Art (New Jersey) and Pratt Institute (New York City). *AWARDS/HONORS/COMMISSIONS:* Gold medalist, Society of Illustrators, New Jersey Art Directors Club, International Association of Business Communicators. Worked with Norman Rockwell on Boy Scout calendars for ten years, taking over the project in 1975; commissioned 1979 to create United States commemorative stamp for Seeing Eye, Inc. *WORKS HANGING:* In the College Football Hall of Fame (Cincinnati, Ohio).

DALI, Louis (1906-). *ARTIST FOR:* Henri d'Arceau & Fils. *STUDIED AT:* Self-taught. *AWARDS/HONORS:* Prix Dessin de Briton, Fellow of the *Salon de l'Ecole Française*, Fellow of the *Salon des Indépendents*. *WORKS HANGING:* In private collections and salons, including the *Salon de la Marine, Salon de la Nationale des Beaux-Arts,* and the *Salon de l'Ecole Française des Indépendents.*

DeGRAZIA, Ted (1909-1982). *ARTIST FOR:* Fairmont, Gorham. *STUDIED AT:* University of Arizona; private study with Diego Rivera and Jose Clemente Orozco. *AWARDS/HONORS:* Achievement Award, University of Arizona (1968). Painting, Los Niños, chosen as annual UNICEF card (1960). *EXHIBITS:* First one-man show at Palace of Fine Arts (Mexico City, 1942). *WORKS HANGING:* In the DeGrazia Museum (Tucson, Arizona).

DURAND, Paul (1925-1977). *ARTIST FOR:* Limoges-Turgot. *STUDIED AT:* In Paris, influenced by Christian Berard, Jacques DeMachy, René Gruau, and André Dignimont. *AWARDS/HONORS:* Selected by Charles de Gaulle to illustrate his 1970 Christmas message to the children of France; presented as candidate for the Hans Christian Andersen Prize (1970). *EXHIBITS:* Festival Cannes (1965); illustrations for numerous French and U.S. publications including Hachette editions, Delagrave editions, Flammarion editions, Golden Press, *Reader's Digest, Le Figaro,* and *Paris Presse.*

DUTHEIL, Jean (1927-). *ARTIST FOR:* Henri d'Arceau & Fils. *STUDIED AT:* L'École de Beaublance (Limoges, France). *AWARDS/HONORS:* Prix de la Ville de Limoges, Prix du Ministre, Grand Prix de Porcelaine de Limoges, and the *Meilleur Ouvrier de France.*

ETÉM, Sue (1931-   ). *ARTIST FOR:* Fairmont. *STUDIED AT:* Self-taught. *AWARDS/HONORS:* NALED Plate of the Year and Collectible of the Year (1981), NALED Artist of the Year (1982 and 1983), California Plate Collectors' convention Artist of the Year (1983), International Plate Collector's convention Plate of the Show (1983). *EXHIBITS:* Extensive tour of the United States and Canada (1981-1982).

GANEAU, François (1912-1983). *ARTIST FOR:* Henri d'Arceau & Fils. *STUDIED AT: L' École Boulle* (Paris, France). *AWARDS/HONORS/COMMISSIONS:* Commissioned by D'Arceau-Limoges to create the Women of the Century series, which bears the United Nations' emblem for the International Women's Year; worked with the Ministry of Economy (France) for exhibitions and fairs in foreign countries. *EXHIBITS:* International fairs and theaters in France, Italy, Holland, and Israel. *WORKS HANGING:* In the *Comédie Française*, Paris Opera House, and the Louvre Museum (all in Paris).

HALLETT, Charlotte and William (Charlotte, 1943-   ), (William, 1940-   ). *ARTISTS FOR:* Hutschenreuther. *STUDIED AT:* Charlotte, at University of Bridgeport (Connecticut); William, at Vesper George School of Art (Boston, Massachusetts). *AWARDS/HONORS:* Local and regional awards, including International Competition at Brown County (Nashville, Indiana); the National Drawing 75 Prize. *EXHIBITS:* Local, regional, and national shows including National Small Paintings exhibition, New Haven Paint Club, and New England Regional Exhibition. *WORKS HANGING:* In the Rutgers University Museum and the private collections of the Archdiocese of New York, the royal families of Saudi Arabia and Spain, and the Mellon family of Philadelphia.

FISHER, Shell (   ). *ARTIST FOR:* Viletta. *STUDIED AT:* Northwestern University, the Art Institute of Chicago, the Academy of Art (Chicago, Illinois). *AWARDS/HONORS:* First prize, Artist's Guild Annual Chicago Artists Show (1977); work commissioned by Queen Elizabeth II and Sammy Davis, Jr. *EXHIBITS:* Crossroads of Sport (New York City, 1972-1973), Artist's Guild (1975); Emilio's Gallery (1978) and Burtwood Gallery (both of Carmel, California); Nepenthe Gallery (Big Sur, California, 1980). *WORKS HANGING:* In the Art Institute of Chicago and Chicago Wildlife Museum.

GEHM, Charles (1929-   ). *ARTIST FOR:* Königszelt Bayern. *STUDIED AT:* Columbus Art School. *AWARDS/HONORS/COMMISSIONS:* Member, Society of Illustrators; cover designs for Saul Bellow books. *EXHIBITS:* James Marks Gallery (California). *WORKS HANGING:* In private collections in the United States.

HIBEL, Edna (1917-   ). *ARTIST FOR:* Hibel Studio, Edwin M. Knowles, Rosenthal, Royal Doulton. *STUDIED AT:* Boston Museum of Fine Arts with Carl Zerbe and Jacovleff (1934-1939); private study with Gregory Michaels in Boston. *AWARDS/HONORS:* Boston Art Festival (1956); International Year of the Child award (1979); Fellow of the Royal Society of Arts (England);

Medal of Honor (The Netherlands, 1982); Medal of Honor from King Baudouin of Belgium and Pope John Paul II (1983). *EXHIBITS:* Numerous one-woman shows since 1962 in the United States, England, Monaco, Germany, and Argentina; recently became the first American woman to exhibit in Jerusalem. *WORKS HANGING:* In the Museum of Fine Arts (Boston, Massachusetts); the Detroit Art Institute (Michigan); the Milwaukee Museum of Art (Wisconsin); Harvard University (Massachusetts); and the Hibel Museum of Art (Florida).

HICKS, Yin-Rei (1933-). *ARTIST FOR:* River Shore. *STUDIED AT:* University of Louisville (Kentucky). *AWARDS/HONORS:* Sculpture prize at Golden Jubilee (Kentucky); Ronvald Kraus sculpture prize; watercolor prize in Brown County (Indiana); first prize in sculpture and painting, and second prize in ceramics and portraiture, Kentucky State Fair (1959). *EXHIBITS:* The J.B. Speed Gallery (Kentucky), University of Louisville, the Floyd County Museum, and other galleries in Kentucky and southern Indiana. *WORKS HANGING:* In private collections in the United States.

HOOVER, G.A. (1943-). *ARTIST FOR:* Longton Crown. *STUDIED AT:* Tulane University (New Orleans, Louisiana) and the John Herron School of Art (Indianapolis, Indiana). *AWARDS/HONORS:* The Roger Gould Walcott travel award to study art abroad; designs, drawings, and illustrations for Little, Brown & Company, McGraw-Hill, Playboy Press, MacMillan and Co., *Reader's Digest,* Harper & Row, and Harcourt Brace and Jovanovich. *EXHIBITS:* Three one-man shows at Bienville Gallery (New Orleans); participant at invitational exhibit (Colombia, South America). *WORKS HANGING:* In the Museum of Art (Medellin, Colombia); Herron Museum of Art (Indianapolis); Tulane University museum (New Orleans), and in private collections on the East Coast of the United States.

HUMMEL, Sister Maria Innocentia (1909-1946). *ARTIST FOR:* Goebel. *STUDIED AT:* The Munich Academy of Applied Art (Germany). *EXHIBITS:* Two exhibitions at the convent at Siessen (Germany). *WORKS HANGING:* At the Goebel Collectors' Club (Tarrytown, New York).

Photograph
not available
at press time

INGARGIOLA, Franco (1944-). *ARTIST FOR:* Studio Dante di Volteradici. *STUDIED AT:* Boy's Town (Rome, Italy); private study with Gino Ruggeri. *AWARDS/HONORS:* First prize, Craftsmen Arts Show (Cecina, Italy).

JANSEN, Leo (1930-1980). *ARTIST FOR:* Kern Collectibles, Royal Bayreuth. *STUDIED AT:* The Academy of Fine Arts (The Netherlands); also in the Pigalle section of Paris, France. *AWARDS/HONORS:* CALED's Plate of the Year (Canada, 1979). *EXHIBITS:* Avron Brothers Corporation (Los Angeles, California). *WORKS HANGING:* In private collections and galleries in the United States and abroad.

KELLER, Hedi (1916-). *ARTIST FOR:* Königszelt Bayern. *STUDIED AT:* The Academy of Art (Stuttgart, West Germany). *EXHIBITS:* Berlin, Munich, Düsseldorf (West Germany).

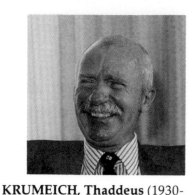

KRUMEICH, Thaddeus (1930-
). *ARTIST FOR:* Anna-Perenna.
STUDIED AT: New York University
and Columbia University (New
York City). *AWARDS/HONORS:* Art
Directors' Award (1970); illustra-
tions for publications such as *Reader's
Digest, Time/Life* books, and *Family
Circle*; work has been selected for
UNICEF greeting cards (1980 and
1981). *EXHIBITS:* Zantman Galleries
(Carmel, California, 1977); the
Bruce Museum (Greenwich, Con-
necticut, 1978); the Bradley Gallery
(New York City, 1978), and the
Southampton Art Museum (South-
ampton, New York, 1980). *WORKS
HANGING:* In the private collections
of Mrs. Paul Mellon, "Doc" Sever-
inson, and the Mali Ambassador to
the United States.

KURSÁR, Raymond (1944-   ).
ARTIST FOR: Edwin M. Knowles.
STUDIED AT: The School of Advertising Art, the University of Oregon,
and the Museum of Modern Art
(Portland, Oregon). *AWARDS/
HONORS/COMMISSIONS:* Twice
recipient of the Award of Merit from
the Society of Illustrators; awards
from the Art Directors' Club and the
Society of Publication Designers;
award-winning posters for the New
York theater; book covers for Random
House publishers; illustrations for
publications such as *Ladies Home*

Journal, Better Homes and Gardens,
and *Good Housekeeping. EXHIBITS:*
Work was included in a world tour
of National Lampoon Art and in
an exhibit in New York City which
later moved to Japan. *WORKS
HANGING:* In private and corporate
collections throughout the United
States.

Photograph
not available
at press time

LALIQUE, Marie-Claude
(   ). *ARTIST FOR:* Lalique.
STUDIED AT: Grand Chaumiere and
*L'École Normale Superiore des Arts
Decoratifs* (Paris, France). *AWARDS/
HONORS:* Currently president of,
and designer for, the firm founded by
her grandfather, René Lalique.

LANGE, Kai (1905-   ). *ARTIST
FOR:* Royal Copenhagen. *STUDIED
AT:* Studied drawing under Carl
Schwenn. *AWARDS/HONORS:* Re-
cipient of several grants; illustrator
for various Danish newspapers;
created wall hangings for numerous
official institutions. *WORKS HANG-
ING: Folkets Hus* (Copenhagen,
Denmark).

LICEA, Eve (1928-   ). *ARTIST
FOR:* Edwin M. Knowles. *STUDIED
AT:* Parson's School of Design
(New York City). *AWARDS/HON-
ORS/ COMMISSIONS:* Illustrations
for numerous publications, including
Good Housekeeping and *Women's
Day*; member of Screen Cartoonists
Guild. *EXHIBITS:* One-woman show
at the Pindar Gallery for Sculpture;
participant in numerous group
shows including those at the Zaner
Gallery (Rochester, New York),
Castle Gallery (New Rochelle, New
York), Carlisle Gallery, First Women's
Bank, Les Mouches, Inc., and the
Lincoln Center (all in New York
City).

LOCKHART, James (1912-   ).
ARTIST FOR: Pickard. *STUDIED AT:*
University of Arkansas; American
Academy of Art and Art Institute
(Chicago, Illinois). *AWARDS/HON-
ORS/COMMISSIONS:* Member,
the Board of Governors of the
Brookfield Zoo (Illinois) and Shedd
Aquarium (Chicago, Illinois); illus-
trator for publications including *The
Saturday Evening Post* and *Sports
Afield. WORKS HANGING:* In private
U.S. collections.

MASSERIA, Francisco J. J. C. (1926-). *ARTIST FOR:* Royal Doulton. *STUDIED AT:* Self-taught. *AWARDS/HONORS:* Gold medalist (at age 14) in the *Salon Annuale de Entre Rios* (Argentina); first prize at the Exposition of Mar Plata (1950), the *Salon Annuale de Santa Fe* (1951), and the *Salon Plasticos* (1959); created NALED's Lithograph of the Year (1982). *EXHIBITS:* Numerous exhibitions throughout Central, South, and North America, and Europe, with one-man shows in Brazil, Chile, Mexico, Spain, and the United States. *WORKS HANGING:* In American galleries and in private collections worldwide.

McCLELLAND, John (1919-). *ARTIST FOR:* Reco. *STUDIED AT:* Auburn University, Grand Central Art School, and Art Career School (New York City); also private studies with Jerry Farnsworth. *AWARDS/HONORS/COMMISSIONS:* NALED's Plate of the Year, Collectible of the Year, and Artist of the Year awards (1980); *Plate World* magazine's Artist of the Year (1982); author of two books on flower and portrait painting. *EXHIBITS:* Numerous exhibits on the United States East Coast; numerous one-man shows including those at the Wilton Gallery, Silvermine Guild, and Carriage Barn (all Connecticut) and

the Birmingham Art Alliance (Alabama). *WORKS HANGING:* In private collections in the United States, the Philippines, and Switzerland.

MONEY, Rusty ( ). *ARTIST FOR:* Ernst Enterprises. *STUDIED AT:* Arizona State University and the Washington School of Art. *AWARDS/HONORS:* International Fine Arts Award competition (1980). *WORKS HANGING:* In numerous private collections, including those of Jean Renoir, Barry Fitzgerald, John Ford, Greer Garson, Robert Aldrich, Gene Fowler, Art Jacobson, Bob Bronson, Telly Savalas, and Peggy Lee.

MUELLER, Hans (1934-). *ARTIST FOR:* Bareuther. *STUDIED AT:* Porcelain Academy of Selb (West Germany) and the Porcelain Trade School of Bavaria (West Germany). *AWARDS/HONORS:* Named chief designer at Bareuther (1968).

NEIMAN, LeRoy (1927-). *ARTIST FOR:* Royal Doulton. *STUDIED AT:* St. Paul Art Center (Minnesota); the University of Chicago and the Art Institute of Chicago (Illinois). *AWARDS/HONORS/COMMISSIONS:* Gold medalist, *Salon d'Art Moderne* (Paris, France); created the Olympian mural at the 1976 and 1980 Olympics; named official artist for the 1984 Olympics; illustrator for publications such as *Vogue, Harper's Bazaar, Glamour;* cover art for *Time, Newsweek,* and *The Saturday Evening Post. EXHIBITS:* Over 30 one-man shows and 40 group shows in the United States, Sweden, Canada, Japan, England, and France. *WORKS HANGING:* In the Hermitage Museum (Leningrad, USSR), the Indianapolis Museum of Art (Indiana), the Minneapolis Institute of Arts (Minnesota), the *Museo de Bellas Artes* (Caracas, Venezuela), the Illinois State Museum (Springfield), the National Museum of Sport in Art (New York City), Wodham College (Oxford, England), the Harding Museum (Chicago, Illinois), the Hayward Museum (California), the University of Texas, the University of Illinois, and numerous private collections.

NEUBACHER, Gerda (1945-). *ARTIST FOR:* Kaiser. *STUDIED AT:* Grace Kelly School of Art (Zurich,

Switzerland). *AWARDS/HONORS:* Numerous awards in Canadian art shows. *EXHIBITS:* National Art Centre (Ottawa, Canada); Christal Galleries (Toronto, Canada); Juliane Galleries (O'Keefe Centre, Toronto), the Galleria (Houston, Texas).

NG, Kee Fung (1941-   ). *ARTIST FOR:* Artists of the World. *STUDIED AT:* Fu San Art School (Canton, China). *EXHIBITS:* Private showings in California. *WORKS HANGING:* In Kee Fung Ng Galleries (San Francisco, California) and Lahaina Gallery (Maui, Hawaii).

NIGHTINGALE, Sandy (1953-   ). *ARTIST FOR:* Porcelaine Georges Boyer. *STUDIED AT:* In England and the south of France. *AWARDS/HONORS/COMMISSIONS:* Book illustrations for the Medici Society (London, England) and illustrations commissioned by the Oxford University Press (Oxford, England). Member of Chelsea Society of Illustrators.

NYLUND, Gunnar (1904-   ). *ARTIST FOR:* Rörstrand. *STUDIED AT:* Studied architecture in Copenhagen (Denmark). *AWARDS/HONORS:* Artist for the Bing & Grøndahl factory (1925). *EXHIBITS:* 1930-1943 in Copenhagen, Denmark, and in Stockholm and Gothenburg, Sweden. *WORKS HANGING:* In various Swedish museums, including National Museum (Stockholm), Roehsska Museet (Gothenburg), Rörstrand Museum (Lidkoeping), and Malmoe Museum (Malmoe).

QUELLIER, André (1925-   ). *ARTIST FOR:* Limoges-Turgot. *STUDIED AT:* L' Ecole des Beaux-Arts. Studied under the direction of Jean Dupas and Edmond Heuze. *AWARDS/HONORS/COMMISSIONS: Prix de l'Institute* (1945), *Prix Casa Velasquez, à Madrid,* the *Médaille d'Or des Artists Français,* and the *Prix Internationale du Gemmeil d'Art Sacré à Lourdes.* Commissioned to decorate a chapel near Saint-Tropez. *EXHIBITS:* United States, Japan, the Soviet Union, Spain, and France, including one of the first exhibitions at the Théâtre des Champs-Elysées in Paris. *WORKS HANGING:* In private collections throughout France. His portrait of Jean Cocteau is in the home of Jean Marais.

RESTIEAU, André (1929-1978). *ARTIST FOR:* Henri d'Arceau & Fils. *STUDIED AT:* Studied under such masters as Lavelle and Fournier. *AWARDS/HONORS/COMMISSIONS:* Lafayette Legacy plate collection (1972). *EXHIBITS: Cercle de la Librairie* (Paris, 1966).

ROCKWELL, Norman (1894-1978). *ARTIST FOR:* Franklin Mint, Gorham, Rockwell Society of America, Royal Devon. *STUDIED AT:* Chase School of Fine and Applied Arts and the National Academy of Design; traditional art training at the Art Student's League (all in New York City). *AWARDS/HONORS/COMMISSIONS:* sold first Saturday Evening Post Cover in 1916, followed by over 300 others. Illustrations for annual Boy Scout Calendars, *Life, Look,* and *Boy's Life.* EXHIBITS: One-man show Milwaukee Art Institute (Wisconsin, 1941) and one-man exhibition at the Dannenberg Galleries (New York City). *WORKS HANGING:* In the Norman Rockwell Museum (Philadelphia, Pennsylvania), the Smithsonian Institution (Washington, D.C.), the Metropolitan Museum of Art (New York City), and other museums throughout the U.S.

ROMANELLI, Carl (1917-   ). *ARTIST FOR:* Incolay. *STUDIED AT:* Apprenticed with his father, sculptor Carlo Romanelli. *AWARDS/HONORS/COMMISSIONS:* Won competition from six top sculptors to create bronze bust of John Henry Cardinal Newman (1960); commissioned by Barron Hilton to create life-size bronze of Elvis Presley for the Las Vegas Hilton. *EXHIBITS:* Peterson Galleries (Beverly Hills, California); Gallerie de Tours (Carmel, California); Painters and Sculptors Club (Los Angeles, California); International Fine Arts Association (New Orleans, Louisiana), and Kachina Gallery (Santa Fe, New Mexico). *WORKS HANGING:* In memorials, churches, and galleries in California, Washington, D.C., the Vatican, and private collections.

Photograph
not available
at press time

RUGGERI, Gino (1902-   ). *ARTIST FOR:* Studio Dante di Volteradici. *STUDIED AT:* Academy of Fine Arts (Sienna, Italy), and the Art Institute (Volterra, Italy). *AWARDS/HONORS/COMMISSIONS:* Three first prizes from the Fine Art Academy (Sienna); Director of the Cooperative Artien since 1942.

RUSSELL, Frank (1921-   ). *ARTIST FOR:* Anna-Perenna. *STUDIED AT:* Art Student's League (New York City). *AWARDS/HONORS:* Prizes in local shows. *EXHIBITS:* One-man shows at Artists' Gallery (New York City); numerous group exhibitions across the country, including Brown University, Philadelphia Museum Annuals, the Brooklyn Museum, and Spiral Group Shows. Joint shows with wife, Gertrude Barrer, in New York, New Jersey, and Connecticut. *WORKS HANGING:* In the collections of the United Nations, the Vatican, Cologne Cathedral, the Art Institute of Chicago, the Whitney Museum, New York University, and the Brooklyn Museum and private collections, including those of Cyrus Vance and Helmut Schmidt.

SCHULZ, Charles (1922-   ). *ARTIST FOR:* Schmid. *STUDIED AT:* Art Instruction, Inc. (Minneapolis, Minnesota). Honorary degree, Anderson College (Indiana, 1963); honorary Doctor of Humane Letters, St. Mary's College (California, 1966). *AWARDS/HONORS:* National Cartoonists' Society "Reuben" Award (1955, 1964); Humorist of the Year award, Yale University (1958); School Bell Award, National Education Society (1960); Best Humor Strip of the Year, National Cartoonists' Society (1962); Big Brother of the Year Award (California, 1973); "Peanuts" characters featured on cover of *Time* (1965). "Peanuts" television specials have won various Peabody and Emmy awards. "Charles Schulz Day" proclaimed by Gov. Ronald Reagan (California, 1967). Grand Marshal of the Tournament of Roses Parade (California, 1974).

SKELTON, Red (1913-   ). *ARTIST FOR:* Crown Parian, Fairmont. *STUDIED AT:* Self-taught artist, as a diversion from his careers in film, television, and music. *AWARDS/HONORS:* Footprints in the Sand of Time award. Numerous awards for his work in television and music. *EXHIBITS:* Center Art Gallery (Los Angeles, California), Center Art Gallery (Honolulu, Hawaii). *WORKS HANGING:* In the collections of the Franklin Mint, the late John Wayne, Jerry Lewis, Ginger Rogers, Dinah Shore, Vincent Price, Debbie Reynolds, the former Queen of Egypt, Burt Reynolds, and Frank Sinatra.

SPAULDING, Don (1926-   ). *ARTIST FOR:* Edwin M. Knowles. *STUDIED AT:* Art Student's League

(New York City). Private studies with Norman Rockwell. *AWARDS/ HONORS:* "Best of Show" awards at shows of Western paintings in the United States; award from Western Collections Group. *EXHIBITS:* Art shows throughout the United States, one-man show at West Point Museum (1979). *WORKS HANGING:* In major private collections throughout the United States and in the permanent collection at the West Point Museum.

SPENCER, Irene ( ). *ARTIST FOR:* Fairmont, Gorham, Pickard. *STUDIED AT:* Art Institute of Chicago and American Academy of Art (both in Chicago, Illinois). *AWARDS/HONORS:* NALED's Lithograph of the Year (1979); NALED's Plate of the Year and Bradford Exchange's New Edition of the Year (1980); NALED's Lithograph of the Year (1982). *EXHIBITS:* Trebor Gallery (Los Angeles and San Francisco, California, 1967-1973). *WORKS HANGING:* In private collections across the country including those of Henry Mancini and Dr. Michael DeBakey, and the Golden West College (California).

STOBART, John (1930-). *ARTIST FOR:* Royal Doulton. *STUDIED AT:* Derby College of Arts and Royal Academy of Art (London, England). *AWARDS/HONORS/ COMMISSIONS:* Paintings featured on covers of *Reader's Digest*, *American Heritage*, *Oceans*, *International Yachtsman*; member of Royal Society of Marine Artists. *EXHIBITS:* Numerous exhibitions in the United States and England; one-man show at Kennedy Galleries (New York City). *WORKS HANGING:* In the Marine Museum of Upper Canada (Toronto, Ontario); National Maritime Museum (Greenwich, England), and the Royal Naval College.

TELLIER, Liliane ( ). *ARTIST FOR:* Haviland. *STUDIED AT: L' École Camondo* (Paris). *AWARDS/HONORS/COMMISSIONS:* Art consultant to UNESCO.

THELANDER, Henry (1902-). *ARTIST FOR:* Bing & Grøndahl. *STUDIED AT:* Paris, London, and Berlin. *AWARDS/HONORS/COMMISSIONS:* Designed government stamps and posters, book illustrations. Commissioned to create advertising illustration, ballet posters (Royal Danish Ballet), by the National Travel Association of Denmark to portray the country's royal history. *WORKS HANGING:* In the Copenhagen Town Hall (Denmark).

VICKERS, Mary (1940-). *ARTIST FOR:* Wedgwood. *STUDIED AT:* St. Martin's School of Art (London, England), England Art Student's League, and Pratt Institute (New York City). *AWARDS/HONORS:* Won her first art contest at age twelve, and numerous awards since. *EXHIBITS:* Since 1969, numerous one-woman shows in Europe and the U.S., including the David Gary Gallery, the Mitch Morse Gallery II, and Merrill Chase Gallery. *WORKS HANGING:* In permanent collections in New York, Chicago, Los Angeles, New Jersey, and Ohio; in the private collections of the Duke and Duchess of Marlborough, Sarah Churchill, and Johnnie Ray.

VINCENT (L. V. Garrison) (1923-). *ARTIST FOR:* Fairmont. *STUDIED AT:* New England School of Art, Boston Museum School, and Scott Carbee School of Art (all in Boston, Massachusetts), and Coronado School of Art (California). *AWARDS/HONORS:* Artists U.S.A. award from San Diego Art Institute and awards from various local competitions and statewide exhibitions. *EXHIBITS:* One-man shows in New York, Los Angeles, Chicago, San Francisco, Las Vegas, Honolulu, and in Mexico. *WORKS HANGING:* In private collections, galleries, and museums around the world.

WIINBLAD, Bjørn (1918-).
ARTIST FOR: Rosenthal. *STUDIED AT:* Royal Academy of Art (Copenhagen, Denmark). *AWARDS/HONORS:* International design awards including the American Interior Designer Award (1965). *EXHIBITS:* First one-man show at Binger's Gallery (1945), one-man shows in Norway and Sweden (1946-1950), and the Georg Jensen Gallery (New York City, 1954). *WORKS HANGING:* In the Museum of Decorative Art (Copenhagen); Museum of National Art (Bergen, Norway); Faenza Museum (Italy), National Museum of Sweden (Stockholm).

XARAS, Theodore (1945-).
ARTIST FOR: Christian Bell Porcelain. *STUDIED AT:* Philadelphia College of Art, Tyler School of Art (Philadelphia, Pennsylvania). *AWARDS/HONORS/COMMISSIONS:* Ely Travel Award for Excellence in Illustration from the Philadelphia College of Art; *Time* magazine cover (1971); cover work for books and railroad magazines. CALED's Plate of the Year. Commissioned by the Franklin Mint to create a series of limited-edition prints of trains. *EXHIBITS:* One-man show at Marion Locks Gallery in Philadelphia. Work included in "50 Great *Time* Covers" at the Time-Life building in New York City (1972). *WORKS HANGING:* In numerous private collections throughout the United States.

Lady Pat Nixon, Governor William Scranton, and Admiral Elmo Zumwalt.

ZOLAN, Donald (1936-).
ARTIST FOR: Pemberton & Oakes, Viletta. *STUDIED AT:* Art Institute of Chicago, American Academy of Art (both of Chicago), apprenticeship with Hadden Sunblum. *AWARDS/HONORS:* Bradford Exchange's Plate of the Year (1979). *EXHIBITS:* Many Midwestern shows. *WORKS HANGING:* In galleries throughout the United States and private collections around the world, including Australia, France, Italy, and South Korea.

Photograph
not available
at press time

WÜLFING, Sulamith (1901-).
ARTIST FOR: Königszelt Bayern. *STUDIED AT:* The Art College (Wuppertal, West Germany). *EXHIBITS:* Frühjahrsmesse (Spring Fair) in Frankfurt, West Germany (1981). *WORKS HANGING:* Original work lost, World War II.

YATES, Michael (1927-).
ARTIST FOR: Morgantown Crystal. *STUDIED AT:* Art Institute of Pittsburgh (Pennsylvania). *EXHIBITS:* Various exhibitions in the United States. *WORKS HANGING:* In numerous public buildings and churches throughout the United States; commissioned works in homes of Gerald Ford, the late Golda Meir, Johnny Cash, former First

Photograph
not available
at press time

ZVORYKIN, Boris (1872-).
ARTIST FOR: Heinrich/Villeroy & Boch. *STUDIED AT:* In Tsarist Russia. Established studio in Paris, 1920. *AWARDS/HONORS/COMMISSIONS:* Commissioned to produce work for Russian Imperial Court. Noted for murals in the Cathedral at Simferopol, Russia. Illustrations chosen for a Russian fairy tales book edited by Jacqueline Kennedy Onassis in 1979. *WORKS HANGING:* In the Metropolitan Museum of Art (New York City).

MAKERS AND SPONSORS
OF OVER-THE-COUNTER ISSUES

Abbey Press (Viletta) **U.S.A.**
Accent on Art **U.S.A.**
Addams Family (Schmid) **U.S.A.**
Allison **U.S.A.**
American Archives (International Silver)
   U.S.A.
American Artists **U.S.A.**
American Arts Services (Viletta) **U.S.A.**
American Commemorative (Gorham) **U.S.A.**
American Express (Gorham) **U.S.A.**
American Express (Lenox) **U.S.A.**
American Heritage Art (Crown Parian)
   U.S.A.
American Historical Plates (Castleton China)
   U.S.A.
American Preservation Guild (Gorham)
   U.S.A.
American Rose Society (Gorham) **U.S.A.**
Anna-Perenna **Ger.**
Anri **Italy**
Antique Trader **U.S.A.**
Arabia **Finland**
Arizona Artisan **U.S.A.**
Arlington Mint **U.S.A.**
Armstrong **U.S.A.**
Arta **Austria**
Artists of the World **U.S.A.**
Audubon Crystal **U.S.A.**
Avondale **U.S.A.**
   See also: Judaic Heritage Society
Aynsley **G.B.**

B & J Art Designs **U.S.A.**
Bareuther **Ger.**
Barthmann **Ger.**
Bayel of France **Fr.**
Bengough **Can.**
Berlin Design **Ger.**
Betourne Studios **Fr.**
Bing & Grøndahl **Den.**
   See also: Ghent Collection
Blue Delft (Schoonhaven) **Neth.**
Boehm Studios **G.B.**
   See also: Hamilton Collection
Bohemia **Czech.**
Bonita Silver **Mex.**
Brantwood Collection **U.S.A.**
Braymer Hall **U.S.A.**
Brentwood Fine Arts (Fairmont) **U.S.A.**
Briarcrest **U.S.A.**

John Brindle Fine Arts **U.S.A.**

Caithness Glass **G.B.**
Calhoun's Collectors Society **U.S.A.**
Calhoun's Collectors Society (Schumann)
   U.S.A.
California Porcelain and Bronze **U.S.A.**
Canadian Collector Plates **Can.**
Capo Di Monte **Italy**
Carlo Monti **Italy**
Carmel Collection **U.S.A.**
Carson Mint (Viletta) **U.S.A.**
Cartier **Fr.**
Castleton China **U.S.A.**
   See also: American Historical Plates
Castleton China (Shenango) **U.S.A.**
Caverswall, see: Ghent Collection
Certified Rarities **U.S.A.**
Chilmark **U.S.A.**
Christian Bell (Schumann) **Can.**
Cleveland Mint **U.S.A.**
Coalport **G.B.**
Collector Creations (Reed & Barton) **U.S.A.**
Collector's Heirlooms (Fairmont) **U.S.A.**
Collector's Heirlooms (Viletta) **U.S.A.**
Collectors Weekly **U.S.A.**
Continental Mint **U.S.A.**
Count Agazzi **Italy**
Creative World **U.S.A.**
Cristal D'Albret **Fr.**
Crown Delft **Neth.**
Crown Parian **U.S.A.**
   See also: American Heritage Art
Crown Staffordshire **G.B.**
Curator Collection **U.S.A.**

Danbury Mint **U.S.A.**
Danish Church **Ger.**
Daum **Fr.**
Stuart Devlin Silver **U.S.A.**
Dresden **Ger.**

Ebeling & Reuss **U.S.A.**
R. J. Ernst Enterprises (Viletta) **U.S.A.**

Fairmont **U.S.A.**
   See also:
   Brentwood Fine Arts
   Collector's Heirlooms
   Ghent Collection

Mistwood Designs
Fenton Glass **U.S.A.**
Firehouse **U.S.A.**
Fleetwood Collection (Gorham) **U.S.A.**
Fostoria **U.S.A.**
Franklin Crystal **U.S.A.**
Franklin Mint **U.S.A.**
Franklin Porcelain **U.S.A.**
Frankoma **U.S.A.**
Fürstenberg **Ger.**

Ghent Collection **U.S.A.**
Ghent Collection (Bing & Grøndahl) **U.S.A.**
Ghent Collection (Caverswall) **U.S.A.**
Ghent Collection (Fairmont) **U.S.A.**
Ghent Collection (Gorham) **U.S.A.**
Ghent Collection (Kaiser) **U.S.A.**
Ghent Collection (Viletta) **U.S.A.**
Glaskunst/Schott Zwiesel **Ger.**
Gnomes United **U.S.A.**
Goebel **Ger.**
Gold Crown Ceramics **Can.**
Golf Digest **U.S.A.**
Gorham **U.S.A.**
   See also:
   American Commemorative
   American Express
   American Preservation Guild
   American Rose Society
   Fleetwood Collection
   Ghent Collection
   Hoyle Products
   Lincoln Mint
   Volair
Gourinat-Dolan **Fr.**
Grafburg **Ger.**
Grande Copenhagen **Den.**
Grande Danica **Den.**
Graphics Buying Service,
   see: Modern Masters/GBS
Greentree Potteries **U.S.A.**
Dave Grossman Designs **U.S.A.**

Hackett American Collectors **U.S.A.**
Hamilton Collection **U.S.A.**
Hamilton Collection (Boehm Studios) **U.S.A.**
Hamilton Collection (Hutschenreuther)
   U.S.A.
Hamilton Collection (Porcelaine Ariel) **U.S.A.**
Hamilton Collection (Royal Devon) **U.S.A.**

Hamilton Collection (Viletta) **U.S.A.**
Hamilton Mint **U.S.A.**
Haviland **Fr.**
Haviland & Parlon **Fr.**
 See also: Kern Collectibles
Heinrich **Ger.**
Hibel Studio (Kaiser) **Ger.**
Hibel Studio (Rosenthal) **Ger.**
Historic Providence Mint **U.S.A.**
Ralph Homan Studios (Viletta) **U.S.A.**
Home Plates (Mingolla) **U.S.A.**
Hornsea **G.B.**
Hoyle Products (Gorham) **U.S.A.**
Hudson Pewter **U.S.A.**
Hutschenreuther **Ger.**
 See also: Hamilton Collection

Imperial **U.S.A.**
Incolay Studios **U.S.A.**
International Museum **U.S.A.**
International Silver **U.S.A.**
 See also: American Archives
Interpace **U.S.A.**

J M Company **U.S.A.**
Georg Jensen **Den.**
Svend Jensen **Den.**
Josair **Fr.**
Joys (Viletta) **U.S.A.**
Judaic Heritage Society **U.S.A.**
Judaic Heritage Society (Avondale) **U.S.A.**
Judaic Heritage Society (Viletta) **U.S.A.**

KPM-Royal Berlin **Ger.**
Kaiser **Ger.**
 See also:
 Ghent Collection
 Hibel Studio
David Kaplan Studio **U.S.A.**
Keller & George (Reed & Barton) **U.S.A.**
Kensington **U.S.A.**
Kera **Den.**
Kern Collectibles **U.S.A.**
Kern Collectibles (Haviland & Parlon) **U.S.A.**
Kern Collectibles (Pickard) **U.S.A.**
Kern Collectibles (Rosenthal) **U.S.A.**
Kern Collectibles (Royal Bayreuth) **U.S.A.**
Kern Collectibles (Sango) **U.S.A.**
Kilkelly **U.S.A.**
Kings **Italy**
Kirk **U.S.A.**
Koschevak Bros. **Czech.**
Kosta **Swed.**
Kurz (Shuler International) **Neth.**

Lake Shore Prints **U.S.A.**
Lapsys **U.S.A.**
Lenox **U.S.A.**
 See also: American Express
Lihs-Lindner **Ger.**
Lincoln Mint **U.S.A.**
Lincoln Mint (Gorham) **U.S.A.**
Litt **U.S.A.**
Lladró **Spain**
Lund & Clausen **Den.**
Lynell Studios **U.S.A.**

Mallek Studios **U.S.A.**
Manjundo **Japan**
Marmot **Ger.**
Mason **G.B.**
Master Engravers of America **U.S.A.**
McCalla Enterprises (Viletta) **U.S.A.**
Meissen **Ger.**
Metal Arts **U.S.A.**

Metawa **Neth.**
Metlox Potteries, see: Vernonware
Metropolitan Museum of Art **U.S.A.**
Mingolla, see: Home Plates
Mistwood Designs (Fairmont) **U.S.A.**
Modern Concepts **U.S.A.**
Modern Masters **U.S.A.**
Modern Masters/GBS **U.S.A.**
Moser **Czech.**
Moussalli **U.S.A.**
Mueller **Ger.**
Museum Editions (Ridgewood) **U.S.A.**
Museum Editions (Viletta) **U.S.A.**

Noritake **Japan**
Nostalgia Collectibles **U.S.A.**

OK Collectibles **U.S.A.**
Ohio Arts **U.S.A.**
Orrefors **Swed.**

Pacific Art **U.S.A.**
Palisander **Den.**
Paramount Classics (Pickard) **U.S.A.**
Pemberton & Oakes (Viletta) **U.S.A.**
Pickard **U.S.A.**
 See also:
 Kern Collectibles
 Paramount Classics
Poillerat **Fr.**
Poole Pottery **G.B.**
Porcelaine Ariel, see: Hamilton Collection
Porcelain Limited **U.S.A.**
Porcelana Granada **Arg.**
Porsgrund **Nor.**
Puiforcat **Fr.**

Ram **U.S.A.**
Raynaud-Limoges **Fr.**
Reco International **U.S.A.**
Reed & Barton **U.S.A.**
 See also:
 Collector Creations
 Keller & George
Rhea Silva **G.B.**
Ridgewood **U.S.A.**
 See also: Museum Editions
River Shore **U.S.A.**
Rockwell Collectors Club **U.S.A.**
Rockwell Museum **U.S.A.**
Roman **U.S.A.**
Roman Ceramica Excelsis **Mex.**
Rörstrand **Swed.**
Rosenthal **Ger.**
 See also:
 Hibel Studio
 Kern Collectibles
Royal Bayreuth, see: Kern Collectibles
Royal Copenhagen **Den.**
Royal Cornwall **China/Taiwan, U.S.A.**
Royal Delft **Neth.**
Royal Devon, see: Hamilton Collection
Royal Doulton **G.B.**
Royal Grafton **G.B.**
Royal Limoges **Fr.**
Royal Oaks **U.S.A.**
Royal Orleans **U.S.A.**
Royal Tettau **Ger.**
Royal Worcester **G.B., U.S.A.**
Royale **Ger.**
Royale Germania **Ger.**
Royalwood **U.S.A.**
John A. Ruthven **U.S.A.**

Sabino **Fr.**

Sango **Japan**
 See also: Kern Collectibles
Santa Clara **Spain**
Sarna **India**
Schmid **Ger., Japan**
 See also: Addams Family
Schoonhaven, see: Blue Delft
Schumann **Ger.**
 See also:
 Calhoun's Collectors Society
 Christian Bell
Sebastian **U.S.A.**
Seeley's Doll Plates **U.S.A.**
Seven Seas **U.S.A.**
Shenango, see: Castleton China
Shuler International, see: Kurz
Signature Collection **U.S.A.**
Silver Creations **U.S.A.**
Smith Glass **U.S.A.**
Sorrina **Can.**
Southern Living Gallery **U.S.A.**
Spode **G.B.**
Sterling America **U.S.A.**
Stieff **U.S.A.**
Stratford Collection **U.S.A.**
Stuart International **U.S.A.**
Stumar **Ger.**
Syracuse China **U.S.A.**

Tirschenreuth **Ger.**
Towle Silversmiths **U.S.A.**

U.S. Historical Society **U.S.A.**

Vague Shadows **U.S.A.**
Val St. Lambert **Belg.**
Veneto Flair **Italy**
Vernonware (Metlox Potteries) **U.S.A.**
Viletta **U.S.A.**
 See also:
 Abbey Press
 American Arts Services
 Carson Mint
 Collector's Heirlooms
 R. J. Ernst Enterprises
 Ghent Collection
 Hamilton Collection
 Ralph Homan Studios
 Joys
 Judaic Heritage Society
 McCalla Enterprises
 Museum Editions
 Pemberton & Oakes
 Warwick
 Westbury
 Edward Weston Editions
Villeroy & Boch **Ger.**
Volair (Gorham) **U.S.A.**

WMF Geislingen **Ger.**
Waldenburg Porcelain **Can.**
Warwick (Viletta) **U.S.A.**
George Washington Mint **U.S.A.**
Wedgwood **G.B.**
Wendell August Forge **U.S.A.**
Westbury (Viletta) **U.S.A.**
Westminster Collectibles **U.S.A.**
Westmoreland **U.S.A.**
Edward Weston Editions (Viletta) **U.S.A.**
Wheaton **U.S.A.**
Whitehall China **U.S.A.**
Wildlife Internationale **U.S.A.**

Zenith Delftware **Neth.**

OVER-THE-COUNTER ISSUES

Over-the-counter plates may be traded, but are not listed, on The Bradford Exchange along with "Bradex" plates, which generally trade with greater regularity and frequency. They are, nonetheless, true collector's plates issued in editions usually limited either to an announced number or to the year of issue as indicated. All editions repetitious of previous editions are excluded.

Over-the-counter issues are arranged alphabetically by country, then alphabetically by maker or maker/sponsor, then chronologically by series. Each entry includes the series name, the year and name of the plate, the edition limit, and the U.S. issue price whenever available.

	Edition Limit	Issue Price (US)
ARGENTINA		
Porcelana Granada		
Peace on Earth		
1971 Annunciation	9,300	$ 12.00
1972 Mary and Elizabeth	6,000	13.00
1973 Road to Bethlehem	5,000	14.00
1974 No Room at Inn	5,000	15.00
1975 Shepherds in Field	5,000	16.50
1976 Nativity	5,000	17.50
1977 Three Kings	5,000	18.00
1978 Young Carpenter	5,000	18.00
1979 Calling of Disciples	5,000	19.00
1980 Loaves and Fishes	5,000	20.00
1981 Suffer Little Children	5,000	21.00
1982 Triumphal Entry	5,000	22.50
AUSTRIA		
Arta		
Mother's Day		
1973 Family with Puppy	1,500	50.00
Christmas		
1973 Nativity—In Manger	1,500	50.00
BELGIUM		
Val St. Lambert		
American Heritage		
1969 Pilgrim Fathers	500	200.00
1970 Paul Revere's Ride	500	200.00
1971 Washington on Delaware	500	200.00
Annual Old Masters		
1969 Rubens & Rembrandt (Pair)	5,000	50.00
1969 Van Gogh & Van Dyck (Pair)	5,000	50.00
1970 Da Vinci & Michelangelo (Pair)	5,000	50.00
1971 El Greco & Goya (Pair)	5,000	50.00
1972 Reynolds & Gainsborough (Pair)	5,000	50.00
(Single issue)		
1970 Rembrandt	Year	25.00

	Edition Limit	Issue Price (US)
CANADA		
Canadian Collector Plates		
Discover Canada		
1980 Sawmill-Kings Landing	10,000	$ 98.00
1981 Quebec Winter	10,000	98.00
1981 Before Bath	10,000	125.00
1982 Grist Mill, Delta	10,000	125.00
1982 Anglican Church at Magnetawan	10,000	125.00
Children of Classics		
1982 Anne of Green Gables	15,000	70.00
1983 Tom Sawyer	15,000	70.00
Days of Innocence		
1982 He Loves Me . . .	15,000	70.00
1982 Butterflies Are Free	15,000	70.00
Christian Bell (Schumann)		
Preserving a Way of Life		
1980 Making Way for Cars	5,000	60.00
1980 Atop Hay Wagon	5,000	60.00
1980 Turning Sod	5,000	60.00
1980 Winter's Morning	5,000	60.00
1981 Sugarbush	10,000	70.00
1981 Fishing for Redfin	10,000	70.00
1981 Wheat Harvest	10,000	70.00
1981 Returning from Village	10,000	70.00
American Steam		
1982 Hiawatha	15,000	65.00
1983 Hittin' Diamond	15,000	65.00
1983 Morning at Depot	15,000	65.00
Men of Rails		
1982 Engineer	30 Days	39.50
1983 Conductor	30 Days	39.50
1983 Pullman Porter	30 Days	39.50
1983 Night Operator	30 Days	39.50
Remember When		
1983 Iceman	NA	45.00
Vanishing Africa		
1983 Sentinel	15,000	55.00
Wild North		
1983 Emperor of North	15,000	55.00
(Single issue)		
1984 Royal Hudson "2860"	25,000	75.00

	Edition Limit	Issue Price (US)
Bengough		
Christmas		
1972 Charles Dickens Christmas Carol	490	$125.00
Northwest Mounted Police		
1972 1898 Dress Uniform	1,000	140.00
1972 First Uniform	1,000	140.00
Royal Canadian Police		
1972 Order Dress	1,000	140.00
Goldcrown Ceramics		
Wild West		
1981 Horse and Rider	1,800	49.95
1982 I-See-You	5,000	49.95
1983 Cowboy	10,000	49.95
1983 Chuckwagon Race	10,000	49.95
Bush Pilot Planes		
1983 Fokker Universal	10,000	49.95
1983 DeHavilland DH80 Puss Moth	10,000	49.95
1984 Ford 6-AT-AS Tri-Motor	10,000	49.95
1984 Fairchild 71B	10,000	49.95
Endangered American Wildlife		
1983 Bald Eagle	15,000	59.95
Famous Fighter Aircraft of World War II		
1983 P-51 D Mustang	10,000	49.95
1983 Chance Vought F4U Corsair	10,000	49.95
1984 Lockheed P-38 Lightning	10,000	49.95
1984 Supermarine Spitfire	10,000	49.95
Sorrina		
Christmas		
1981 Gingerbread House	5,000	40.00
1982 Christmas Eve at Jesuit House	5,000	42.50
1983 Main Street, Barkerville	5,000	45.00
Country Friends		
1983 Meeting at Fence	10,000	65.00
Every Boy's Dream		
1983 Going to Rink	7,500	70.00

	Edition Limit	Issue Price (US)
Waldenburg Porcelain		
Punkinhead Happy Little Bear		
1983 Punkinhead and His Friends	5,000	$ 34.50
1983 Punkinhead and Santa Claus	5,000	34.50
CHINA (TAIWAN)		
Royal Cornwall		
Five Perceptions of Woo Cho		
1979 Sense of Touch	19,500	55.00
1979 Sense of Sight	19,500	55.00
1979 Sense of Taste	19,500	55.00
1979 Sense of Hearing	19,500	55.00
1979 Sense of Smell	19,500	55.00
CZECHOSLOVAKIA		
Bohemia		
Mother's Day		
1974 Mother's Day	500	130.00
1975 Mother's Day	500	140.00
1976 Mother's Day	500	150.00
Koschevak Bros.		
Mary Gregory Christmas		
1973 Christmas	1,000	55.00
1974 Christmas	1,000	60.00
1975 Christmas	1,000	60.00
1976 Christmas	500	65.00
Mary Gregory Mother's Day		
1973 Mother's Day	500	55.00
1974 Mother's Day	300	60.00
1975 Mother's Day	300	60.00
1976 Mother's Day	500	65.00
Moser		
Christmas (Vanoce)		
1970 Hradcany Castle	400	75.00
1971 Karlstein Castle	1,365	75.00
1972 Old Town Hall	1,000	85.00
1973 Karlovy Vary Castle	500	90.00
Mother's Day (Den Matek)		
1971 Peacocks	350	75.00
1972 Butterflies	750	85.00
1973 Squirrels	200	90.00

DENMARK

Bing & Grøndahl

Olympic Games	Edition Limit	Issue Price (US)
1972 Olympiade—Munich	Year	$ 20.00
1976 Olympic Montreal	Year	29.50
1980 Moscow by Night	Year	43.00
1984 Los Angeles	Year	45.00

Bicentennial		
1976 E. Pluribus Unum	Year	50.00

Heritage		
1976 Norseman	5,000	30.00
1977 Navigators	5,000	30.00
1978 Discovery	5,000	39.50
1979 Exploration	5,000	39.50
1980 Helmsman	NA	45.00
1981 Swordsman	NA	49.50

Carl Larsson (Sets of four)		
1977 Flowers on Windowsill		
1977 Breakfast under Big Birch		
1977 Yard & Warehouse		
1977 Kitchen	7,500	150.00
1978 First Born		
1978 Room for Mother and Children		
1978 Portrait of Inga-Maria Thiel		
1978 Iduna	7,500	170.00
1979 Forestry		
1979 Cutting Grass		
1979 Potato Harvest		
1979 Fishery	7,500	165.00

(Single issue)		
1977 Madonna	10,000	45.00

(Single issue)		
1978 Seagull	7,500	75.00

Mother's Day Jubilee		
1979 Mother's Day Jubilee	Year	55.00

Year of Viking (Single issue)		
1980 Viking	10,000	65.00

New Generation		
1982 Fledglings	10,000	29.50
1982 Kittens	10,000	29.50
1982 Bunnies	10,000	29.50
1982 Fawns	10,000	29.50

Seasons Remembered		
1984 Promise of Spring	7,500	35.00
1984 Wildflowers of Summer	7,500	35.00

See also: Ghent Collection (U.S.A.)

Grande Copenhagen

Bicentennial (Single issue)		
1976 Great Seal	Year	35.00

Grande Danica

Mother's Day		
1977 Dog with Puppies	10,000	25.00
1978 Storks	10,000	25.00
1979 Badgers	10,000	25.00

Georg Jensen

Christmas		
1972 Doves	Year	15.00
1973 Christmas Eve	Year	15.00
1974 Christmas Story	Year	17.50
1975 Winter Scene	Year	22.50
1976 Christmas in Country	Year	22.50

Chagall (Single issue)		
1972 Lovers	12,500	50.00

Mother's Day		
1973 Mother & Child	Year	15.00
1974 Sweet Dreams	Year	17.50
1975 Mother's World	Year	22.50

Svend Jensen

Christmas		
1970 H.C. Andersen House	Year	14.50
1971 Little Match Girl	Year	15.00
1972 Mermaid of Copenhagen	Year	16.50
1973 Fir Tree	Year	22.00
1974 Chimney Sweep	Year	25.00
1975 Ugly Duckling	Year	27.50
1976 Snow Queen	Year	27.50
1977 Snowman	Year	29.50
1978 Last Dream of Old Oak	Year	32.00
1979 Old Street Lamp	Year	36.50
1980 Willie Winky	Year	42.50
1981 Uttermost Parts of Sea	Year	49.50
1982 Twelve by Mailcoach	Year	54.50
1983 Story of Year	Year	54.50

Mother's Day		
1970 Bouquet for Mother	Year	14.50
1971 Mother's Love	Year	15.00
1972 Good Night	Year	16.50
1973 Flowers for Mother	Year	$ 20.00
1974 Daisies for Mother	Year	25.00
1975 Surprise for Mother	Year	27.50
1976 Complete Gardener	Year	27.50
1977 Little Friends	Year	29.50
1978 Dreams	Year	32.00
1979 Promenade	Year	36.50
1980 Nursery Scene	Year	42.50
1981 Daily Duties	Year	49.50
1982 My Best Friend	Year	54.50
1983 An Unexpected Meeting	Year	54.50

Anniversary		
1980 Hans Christian Andersen's Home	NA	60.00

Kera

Christmas		
1967 Kobenhavn	Year	6.00
1968 Forste	Year	6.00
1969 Andersen's House	Year	6.00
1970 Langelinie	Year	6.00
1971 Lille Peter	Year	6.00

Moon		
1969 Apollo 11	Year	6.00
1970 Apollo 13	Year	6.00

Mother's Day		
1970 Mother's Day	Year	6.00
1971 Mother's Day	Year	6.00

Lund & Clausen

Moon		
1969 Moon Landing— Apollo 11	Year	10.00
1971 Apollo 13	Year	15.00

Mother's Day		
1970 Rose	Year	10.00
1971 Forget-Me-Nots	Year	10.00
1972 Bluebell	Year	15.00
1973 Lily of Valley	Year	16.00

Christmas		
1971 Animal Garden	Year	13.50
1972 Stave Church	Year	13.50
1973 Christmas Scene	Year	13.50

Palisander

Christmas		
1971 Red Robin on Holly	1,200	50.00
1972 Flying Geese	1,200	50.00
1973 Christmas	1,200	50.00

Presidential		
1971 George Washington	1,000	50.00
1972 Thomas Jefferson	1,000	50.00
1973 John Adams	1,000	50.00

(Single issue)		
1973 Bicentennial	250	50.00

Royal Copenhagen

Historical		
1975 R. C. Bicentennial	Year	30.00
1976 U.S. Bicentennial	Year	35.00
1977 Electro-Magnetism	Year	35.00
1978 Capt. Cook	Year	37.50
1979 Adam Oehlenschlager	Year	42.50
1980 Amagertorv	Year	52.50

National Parks of America		
1978 Yellowstone	5,000	75.00
1979 Shenandoah	5,000	75.00
1980 Yosemite	5,000	75.00
1980 Mt. McKinley	5,000	75.00
1981 Everglades	5,000	75.00
1981 Grand Canyon	5,000	75.00

(Single issue)		
1980 Year of Viking	5,000	55.00

Hans Christian Andersen		
1983 Shepherdess and Chimney Sweep	Year	39.50

FINLAND

Arabia

Christmas 100 Years Ago		
1978 Inland Village Scene	Year	49.00
1979 Forest Village Scene	Year	72.00
1980 Seaside Village Scene	Year	79.00
1981 Farm Village Scene	Year	87.00
1982 Country Village Scene	Year	95.00

Pictures of Lapland		
1981 Laplander Village	7,000	175.00

(Single issue)		
1981 Rose	2,000	360.00

FRANCE

Bayel of France

Flowers		
1972 Rose	300	50.00
1973 Lilies	300	50.00
1973 Orchid	300	$ 50.00

Bicentennial		
1974 Liberty Bell	500	50.00
1975 Independence Hall	500	60.00
1976 Spread Eagle	500	60.00

Eagles		
1974 Eagle Head	300	50.00
1974 Eagle in Flight	300	50.00

Betourne Studios

Jean-Paul Loup Christmas		
1971 Noel	300	125.00
1972 Noel	300	150.00
1973 Noel	300	175.00
1974 Noel	400	200.00
1975 Noel	250	250.00
1976 Noel	150	300.00

Mother's Day (Champleve)		
1974 Mother & Child	500	250.00

Mother's Day (Enamel)		
1975 Mother's Day	400	285.00
1976 Mother & Child	250	300.00

Cartier

Cathedral		
1972 Chartres Cathedral	12,500	50.00
1974 Chartres, Millous	500	130.00

Cristal D'Albret

Four Seasons		
1972 Summer	1,000	75.00
1973 Autumn	648	75.00
1973 Spring	312	75.00
1974 Winter	1,000	88.00

(Single issue)		
1972 Bird of Peace	3,700	64.00

Daum

Four Seasons		
1969 Autumn (Amethyst)	2,000	150.00
1970 Winter (Aquamarine)	2,000	150.00
1970 Spring (Emerald)	2,000	150.00
1970 Summer (Topaz)	2,000	150.00

Famous Musicians		
1970 Bach (Emerald)	2,000	60.00
1970 Beethoven (Amethyst)	2,000	60.00
1971 Mozart (Tourmaline)	2,000	60.00
1971 Wagner (Peridot)	2,000	60.00
1972 Debussy (Topaz)	2,000	60.00
1972 Gershwin (Sapphire)	2,000	60.00

Dali		
1971 Ceci N'est Pas Une Assiette	2,000	200.00
1971 Triomphale	2,000	200.00

Nymphea		
1979 Waterlilies	4,000	125.00
1980 Lily Pond	4,000	150.00
1981 Swan	4,000	170.00

Gourinat-Dolan

(Single issue)		
1978 Doves of Peace	3,000	60.00

Haviland

Historical		
1968 Martha Washington	2,500	35.00
1969 Lincoln	2,500	100.00
1970 Grant	3,000	100.00
1971 Hayes	2,500	110.00

Bicentennial		
1972 Burning of Gaspee	10,000	39.95
1973 Boston Tea Party	10,000	39.95
1974 First Continental Congress	10,000	39.95
1975 Ride of Paul Revere	10,000	40.00
1976 Declaration of Independence	10,000	48.00

French Collection		
1973 Breakfast	10,000	29.95
1974 Wash	10,000	29.95
1975 In Park	10,000	30.00
1976 To Market	10,000	38.00
1977 A Wash Before Dinner	10,000	38.00
1978 An Evening at Home	10,000	40.00
1979 Happy Mother's Day	10,000	45.00

Theatre Des Saisons		
1978 Spring	5,000	120.00
1978 Summer	5,000	120.00
1978 Autumn	5,000	120.00
1978 Winter	5,000	120.00

Mother's Day		
1980 Child and His Animals	Year	55.00

Visit from Saint Nicholas		
1980 Twas Night Before Christmas	Year	55.00
1981 Children Were Nestled	Year	60.00
1982 Tore Open Shutters	Year	60.00
1983 What to Wondering Eyes	1,500	$ 60.00

Fleurs et Rubens		
1980 Orchidée	7,500	120.00
1981 Hibiscus	7,500	120.00
1982 Poppy	7,500	120.00

Haviland & Parlon

Nan Lee (Single issue)		
1973 Peaceable Kingdom	5,000	30.00

Mother's Day		
1975 Laura and Child	15,000	37.50
1976 Pinky and Baby	15,000	42.50
1977 Amy and Snoopy	10,000	45.00

King Tut (Single issue)		
1977 Scarab	2,500	80.00

Zodiac (Single issue)		
1977 Astrological Man	5,000	50.00

Enchanted Forest		
1982 Entrance to Forest	10,000	65.00

See also: Kern Collectibles (U.S.A.)

Josair

Bicentennial		
1972 American Eagle	400	250.00
1973 American Flag	400	250.00
1974 Abraham Lincoln	400	250.00
1975 George Washington	400	250.00
1976 Declaration of Independence	400	250.00

Poillerat

Christmas		
1972 Three Kings	500	350.00
1973 Rose	250	350.00

Puiforcat

Cartes a Jouer		
1972 (Set of five)	2,000	300.00

(Single issue)		
1973 Exodus (Silver)	2,000	200.00

Raynaud-Limoges

Castles		
1979 Bodiam Castle	5,000	48.00
1979 Glamis Castle	5,000	48.00
1979 Tower of London	5,000	48.00

Wildlife Collection		
1978 Tiger Bouquet	Year	50.00

Royal Limoges

Christmas		
1972 Nativity	5,000	25.00
1973 Three Wise Men	5,000	27.50

Sabino

Annual Crystal		
1970 King Henry IV & Maria De Medici	1,500	65.00
1971 Milo & Beasts	1,500	65.00

GERMANY

Anna-Perenna

Birds of Fancy		
1978 Firebird	5,000	110.00

Floral Fantasies		
1978 Empress Gold	5,000	110.00

Enchanted Gardens		
1978 June Dream	5,000	75.00
1979 Summer Day	5,000	95.00

Oriental Tranquility		
1978 Chun Li at Pond	5,000	100.00
1979 Ming Tao on Path of Faith	5,000	110.00

Joy of Motherhood		
1979 Gesa and Children	5,000	165.00
1980 Alexandra and Children	5,000	175.00

American Silhouettes I—Children		
1981 Fiddlers Two	5,000	75.00
1981 Mary with Lambs	5,000	75.00
1981 Waiting for Tom	5,000	75.00
1981 Ring Around Rosie	5,000	75.00

American Silhouettes II—Family		
1982 Family Outing	5,000	75.00
1982 John and Mary	5,000	75.00
1982 Homemakers A-Quilting	5,000	75.00
1982 Leisure Time	5,000	75.00

American Silhouettes III—Valley Life		
1983 Frosty Frolic	5,000	75.00
1983 Hayride	5,000	75.00
1983 Sunday Ride	5,000	75.00
1983 Market Day	5,000	75.00

Bashful Bunnies		
1981 Spring's Surprise	15,000	62.50
1981 Summer's Sunshine	15,000	62.50

	Edition Limit	Issue Price (US)
1982 Fall's Frolic	15,000	$ 62.50
1982 Winter's Wonder	15,000	62.50
Children of Mother Earth		
1982 Spring	2,500	275.00
Happy Village		
1982 Spring	5,000	55.00
1982 Summer on Pond	5,000	55.00
1982 Autumn Harvest	5,000	55.00
1982 Winter Snow Kids	5,000	55.00
Masquerade Fantasy		
1982 Masquerade Party	9,800	95.00
1982 Clowns and Unicorns	9,800	95.00
1982 Merry-Go-Round Ballet	9,800	95.00
Uncle Tad's Holiday Cats		
1982 Jingle Bells	9,800	75.00
1983 Pollyanna	9,800	75.00
Arctic Spring		
1983 Patience	9,500	75.00
Flowers of Count Bernadotte		
1983 Iris	17,800	75.00
1983 Carnation	17,800	75.00
Rhythm and Dance		
1983 Ballroom	5,000	29.50
1983 Two-Step	5,000	29.50
1983 Strut	5,000	29.50
1983 Swing	5,000	29.50
1983 Aerobics	5,000	29.50
1983 Jazz	5,000	29.50
1983 Charleston	5,000	29.50
1983 Cake-Walk	5,000	29.50
Bareuther		
Mother's Day		
1969 Mother & Children	5,000	12.00
1970 Mother & Children	5,000	12.00
1971 Mother & Children	5,000	13.50
1972 Mother & Children	5,000	15.00
1973 Mother & Children	5,000	15.00
1974 Musical Children	5,000	19.00
1975 Spring Outing	5,000	21.50
1976 Rocking Cradle	5,000	23.00
1977 Noon Feeding	5,000	24.50
1978 Blind Man's Bluff	5,000	27.50
1979 Mother's Love	5,000	35.00
1980 First Cherries	5,000	37.50
1981 Playtime	5,000	39.50
1982 Suppertime	5,000	39.50
1983 On Farm	5,000	39.50
1984 Village Children	5,000	42.50
Thanksgiving		
1971 First Thanksgiving	2,500	13.50
1972 Harvest	2,500	14.50
1973 Country Road in Autumn	2,500	15.00
1974 Old Mill	2,500	19.00
1975 Wild Deer in Forest	2,500	21.50
1976 Thanksgiving on Farm	2,500	23.50
1977 Horses	2,500	24.50
1978 Apple Harvest	2,500	27.50
1979 Noontime	2,500	35.00
1980 Longhorns	2,500	37.50
1981 Gathering Wheat	2,500	39.50
1982 Autumn	2,500	39.50
Barthmann		
Christmas		
1977 Mary with Child	300	236.00
1978 Adoration of Child	500	326.00
1979 Holy Mother of Kasanskaja	500	361.00
1980 Holy Mother by Kykos	500	385.00
Berlin Design		
Father's Day (Historical)		
1971 Brooklyn Bridge on Opening Day	12,000	14.50
1972 Continent Spanned	3,000	15.00
1973 Landing of Columbus	2,000	18.00
1974 Adorn's Balloon	Year	25.00
1975 Washington Crossing Delaware	Year	30.00
1976 Tom Thumb	Year	32.00
1977 Zeppelin	Year	32.00
1978 Carl Benz	Year	36.00
1979 Johannes Gutenberg at Mainz	Year	47.50
Mother's Day		
1971 Grey Poodles	20,000	14.50
1972 Fledglings	10,000	15.00
1973 Duck Family	6,000	16.50
1974 Squirrels	6,000	22.50
1975 Cats	6,000	30.00
1976 Doe and Her Fawn	6,000	32.00
1977 Storks	6,000	32.00
1978 Mare with Foal	6,000	36.00

	Edition Limit	Issue Price (US)
1979 Swans and Cygnets	6,000	$ 47.50
1980 Goat Family	6,000	55.00
1981 Dachshund Family	6,000	55.00
1982 Partridge Family	6,000	55.00
Danish Church		
Church		
1968 Roskilde Cathedral	Year	12.00
1969 Ribe Cathedral	Year	13.00
1970 Marmor Church	Year	13.00
1971 Ejby Church	Year	13.00
1972 Kalundborg Church	Year	13.00
1973 Grundtvig Church	Year	15.00
1974 Broager Church	Year	15.00
1975 Sct. Knuds Church	Year	18.00
1976 Osterlars Church	Year	22.00
1977 Budolfi Church	Year	15.95
1978 Haderslev Cathedral	Year	19.95
1979 Holmens Church	Year	19.95
1980 Sct. Bendts Church	Year	24.00
1981 Vor Frue Church	Year	32.50
1982 Fjennesler Church	Year	33.00
Dresden		
Christmas		
1971 Shepherd Scene	3,500	14.50
1972 Niklas Church	6,000	18.00
1973 Schwanstein Church	6,000	18.00
1974 Village Scene	5,000	20.00
1975 Rothenberg Scene	5,000	24.00
1976 Bavarian Village Church	5,000	26.00
1977 Old Mill in Hexenloch	5,000	28.00
Mother's Day		
1972 Doe and Fawns	8,000	15.00
1973 Mare and Colt	6,000	16.00
1974 Tiger and Cub	5,000	20.00
1975 Dachshund Family	5,000	24.00
1976 Mother Owl and Young	5,000	26.00
1977 Chamois	5,000	28.00
Fürstenberg		
Easter		
1971 Sheep	3,500	15.00
1972 Chicks	4,000	15.00
1973 Bunnies	4,000	16.00
1974 Pussywillow	4,000	20.00
1975 Village Church	4,000	24.00
1976 Country Watermill	4,000	25.00
Christmas		
1971 Rabbits	7,500	14.00
1972 Snowy Village	6,000	15.00
1973 Christmas Eve	3,000	18.00
1974 Sparrows	4,000	20.00
1975 Deer Family	4,000	24.00
1976 Winter Birds	4,000	25.00
Deluxe Christmas		
1971 Three Wise Men	1,500	45.00
1972 Holy Family and Angel	2,000	45.00
1973 Christmas Eve	2,000	60.00
Mother's Day		
1972 Hummingbird	5,000	15.00
1973 Hedgehogs	5,000	16.00
1974 Doe with Fawn	4,000	20.00
1975 Swan Family	4,000	24.00
1976 Koala Bear	4,000	25.00
Olympic		
1972 Olympics—Munich	5,000	20.00
1976 Olympics—Montreal	5,000	37.50
New York City Landscape		
1981 City Hall	3,500	75.00
1981 Central Park	3,500	75.00
Glaskunst/Schott-Zwiesel		
Christmas		
1977 Three Wise Man	NA	105.00
1978 Holy Family	NA	112.50
1979 Shepherd of Field	NA	115.00
1980 Annunciation of Maria	NA	118.00
Goebel		
Charlot Byj		
1973 Santa at Tree	Year	16.50
1974 Santa and Girl	Year	22.00
1975 Up and Away	Year	25.00
1976 Boy with Teddy Bear	Year	25.00
1977 Joy to World	Year	25.00
Wildlife		
1974 Robin	Year	45.00
1975 Blue Titmouse	Year	50.00
1976 Barn Owl	Year	50.00
1977 Bullfinch	Year	50.00
1978 Sea Gull	Year	55.00
1979 Mallard	10,000	90.00
1980 Cardinal	10,000	90.00
1981 Peregrine Falcon	10,000	NA

	Edition Limit	Issue Price (US)
Mothers		
1975 Rabbits	Year	$ 45.00
1976 Cats	Year	45.00
1977 Panda Bears	Year	45.00
1978 Doe and Fawn	Year	50.00
1979 Long-Eared Owl	10,000	65.00
1980 Raccoon and Baby	10,000	75.00
1981 Ringed Seal	10,000	80.00
1982 Swan	10,000	80.00
Robson Christmas		
1975 Flight to Egypt (Porcelain)	Year	50.00
1975 Flight to Egypt (Pewter)	Year	45.00
Annual Crystal		
1978 Praying Girl	Year	45.00
1979 Praying Boy	Year	50.00
1980 Praying Angel	15,000	50.00
1981 Girl with Teddy Bear	10,000	50.00
American Heritage		
1978 Freedom & Justice Soaring	Year	100.00
1979 Wild & Free	10,000	100.00
1980 Where Buffalo Roam	4,000	125.00
Old Testament Themes		
1978 Twelve Tribes of Israel	10,000	125.00
1979 Ten Commandments	10,000	175.00
1980 Traditions	10,000	225.00
Crystal Mother's Day		
1979 Butterfly	Year	50.00
1980 Sparrow	15,000	50.00
1981 Doves	5,000	50.00
(Single issue)		
1979 Christmas	200	500.00
Bratsoff		
1979 Star Steed	15,000	125.00
Bavarian Forest		
1980 Owls	7,500	150.00
1981 Deer	7,500	150.00
1982 Pheasants	7,500	150.00
North American Wildlife		
1980 Beaver	10,000	125.00
1981 Harp Seal	10,000	125.00
1982 Polar Bear	10,000	125.00
Christmas in Kinderland		
1982 A Gift of Joy	10,000	49.50
1983 A Midnight Clear	10,000	49.50
Christmas Morning in Dingle Dell		
1982 Dolly Dingle	10,000	30.00
1983 Billy Bumps	10,000	30.00
Dolly Dingle World Traveler		
1982 Dolly Visits Germany	10,000	30.00
1982 Dolly Visits Italy	10,000	30.00
1982 Dolly Visits Holland	10,000	30.00
1982 Dolly Visits Spain	10,000	30.00
Native Companions		
1982 Rachel	10,000	49.50
1983 Hummingbird	10,000	49.50
1983 Rabbit Dancer	10,000	49.50
1984 Celebration	10,000	49.50
Winged Fantasies		
1982 Strawberries	10,000	49.50
1983 Bacchanalia	10,000	49.50
1983 Cerises	10,000	49.50
1983 Brambleberries	10,000	49.50
Blue-Button Twins Christmas		
1983 By Fireplace	10,000	30.00
1983 Down Stairs	10,000	30.00
English Countryside Cat		
1983 James	10,000	35.00
1983 Henry	10,000	35.00
1983 Lucy	10,000	35.00
(Single issue)		
1984 Skater's Waltz	10,000	33.00
Grafburg		
Christmas		
1975 Black-Capped Chickadee	5,000	20.00
1976 Squirrels	5,000	22.00
Heinrich		
UNICEF Children in World		
1977 Europe	Year	30.00
1978 Asia	Year	30.00
1979 Africa	Year	30.00
1980 America	Year	30.00
1981 Malaysia	Year	30.00
1982 Mexico	Year	35.00
(Single issue)		
1979 International Year of Child	Year	35.00
Flower Fairies Collection		
1979 Lavender Fairy	21 Days	35.00
1980 Sweet Pea Fairy	21 Days	35.00

	Edition Limit	Issue Price (US)
1980 Candytuft Fairy	21 Days	$ 35.00
1980 Heliotrope Fairy	21 Days	35.00
1981 Black Thorne Fairy	21 Days	35.00
1981 Apple Blossom Fairy	21 Days	35.00
Hibel Studio (Kaiser)		
World I Love		
1981 Leah's Family	17,500	85.00
1982 Kaylin	17,500	85.00
1983 Edna's Music	17,500	85.00
1984 O-Hana	17,500	85.00
Hibel Studio (Rosenthal)		
Famous Women and Children		
1980 Pharoah's Daughter and Moses	3,000	350.00
Hutschenreuther		
Songbirds of America		
1972 Eastern Bluebird and Goldfinch (Pair)	5,000	100.00
1973 Mockingbird and Robin (Pair)	5,000	100.00
*Christmas**		
1972 On Way to Egypt	5,000	NA
1973 Adoration	5,000	NA
1974 Annunciation	5,000	NA
*Series not available in U.S.		
Canada Christmas		
1973 Parliament Building	Year	15.00
1974 Moose	Year	16.00
1975 Basilica	Year	21.00
1976 Winter on Prairies	Year	23.00
1977 Bluenose	Year	23.00
1978 Lost Lagoon	Year	27.00
1979 Yukon Highway Bridge	Year	33.00
1980 Covered Bridge	Year	38.00
1981 Saskatchewan Winter	Year	38.00
1982 Christmas to Celebrate	Year	38.00
Bicentennial		
1976 Freedom in Flight	5,000	100.00
1976 Freedom in Flight (Gold)	200	200.00
Plates of Month (Set of 12)		
1977 January—December	5,000	780.00
Mother and Child Annual		
1978 Mother and Child	Year	55.00
1979 Mother and Child	Year	65.00
1980 Mother and Child	Year	87.50
1981 Mother and Child	Year	87.50
Birthday Annual		
1978 Birthday Plate	10,000	165.00
Winter Christmas		
1978 Silent Night	Year	260.00
1979 Saint Lucia	Year	295.00
1980 Christmas Pavillion	Year	325.00
1981 Christmas Sleigh	Year	400.00
1982 Joy to World	Year	400.00
Friendship Annual		
1978 Friendship Plate	Year	80.00
Dolores Valenza Enchantment		
1979 Princess Snowflake	5,000	50.00
1979 Blossom Queen	5,000	62.50
1980 Princess Marina	5,000	87.50
1980 Princess Starbright	5,000	87.50
1981 Princess Aura	5,000	87.50
1981 Harvest Queen	5,000	87.50
Wedding Annual		
1978 Wedding Plate	10,000	210.00
Zodiac Collection (Set of 12)		
1978 Aries—Pisces	1,500	1500.00
Hans Achtziger Annual		
1979 Heading South	4,000	150.00
1980 Playful Flight	5,000	187.50
1981 Tropical Skies	5,000	245.00
1982 Carried by Wind	2,500	250.00
Arzberg Christmas		
1979 Christmas	2,500	60.00
(Single issue)		
1979 Celebration Plate	Year	67.50
(Single issue)		
1979 Anniversary Plate	Year	120.00
(Single issue)		
1977 Allegro Ensemble	7,500	120.00
Hibel Museum (Single issue)		
1977 Flower Girl of Provence	12,750	175.00
Floral Heirlooms		
1977 Zinnias in Sugar Bowl	5,000	65.00
1978 Pansies in Antique Tin	5,000	65.00
1979 Primroses in Staffordshire Pitcher	5,000	65.00
Birds of Paradise		
1981 Bluebird of Paradise	10,000	175.00

	Edition Limit	Issue Price (US)
1982 Raggis Great Bird of Paradise	10.000	$175.00
Glory of Christmas		
1982 Nativity	25,000	80.00
1983 Angels	25,000	80.00
Legendary Animals (Set of four)		
1982 Unicorn		
1982 Griffin		
1982 Dragon		
1982 Pegasus	12,500	175.00
Songbirds of North America		
1982 Eastern Bluebird	12,500	60.00
1982 Mockingbird	12,500	60.00
1982 American Goldfinch	12,500	60.00
1982 Rosebreasted Grosbeak	12,500	60.00
Early Memories		
1983 Do They Bite?	7,500	72.50
Water Babies		
1983 Tom and Dragon-Fly	15 Days	45.00
1983 Fairies Take Care of Tom	15 Days	45.00
1983 Tom and Mrs. Do-As-You-Would	15 Days	45.00
1983 Tom and Mrs. Be-Done-By	15 Days	45.00
1984 Tom and Sweet Chest	15 Days	45.00
1984 Ellie Teaches Tom	15 Days	45.00
1984 Tom Takes Care of Baby	15 Days	45.00
1984 Tom and Ellie	15 Days	45.00
Unicorns in Dreamer's Garden (Set of five)		
1984 Sound of Melodies		
1984 Sight of Wonders		
1984 Smell of Roses		
1984 Taste of Sweetness		
1984 Touch of a Dream	12,500	197.50

See also:
Hamilton Collection (U.S.A.)

Kaiser

	Edition Limit	Issue Price (US)
(Single issue)		
1970 Oberammergau Passion Play	Year	18.00
(Single issue)		
1970 Royal Horse Show—Toronto	1,000	29.00
Great Yachts		
1971 Cetonia	1,000	50.00
1971 Westward	1,000	50.00
Anniversary		
1972 Love Birds	Year	16.50
1973 In Park	Year	18.00
1974 Canoeing Down River	7,000	22.00
1975 Tender Moment	7,000	25.00
1976 Serenade for Lovers	Year	25.00
1977 A Simple Gift	Year	25.00
1978 Viking Toast	Year	30.00
1979 Romantic Interlude	Year	32.00
1980 Love at Play	Year	40.00
1981 Rendezvous	Year	40.00
1982 Betrothal	Year	40.00
1983 Sunday Afternoon	Year	40.00
Feathered Friends		
1978 Blue Jays	10,000	70.00
1979 Cardinals	10,000	80.00
1980 Cedar Waxwings	10,000	80.00
King Tut		
1978 Golden Mask	15,000	65.00
Little Men		
1978 Magical Moment	9,500	60.00
People of the Midnight Sun		
1978 Northern Lullaby	15,000	65.00
1979 Ilaga, My Friend	15,000	75.00
1980 Motherhood	15,000	85.00
1981 Odark and Son Samik	15,000	90.00
1982 Anana with Little Nutak	15,000	90.00
1983 Hunter's Reward	15,000	90.00
Yesterday's World		
1978 Time for Dreaming	5,000	70.00
1979 Summer is Forever	5,000	75.00
1980 Sunday Afternoon	5,000	80.00
Four Seasons (Set of four)		
1981 Spring		
1981 Summer	1981 Fall	
1981 Winter	NA	200.00
Happy Days		
1981 Aeroplane	5,000	75.00
Little Clowns		
1981 Red Mask	9,500	35.00
1982 Pigtails and Puppies	9,500	35.00
Nativity		
1981 Old Country Christmas	Year	20.00
Romantic Portraits		
1981 Lilie	5,000	175.00
1982 Camelia	5,000	175.00
1983 Rose	5,000	$175.00
1984 Daisy	5,000	175.00
Children's Prayers		
1982 Now I Lay Me Down to Sleep	5,000	29.50
Christmas		
1983 Wonder of Christmas	Year	42.50
Famous Horses		
1983 Snow Knight	3,000	95.00
Traditional Fairy Tales		
1983 Cinderella	NA	39.50
1983 Jack and Beanstalk	NA	39.50
Woodland Creatures		
1984 Springtime Frolic	10 Days	34.95
1984 Fishing Trip	10 Days	34.95

See also:
Ghent Collection (U.S.A.)
Hibel Studio (Ger.)

KPM—Royal Berlin

	Edition Limit	Issue Price (US)
Christmas		
1969 Christmas Star	5,000	28.00
1970 Three Kings	5,000	28.00
1971 Christmas Tree	5,000	28.00
1972 Christmas Angel	5,000	31.00
1973 Christchild on Sled	5,000	33.00
1974 Angel & Horn	5,000	35.00
1975 Shepherds	5,000	40.00
1976 Star of Bethlehem	5,000	43.00
1977 Mary at Crib	5,000	46.00
1978 Three Wise Men	5,000	49.00
1979 At Manger	5,000	55.00
1980 Shepherd	5,000	59.00

Lihs-Lindner

	Edition Limit	Issue Price (US)
Christmas		
1972 Little Drummer Boy	6,000	25.00
1973 Little Carolers	6,000	25.00
1974 Peace on Earth	6,000	25.00
1975 Christmas Cheer	6,000	30.00
1976 Joy of Christmas	6,000	30.00
1977 Holly-Jolly Christmas	6,000	30.00
Mother's Day		
1972 Mother and Child	1,000	25.00
1973 Mother and Child	2,000	25.00
1974 Bouquet for Mother	2,000	25.00
1975 We Wish You Happiness	2,000	28.00
Union Pacific Railroad		
1972 Union Pacific	1,500	22.00
1973 Union Pacific Big Boy	1,500	25.00
History		
1973 Tribute to Flag	3,000	60.00
1974 Golden Spike Centennial	1,500	40.00
Easter		
1973 Happy Easter	1,500	25.00
1974 Springtime	1,500	25.00
1975 With Love to You at Easter	1,500	28.00
America Beautiful		
1975 Independence Hall	1,500	42.00
1975 Statue of Liberty	1,500	42.00
1975 Niagara Falls	1,500	42.00
1975 Grand Canyon	1,500	42.00
1975 Golden State	1,500	42.00
1975 Capitol	1,500	42.00
Bicentennial		
1976 Freedom Train	1,500	45.00
1976 Spirit of America	3,500	45.00
Playmates		
1976 Timmy and His Pal	5,000	45.00
1977 Heidi and Playmate	5,000	45.00
Golden Spike Centennial		
1977 Central Pacific Jupiter	1,500	25.00
1977 Union Pacific 119	1,500	25.00
A Child's Christmas		
1978 Holy Night	5,000	40.00

Marmot

	Edition Limit	Issue Price (US)
Father's Day		
1970 Stag	3,500	12.00
1971 Horse	3,500	12.50
Christmas		
1970 Polar Bear	5,000	13.00
1971 Buffalo	5,000	14.00
1972 Boy & Grandfather	5,000	20.00
1973 Snowman	3,000	20.00
1974 Dancing Children	2,000	24.00
1975 Covey of Quail	2,000	30.00
1976 Windmill	2,000	30.00
Presidents		
1971 Washington	1,500	25.00
1972 Jefferson	1,500	25.00
1973 John Adams	1,500	25.00
Mother's Day		
1972 Seal	6,000	$ 16.00
1973 Polar Bear	2,000	20.00
1974 Penguins	2,000	24.00
1975 Raccoons	2,000	30.00
1976 Ducks	2,000	40.00

Meissen

	Edition Limit	Issue Price (US)
Annual		
1973 Winter Countryside by Sleigh	5,000	71.00
1974 Sleeping Beauty	5,000	75.00
1975 Archway to Albrecht's Castle	5,500	92.00
1976 Doge's Palace in Venice	5,000	92.00
1977 Fra Holle	5,000	114.00
1978 Ice Crystal with Children	7,000	123.00
1979 Winter Fairy Tale	7,000	151.00
1980 Booted Cat	NA	155.00

Mueller

	Edition Limit	Issue Price (US)
Christmas		
1971 Christmas in Tyrol	Year	20.00
1972 Christmas Messenger	Year	15.00
1973 Bringing Home Tree	Year	20.00
1974 Trimming Tree	Year	25.00
1975 Family on Christmas Morning	Year	27.50
1976 Christmas Fire	Year	28.50
1977 Ice Skating	Year	28.50
Father's Day		
1973 Three Generations	NA	17.50
1974 Fishing	NA	20.00
1975 Hiking	NA	27.50

Porcelaine Ariel

See: Hamilton Collection (U.S.A.)

Rosenthal

	Edition Limit	Issue Price (US)
Annual (Porcelain)		
1971 Tapio Wirkkala	3,000	NA
1972 Natale Sapone	3,000	NA
1973 Otto Piene	3,000	NA
1974 Gunther Fruhtrunk	3,000	NA
1975 Srivastava Narendra	3,000	NA
1976 Salvador Dali	3,000	NA
1977 Victor Vasarely	3,000	NA
1978 E. Paolozzi	3,000	NA
1979 Arnold Leissler	3,000	NA
1980 O.H. Hajek	3,000	NA
*Artist Plates**		
1973 NR 1 Gunter Grass	5,000	NA
1974 NR 2 Jean Cocteau	5,000	NA
1974 NR 3 Eugen Gomringer	5,000	NA
1974 NR 4 Otto Piene	5,000	NA
1975 NR 5 Max Bill	5,000	NA
1975 NR 6 Hans-Werner Henze	5,000	NA
1975 NR 7 Bjørn Wiinblad	5,000	NA
1975 NR 8 Kriwet	5,000	NA
1976 NR 9 Hildegard Knef	5,000	NA
1977 NR10 Yehudi Menuhin	5,000	NA
1977 NR11 Emilio Pucci	5,000	NA
1978 NR12 Salvador Dali	5,000	NA
1978 NR13 Victor Vasarely	5,000	NA
1978 NR14 Almir Mazignier	5,000	NA
1979 NR15 Ivan Rapuzin	5,000	NA
1979 NR16 Ottmar Alt	5,000	NA
*Series not available in U.S.		
*Satire Plates**		
NR1 Konrad Adenauer	5,000	NA
NR2 Willy Brandt	5,000	NA
NR3 Theodor Heuss	5,000	NA
NR4 Walter Scheel	5,000	NA
NR5 Helmut Schmidt	5,000	NA
NR6 Franz-Josef Strauss	5,000	NA
NR7 Helmut Kohl	5,000	NA
NR8 Heinz Ruhmann	5,000	NA
NR9 Herbert Von Karajan	5,000	NA
NR10 Marlene Dietrich	5,000	NA
NR11 Mao-Tse-Tung	5,000	NA
NR12 Bruno Kreisky	5,000	NA
*Series not available in U.S.		
Annual (Crystal)		
1974 Otto Piene (Clear)	3,000	200.00
1974 Otto Piene (Gold Inlaid)	3,000	250.00
1974 Otto Piene (Platinum Inlaid)	3,000	250.00
1975 G. Uecker	3,000	200.00
1976 Bjørn Wiinblad	3,000	NA
1977 Gunter F. Ris	3,000	NA
1978 Ivan Rapuzin	3,000	600.00
1979 Salvador Dali	3,000	NA
1980 Ernst Fuchs	3,000	NA
Lorraine Trester		
1975 Once Upon a Summertime	5,000	$ 60.00
1976 One Lovely Yesterday	5,000	70.00
Fantasies and Fables		
1976 Oriental Night Music	NA	50.00
1977 Mandolin Players	NA	55.00
Wiinblad Studio-Linie		
1976 Madonna	2,000	150.00
1977 Annunciation	2,000	195.00
1978 Three Kings	2,000	225.00
1979 Holy Family	2,000	230.00
1980 Appearance of Angels	2,000	240.00
1981 Adoration of Shepherds	2,000	295.00
Aladdin		
1979 Aladdin and Lamp	NA	65.00
1979 Aladdin and Street Urchins	NA	65.00
1980 Aladdin and Magician	NA	65.00
1980 Aladdin in Garden	NA	65.00
1981 Aladdin and Spirit	NA	85.00
1981 Aladdin and Princess	NA	85.00
1982 Aladdin's Mother and Genie	NA	85.00
1982 Aladdin's Mother and Sultan	NA	85.00
1983 Aladdin Rides to Palace	NA	85.00
1983 Genie Builds Palace	NA	85.00
Christmas Carols		
1983 Silent Night	NA	195.00

See also:
Hibel Studio (Ger.)
Kern Collectibles (U.S.A.)

Royal Bayreuth

See: Kern Collectibles (U.S.A.)

Royal Tettau

	Edition Limit	Issue Price (US)
Papal Plates		
1971 Pope Paul VI	5,000	100.00
1972 Pope John XXIII	5,000	100.00
1973 Pope Pius XII	5,000	100.00
Christmas (Single issue)		
1972 Carriage in Village	NA	12.50

Royale

	Edition Limit	Issue Price (US)
Christmas		
1969 Christmas Fair in Ebeltoft	6,000	12.00
1970 Kalundborg Church	10,000	13.00
1971 Christmas Night	8,000	16.00
1972 Elks	8,000	16.00
1973 Christmas	6,000	20.00
1974 Village at Christmas	5,000	22.00
1975 Feeding Time	5,000	26.00
1976 Christmas at Seaport	5,000	27.50
1977 Sledding	5,000	30.00
Mother's Day		
1970 Swan and Brood	6,000	12.00
1971 Doe and Fawn	9,000	13.00
1972 Rabbit Family	9,000	16.00
1973 Owl Family	6,000	18.00
1974 Duck Family	5,000	22.00
1975 Lynx Family	5,000	26.00
1976 Woodcock and Young	5,000	27.50
1977 Koala Bear	5,000	30.00
Father's Day		
1970 U.S. Frigate Constitution	5,000	13.00
1971 Man Fishing	5,000	13.00
1972 Mountain Climber	6,000	16.00
1973 Camping	4,000	18.00
1974 Eagle	2,500	22.00
1975 Regatta	2,500	26.00
1976 Hunting Scene	2,500	27.50
1977 Fishing	5,000	30.00
Game		
1972 Setters Pointing Quail	500	180.00
1973 Fox	500	200.00
1974 Osprey	250	250.00
1975 California Quail	250	265.00

Royale Germania

	Edition Limit	Issue Price (US)
Annual		
1970 Orchid (Blue)	600	200.00
1971 Cyclamen (Red)	1,000	200.00
1972 Silver Thistle (Green)	1,000	250.00
1973 Tulips (Lilac)	600	275.00
1974 Sunflowers (Topaz)	500	300.00
1975 Snowdrops (Amber)	350	450.00
1976 Flaming Heart (Red)	350	450.00
Mother's Day		
1971 Roses (Red)	250	135.00
1972 Elephant (Green)	750	180.00
1973 Koala Bear (Lilac)	600	200.00

	Edition Limit	Issue Price (US)
1974 Squirrels (Topaz)	500	$240.00
1975 Swan Family (Amber)	350	250.00
Schmid		
Bavarian Christmas		
1971 Family Portrait	5,000	25.50
1972 On Horseback	5,000	26.50
1973 Bringing Home Tree	5,000	26.50
1974 Decorating Tree	5,000	26.50
1975 Opening Presents	5,000	26.50
1976 By Fireside	5,000	26.50
1977 Skating	5,000	28.50
1978 Family Picking Tree	5,000	36.00
1979 Breakfast by Tree	5,000	45.00
1980 Feeding Animals	5,000	55.00
Ferrandiz Christmas		
1972 Christ in Manger	Year	30.00
1973 Christmas	Year	30.00
Golden Moments		
1978 Tranquility	15,000	250.00
Christmas (Pewter)		
1977 Santa	5,000	30.00
1978 Beautiful Snow	5,000	45.00
1979 I Hear America Singing	6,000	50.00
Ferrandiz Mother and Child		
1977 Orchard Mother	10,000	65.00
1978 Pastoral Mother	10,000	75.00
1979 Floral Mother	10,000	95.00
1980 Avian Mother	10,000	100.00
Beatrix Potter (Pewter)		
1978 Peter Rabbit	5,000	50.00
1979 Jemima-Puddle Duck	5,000	50.00
Reflections of Life		
1980 Quiet Reflections	10,000	85.00
1981 Tree of Life	10,000	85.00
Country Pride		
1981 Surprise in Cellar	7,500	35.00
1981 Plum Tuckered Out	7,500	35.00
1981 Duke's Mixture	7,500	35.00
1982 Bustin with Pride	7,500	35.00
Music Makers		
1981 Flutist	10,000	25.00
1982 Entertainer	10,000	25.00
1982 Magical Medley	10,000	25.00
1982 Sweet Serenade	10,000	25.00
My Name Is Star		
1981 Star's Spring	10,000	30.00
1981 Star's Summer	10,000	30.00
1982 Star's Autumn	10,000	30.00
1982 Star's Winter	10,000	30.00
Beautiful Bounty		
1982 Summer's Golden Harvest	10,000	40.00
1982 Autumn's Blessing	10,000	40.00
1983 A Mid-Winter's Dream	10,000	40.00
1983 Spring Blossoms	10,000	40.00
Cat Tales		
1982 Right Church, Wrong Pew	12,500	37.50
1982 Company's Coming	12,500	37.50
1983 Flew Coop	12,500	37.50
1983 On Move	12,500	37.50
Prairie Women		
1982 Maiden	12,500	35.00
1982 Courtship Blanket	12,500	35.00
1983 Mother Now	12,500	35.00
1983 Passing of Moons	12,500	35.00
Carousel Fantasies		
1983 A Fairy Tale Princess	7,500	50.00
Lowell Davis Christmas		
1983 Country Christmas	7,500	45.00
(Single issue)		
1983 Critics	12,500	45.00
Nature's Treasures		
1984 Rose Haven/Sparrow	5,000	45.00
1984 Tulip Nest/Robin	5,000	45.00
1984 Leafy Bower/Oriole	5,000	45.00
1984 Nesting/Mockingbird	5,000	45.00
Prime Time		
1984 Love Boat	NA	30.00
1984 Dynasty	NA	30.00
1984 Dallas	NA	30.00
Statuette		
1984 Hark Herald	Year	40.00
See also: Addams Family (U.S.A.)		
Schumann		
Composers		
1970 Beethoven	NA	8.00
1972 Mozart	NA	13.00
Christmas		
1971 Snow Scene	10,000	12.00
1972 Deer in Snow	15,000	12.00
1973 Weihnachten	5,000	12.00

	Edition Limit	Issue Price (US)
1974 Church in Snow	5,000	$ 12.00
1975 Fountain	5,000	12.00
See also:		
Christian Bell (Can.)		
Calhoun's Collector's Society (U.S.A.)		
Stumar		
Christmas		
1970 Angel	10,000	8.00
1971 Old Canal	10,000	8.00
1972 Countryside	10,000	8.00
1973 Friendship	10,000	10.00
1974 Making Fancy	10,000	10.00
1975 Preparation	10,000	10.00
1976 Drummer Boy	10,000	10.00
1977 Joyful Expectations	10,000	15.00
1978 Christmas	10,000	19.50
Mother's Day		
1971 Amish Mother & Daughter	10,000	8.00
1972 Children	10,000	8.00
1973 Mother Sewing	10,000	10.00
1974 Mother Cradle	10,000	10.00
1975 Baking	10,000	10.00
1976 Reading to Children	10,000	15.00
1977 Comforting Child	10,000	15.00
1978 Tranquility	10,000	19.50
Egyptian		
1977 Ancient Egyptian Trilogy	5,000	45.00
1978 Charioteer	5,000	54.00
Tirschenreuth		
Christmas		
1969 Homestead	3,500	12.00
1970 Church	3,500	12.00
1971 Star of Bethlehem	3,500	12.00
1972 Elk Silhouette	2,000	13.00
1973 Christmas	Year	14.00
Villeroy & Boch		
Christmas		
1977 Holy Family	10,000	175.00
1978 Three Holy Kings	20,000	175.00
1979 Mary with Child	10,000	198.00
1980 Madonna in Glory	10,000	200.00
1981 Mary Glorious	10,000	210.00
World Wildlife		
1982 Panda Bear	Year	38.00
1983 Tiger	Year	38.00
1984 Otter	Year	38.00
Fairyland Lovers		
1982 Prince	NA	39.00
1982 Ivan and Chestnut Horse	NA	39.00
1983 Princess and Enchanted Stag	NA	39.00
1983 Goose Girl	NA	39.00
Flower Fairy		
1983 Columbine	NA	39.00
French Fairy Tales		
1983 Fortunata and Hen	19,750	70.00
1983 King of Peacocks	19,750	70.00
1983 King and Puss in Boots	19,750	70.00
WMF Geislingen		
Annual		
1978 Rose-Motif I	2,500	117.50
1979 Rose-Motif-II	2,500	120.00
1980 Rose-Motif III	2,500	120.00
Christmas		
1978 Birth of Christ	2,500	117.50
1979 Praising King	2,500	120.00
1980 Praising Shepherd	2,500	120.00

GREAT BRITAIN

	Edition Limit	Issue Price (US)
Aynsley		
A Christmas Carol		
1979 Mr. Fezziwig's Ball	Year	30.00
1980 Marley's Ghost	Year	36.00
1981 Cratchit Family	Year	41.00
1982 Christmas Day	Year	41.00
Boehm Studios		
European Bird Plates		
1973 Swallow	5,000	48.75
1973 Chaffinch	5,000	48.75
1973 Coal Tit	5,000	48.75
1973 Tree Sparrow	5,000	48.75
1973 King Fisher	5,000	48.75
1973 Gold Crest	5,000	48.75
1973 Blue Tit	5,000	48.75
1973 Linnet	5,000	48.75
Honor America		
1974 American Bald Eagle	12,000	85.00

	Edition Limit	Issue Price (US)
Butterfly		
1975 Blue Mountain Swallowtails	100	$450.00
1975 Jezabels	100	450.00
1976 Comma with Loops	100	450.00
1976 African Butterflies	100	450.00
1976 Solandras Maxima	100	450.00
Hard Fruit		
1975 Plums	100	450.00
1975 Pears	100	450.00
1976 Peaches	100	450.00
1976 Apples	100	450.00
Oriental Birds		
1975 Bluebacked Fairy Bluebirds	100	400.00
1975 Azure-Winged Magpies	100	400.00
1976 Golden-Fronted Leafbird	100	400.00
1976 Golden-Throated Barbet	100	400.00
Seashell		
1975 Violet Spider Conch	100	450.00
1975 Rooster Tail Conch	100	450.00
1976 Orange Spider Conch	100	450.00
1976 Chiragra Spider Conch	100	450.00
Soft Fruit		
1975 Loganberries	100	450.00
1975 Cherries	100	450.00
1976 Strawberries	100	450.00
1976 Grapes	100	450.00
Butterflies of World		
1978 Monarch and Daisy	5,000	62.00
1978 Red Admiral and Thistle	5,000	62.00
Flower		
1975 Lilies	100	450.00
1975 Passion Flowers	100	450.00
1976 Double Clematis	100	450.00
Favorite Floral		
1978 Clematis	2,500	58.00
1978 Rhododendron	2,500	58.00
1979 Boehm Orchid	2,500	58.00
1979 Yellow Rose	2,500	58.00
1980 Spider Orchid	2,500	58.00
1980 Dahlia	2,500	58.00
See also: Hamilton Collection (U.S.A.)		
Caithness Glass		
America's Favorite Birds		
1979 Crystal Wren	5,000	79.50
Coalport		
Christmas		
1976 Christmas Eve	Year	12.00
1977 Dangerous Skating	Year	16.00
1978 Alas! Poor Bruin	Year	18.00
1979 Christmas Morning	Year	22.00
1980 Blind Man's Bluff	Year	27.00
1981 Skating	Year	32.50
1982 Snapdragon	Year	35.00
1983 Trafalgar Square	Year	35.00
Mother's Day		
1978 Clematis	Year	16.00
1979 Orchid	Year	21.00
1980 Peony	Year	27.00
1981 Rose	Year	30.00
(Single issue)		
1972 Indy 500	2,000	49.95
Crown Staffordshire		
Wildlife in Winter		
1982 Tranquility	10,000	55.00
1983 Winter's Orphan	10,000	55.00
1983 Early Awakening	10,000	55.00
Hornsea		
Christmas		
1979 "C"—Nativity	10,000	21.00
1980 "H"—Mary and Child	10,000	25.00
1981 "R"—Three Wise Men	10,000	30.00
1982 "I"—At Inn	10,000	32.50
1983 "S"—Shepherds	10,000	35.00
Mason		
Christmas		
1975 Windsor Castle	Year	75.00
1976 Holyrood House	Year	75.00
1977 Buckingham Palace	Year	75.00
1978 Balmoral Castle	Year	75.00
1979 Hampton Court	Year	75.00
1980 Sandringham House	Year	75.00
Poole Pottery		
Medieval Calendar		
1972 Drinking Wine by Fire (January)	1,000	100.00

	Edition Limit	Issue Price (US)
1972 Chopping Wood (February)	1,000	$100.00
1973 Digging in Fields and Setting Seeds (March)	1,000	125.00
1973 Carrying Flowering Branch (April)	1,000	125.00
1974 Hawking (May)	1,000	125.00
1974 Mowing Hay (June)	1,000	125.00
1975 Cutting Corn with Sickle (July)	1,000	125.00
1975 Threshing with Flail (August)	1,000	125.00
1976 Picking Grapes (September)	1,000	125.00
1976 Sowing Winter Corn (October)	1,000	125.00
1977 Gathering Acorns to Feed Pigs (November)	1,000	125.00
1977 Pig Killing (December)	1,000	125.00
Cathedral		
1973 Christ on Cross	11,000	125.00
Christmas		
1973 Adoration of Magi	1,000	125.00
1973 Flight into Egypt	1,000	125.00
Home at Christmas		
1978 Santa's Helpers	10,000	37.50
1979 Three Wisemen	10,000	37.50
Birds of North America		
1979 Great Horned Owl	10,000	37.50
Mother's Day		
1979 Tenderness	10,000	37.50
Rhea Silva		
Feline Favourites		
1982 Long Haired Ladies	10,000	47.00
1982 Siamese & Apple Blossoms	10,000	47.00
Child's Garden of Verses		
1983 Land of Counterpane	17,500	39.00
Portraits of Countryside		
1983 Autumn Wayside	5,000	79.00
Endangered Birds		
1984 Whooping Crane	5,000	60.00
Royal Doulton		
Flower Garden		
1975 Spring Harmony	15,000	60.00
1976 Dreaming Lotus	15,000	65.00
1977 Poet's Garden	15,000	70.00
1978 Country Bouquet	15,000	70.00
1980 From My Mother's Garden	15,000	85.00
Ports of Call		
1975 San Francisco	15,000	60.00
1976 New Orleans	15,000	65.00
1977 Venice	15,000	70.00
1978 Montmartre	15,000	70.00
Reflections on China		
1976 Garden of Tranquility	15,000	70.00
1977 Imperial Palace	15,000	70.00
1978 Temple of Heaven	15,000	75.00
1980 Lake of Mists	15,000	85.00
I Remember America		
1977 Pennsylvania Pastorale	15,000	70.00
1978 Lovejoy Bridge	15,000	70.00
1979 Four Corners	15,000	75.00
1980 Marshlands	15,000	95.00
Victorian Christmas		
1977 Skater	Year	25.00
1978 Victorian Girl	Year	27.50
1979 Sleigh Ride	Year	29.95
1980 St. Nick's Arrival	Year	32.50
1981 Carolers	Year	37.50
1982 Santa Claus	Year	37.50
1983 Silent Night	Year	37.50
All God's Children		
1978 Brighter Day	10,000	60.00
1979 Village Children	10,000	65.00
1980 Noble Heritage	10,000	85.00
1981 Buddies	10,000	85.00
1982 Little Brother	10,000	95.00
American Tapestries		
1978 Sleigh Bells	10,000	70.00
1979 Pumpkin Patch	10,000	70.00
1980 General Store	10,000	95.00
1981 Fourth of July	10,000	95.00
Jungle Fantasy		
1979 Ark	10,000	75.00
1980 Compassion	10,000	95.00
1981 Patience	10,000	95.00
1982 Refuge	10,000	95.00
Behind Painted Masque		
1982 Painted Feelings	10,000	95.00

	Edition Limit	Issue Price (US)
1982 Pleasing Performance	10,000	$ 95.00
1983 Make Me Laugh	10,000	95.00
1983 Minstrel Serenade	10,000	95.00
Celebration of Faith		
1982 Rosh Hashanah	7,500	250.00
1982 Passover	7,500	250.00
1983 Yom Kippur	7,500	250.00
1983 Chanukah	7,500	250.00
Children of Pueblo		
1983 Apple Flower	10,000	60.00
1983 Morning Star	10,000	60.00
Christmas Carol		
1983 Silent Night	NA	39.95
Festival Children of World		
1983 Mariani (Bali)	15,000	65.00
1983 Michiko (Japan)	15,000	65.00
1984 Magdalena (Mexico)	15,000	65.00
1984 Monika (Poland)	15,000	65.00
Royal Grafton		
Twelve Days of Christmas		
1976 Partridge in Pear Tree	3,000	17.50
1977 Two Turtle Doves	3,000	17.50
1978 Three French Hens	3,000	21.50
1979 Four Colly Birds	3,000	26.50
1980 Five Gold Rings	3,000	35.00
1981 Six Geese A'Laying	3,000	38.50
1982 Seven Swans A'Swimming	3,000	40.00
1983 Eight Maids A'Milking	3,000	41.00
Royal Worcester		
Doughty Bird		
1972 Redstarts and Beech	2,750	125.00
1973 Myrtle Warbler/ Cherry	3,000	175.00
1974 Blue-Grey Gnatcatchers	3,000	195.00
1975 Blackburnian Warbler	3,000	195.00
1976 Blue-Winged Sivas	3,000	195.00
1977 Paradise Wydah	3,000	195.00
1978 Bluetits/Witch Hazel	3,000	195.00
1979 Mountain Bluebird	3,000	195.00
1980 Cerulean Warblers	3,000	315.00
1981 Willow Warbler	3,000	330.00
1982 Ruby-Crowned Kinglets	3,000	330.00
1983 Bewick's Wren	3,000	330.00
Bicentennial		
1976 Independence	10,000	150.00
Fabulous Birds		
1976 Peacocks I	10,000	65.00
1977 Peacocks II	10,000	65.00
Audubon Birds		
1977 Warbler & Jay	5,000	150.00
1978 Kingbird & Sparrow	10,000	150.00
Chinoiserie		
1977 Bishop Summer	Year	65.00
English Christmas		
1979 Christmas Eve	Year	60.00
1980 Christmas Morning	Year	65.00
1981 Christmas Day	Year	70.00
1982 Christmas Evening	Year	70.00
Spode		
Ray Harm Birds (Set of 12)		
1970 Rufus-Sided Towhee		
1970 Winter Wren		
1971 Eastern Bluebird		
1971 Stellar's Jay		
1971 Eastern Mockingbird		
1971 Barn Swallow		
1971 Rose-Breasted Grosbeak		
1971 Cardinal		
1972 Western Tanager		
1972 Woodpecker		
1972 Chickadee		
1972 American Goldfinch	5,000	300.00
Maritime Plates (Set of six)		
1980 USS United States and HMS Macedonian		
1980 USS President and HMS Little Belt		
1980 HMS Shannon and USS Chesapeake		
1980 USS Constitution and HMS Guerriere		
1980 USS Constitution and HMN Java		
1980 HMS Pelican and USS Argus	2,000	300.00
Christmas Pastimes		
1982 Sleigh Ride	Year	75.00

	Edition Limit	Issue Price (US)
Wedgwood		
Calendar		
1971 Zodiac Sign	Year	$ 12.00
1972 Carousel	Year	12.95
1973 Bountiful Butterfly	Year	12.95
1974 Knights of Camelot	Year	14.00
1975 Children's Game	Year	15.00
1976 Robin	Year	25.00
1977 Tonateuk—Aztec Sun	Year	30.00
1978 Samurai	Year	30.00
1979 Sacred Scarab	Year	35.00
1980 Safari	Year	35.00
1981 Horses	Year	37.50
1982 Wild West	Year	40.00
1983 Age of Reptiles	Year	45.00
1984 Dogs	Year	54.00
Children's Story		
1971 Sandman	Year	30.00
1972 Tinder Box	Year	30.00
1973 Emperor's New Clothes	Year	30.00
1974 Ugly Duckling	Year	10.00
1975 Little Mermaid	Year	14.00
1976 Hansel & Gretel	Year	17.00
1977 Rumpelstiltskin	Year	17.00
1978 Frog Prince	Year	15.00
1979 Golden Goose	Year	15.00
1980 Rapunzel	Year	16.00
1981 Tom Thumb	Year	18.00
1982 Lady and Lion	Year	20.00
1983 Elves and Shoemaker	Year	20.00
1984 King Roughbeard	Year	20.00
(Single issue)		
1978 Tri-Color Decade Christmas	10,000	325.00
(Single issue)		
1978 Anniversary Christmas	Year	130.00
Trophy		
1978 Tutankhamun	500	1000.00
1978 Ankhesenamum	500	1000.00
Child's Christmas		
1979 Snowman	Year	35.00
1980 Bringing Home Tree	Year	37.50
1981 Tobogganing	Year	37.50
1982 Skaters	Year	37.50
1983 Carolers	Year	40.00
Queen's Ware Christmas		
1980 Windsor Castle	Year	24.95
1981 Trafalgar Square	Year	27.00
1982 Piccadilly Circus	Year	32.50
1983 St. Paul's Cathedral	Year	32.50
Remarkable World of Charles Dickens		
1980 Oliver Twist and Fagin	19,500	60.00
1980 Scrooge and Marley's Ghost	19,500	60.00
1980 Bob Cratchit	19,500	60.00
1980 David Copperfield	19,500	60.00
1981 Micawber/Uriah Heep	19,500	60.00
1981 Little Nell	19,500	60.00
1981 Madame Defarge	19,500	60.00
1981 Mr. Pickwick	19,500	60.00
Eyes of a Child		
1983 Little Lady Love	15,000	65.00
(Single issue)		
1983 200 Years of Ballooning	Year	35.00
INDIA		
Sarna		
Christmas		
1975 Holy Family	4,000	17.50
ITALY		
Anri		
Mother's Day		
1972 Alpine Mother & Children	5,000	35.00
1973 Alpine Mother & Children	5,000	40.00
1974 Alpine Mother & Children	5,000	50.00
1975 Alpine Stroll	5,000	60.00
1976 Knitting	5,000	60.00
Father's Day		
1972 Alpine Father & Children	5,000	35.00
1973 Alpine Father & Children	5,000	40.00
1974 Cliff Gazing	5,000	50.00
1975 Sailing	5,000	60.00
Ferrandiz Birthday		
1972 Birthday Girl	Year	15.00
1972 Birthday Boy	Year	15.00
1973 Birthday	Year	20.00
1974 Birthday Girl	Year	22.00

	Edition Limit	Issue Price (US)
1974 Birthday Boy	Year	$ 22.00
1975 Birthday Girl	Year	35.00
Ferrandiz Mother's Day		
1972 Mother Sewing	2,500	35.00
1973 Mother & Child	1,500	40.00
1974 Mother & Child	1,500	50.00
1975 Mother Holding Dove	1,500	60.00
1976 Mother & Child	1,500	60.00
1977 Girl with Flowers	1,500	65.00
1978 Beginning	3,000	77.50
1979 All Hearts	3,000	120.00
1980 Spring Arrivals	3,000	150.00
1981 Harmony	3,000	150.00
1982 With Love	3,000	150.00
Ferrandiz Christmas		
1972 Finishing Cradle	2,500	35.00
1973 Boy with Lamb	Year	40.00
1974 Nativity	Year	40.00
1975 Flight into Egypt	Year	40.00
1976 Mary & Joseph Pray	Year	40.00
1977 Girl with Tree	4,000	65.00
1978 Leading Way	4,000	77.50
1979 Drummer Boy	4,000	120.00
1980 Rejoice	4,000	150.00
1981 Spreading Word	4,000	150.00
1982 Shepherd Family	4,000	150.00
1983 Peace Attend Thee	4,000	150.00
Ferrandiz Wedding Day		
1972 Wedding	Year	40.00
1973 Wedding	Year	40.00
1974 Wedding	Year	48.00
1975 Wedding	Year	60.00
1976 Wedding	Year	60.00
(Single issue)		
1982 Riding Thru Rain	2,500	550.00
Ferrandiz Annual		
1984 Pastoral Journey	2,000	180.00
Sarah Kay Annual		
1984 A Time for Secrets	2,500	120.00
Capo Di Monte		
Christmas		
1972 Cherubs	500	55.00
1973 Bells & Holly	500	55.00
1974 Christmas	1,000	60.00
1975 Christmas	1,000	60.00
1976 Christmas	250	65.00
Mother's Day		
1973 Mother's Day	500	55.00
1974 Mother's Day	500	60.00
1975 Mother's Day	500	60.00
1976 Mother's Day	500	65.00
Carlo Monti		
Mother's Day		
1973 Madonna & Child	2,000	35.00
Count Agazzi		
Famous Personalities		
1968 Famous Personalities	600	8.00
1970 Famous Personalities	1,000	12.50
1973 Famous Personalities	600	15.00
(Single issue)		
1969 Apollo II	1,000	17.00
Children's Hour		
1970 Owl	2,000	12.50
1971 Cat	2,000	12.50
1972 Pony	2,000	12.50
1973 Panda	2,000	12.50
Easter		
1971 Playing Violin	600	12.50
1972 At Prayer	600	12.50
1973 Winged Cherub	600	12.50
Mother's Day		
1972 Mother's Day	144	35.00
1973 Mother's Day	720	19.50
Father's Day		
1972 Father's Day	144	35.00
1973 Father's Day	288	19.50
Christmas		
1973 Christmas	1,000	19.50
(Single issue)		
1973 Peace	720	12.50
Kings		
Mother's Day		
1973 Dancing Girl	1,500	100.00
1974 Dancing Boy	1,500	115.00
1975 Motherly Love	1,500	140.00
1976 Maiden	1,500	180.00
Christmas		
1973 Adoration	1,500	150.00
1974 Madonna	1,500	150.00
1975 Heavenly Choir	1,500	160.00
1976 Girl and Brother	1,500	200.00

	Edition Limit	Issue Price (US)
Veneto Flair		
Christmas		
1971 Three Kings	1,500	$ 45.00
1972 Shepherds	2,000	45.00
1973 Christ Child	2,000	55.00
1974 Angel	2,000	55.00
Wildlife		
1971 Deer	500	37.50
1972 Elephant	1,000	37.50
1973 Puma	2,000	37.50
1974 Tiger	2,000	40.00
Birds		
1972 Owl	2,000	37.50
1973 Falcon	2,000	37.50
1974 Mallard Duck	2,000	45.00
Dogs		
1972 German Shepherd	2,000	37.50
1973 Poodle	2,000	37.50
1974 Doberman	2,000	37.50
1975 Collie	2,000	40.00
1976 Dachshund	2,000	45.00
Mother's Day		
1972 Madonna and Child	2,000	55.00
1973 Madonna and Child	2,000	55.00
1974 Mother and Son	2,000	55.00
1975 Daughter and Doll	2,000	45.00
1976 Son and Daughter	2,000	55.00
1977 Mother and Child	2,000	50.00
Easter		
1973 Rabbits	2,000	50.00
1974 Chicks	2,000	50.00
1975 Lamb	2,000	50.00
1976 Composite	2,000	55.00
Goddess		
1973 Pomona	1,500	75.00
1974 Diana	1,500	75.00
Mosaic		
1973 Justinian	500	50.00
1974 Pelican	1,000	50.00
1977 Theodora	500	50.00
Cats		
1974 Persian	2,000	40.00
1975 Siamese	2,000	45.00
1976 Tabby	2,000	45.00
Christmas Card		
1975 Christmas Eve	5,000	45.00
1976 Old North Church	5,000	50.00
1977 Log Cabin Christmas	5,000	50.00
1978 Dutch Christmas	5,000	50.00
Valentine's Day		
1977 Valentine Boy	3,000	45.00
1978 Valentine Girl	3,000	45.00
Flower Children		
1978 Rose	3,000	45.00
1979 Orchid	3,000	60.00
1980 Camillia	3,000	65.00
La Belle Femme		
1978 Lily	9,500	70.00
1978 Gigi	9,500	76.50
1980 Dominique	9,500	76.50
1980 Gabrielle	9,500	76.50
American Landscape		
1979 Hudson Valley	7,500	75.00
1980 Northwest Cascade	7,500	75.00
Children's Christmas		
1979 Carolers	7,500	60.00
1980 Heading Home	7,500	70.00
1981 Night Before	7,500	95.00
1982 A Visit to Santa	7,500	80.00
Mother and Child		
1981 Buffalos	5,000	95.00
1981 Elephants	5,000	95.00
1981 Koalas	5,000	95.00
1981 Lions	5,000	95.00
1981 Loons	5,000	95.00
1981 Polar Bears	5,000	95.00
Young Love		
1981 Young Love	5,000	95.00
JAPAN		
Manjundo		
Chinese Lunar Calendar		
1972 Year of Rat	5,000	15.00
1973 Year of Ox	5,000	15.00
Noritake		
Christmas		
1975 Madonna with Child	3,000	42.00
1976 Gratia Hoso Kawa	3,000	54.00
1977 Julia Otaa	3,000	83.00
1978 Amakusa Shiro	3,000	109.00
1979 Munzio Ito	3,000	124.00
1980 Furst Takayama	3,000	125.00

	Edition Limit	Issue Price (US)
Annual		
1977 Paradise Birds	3,000	$380.00
1978 Chrysanthemums	3,000	494.00
1979 Cranes	3,000	556.00
1980 Water Lilies and Butterflies	3,000	575.00
Sango		
Christmas		
1976 Undesired Slumber	7,500	25.00
1977 Togetherness	7,500	25.00
Mother's Day		
1976 Spring Delight	7,500	20.00
1977 Broken Wing	5,000	22.50
See also: Kern Collectibles (U.S.A.)		
Schmid		
Raggedy Ann Christmas		
1975 Gifts of Love	Year	12.50
1976 Raggedy Ann Skates	Year	13.00
1977 Decorating Tree	Year	13.00
1978 Checking List	Year	15.00
1979 Little Helper	15,000	17.50
Raggedy Ann Mother's Day		
1976 Motherhood	Year	13.00
1977 Bouquet of Love	Year	13.00
1978 Hello Mom	Year	15.00
1979 High Spirits	10,000	17.50
Raggedy Ann Valentine's Day		
1978 As Time Goes By	Year	13.00
1979 Daisies Do Tell	Year	17.50
Disney Valentine's Day		
1979 Hands and Hearts	Year	17.50
1980 Mickey's I Love You	Year	17.50
1981 Be Mine	Year	17.50
A Year with Paddington Bear		
1979 Pyramid Presents	25,000	12.50
1980 Springtime	25,000	12.50
1981 Sandcastles	25,000	12.50
1981 School Days	25,000	12.50
Peanuts 30th Anniversary (Single issue)		
1980 Happy Anniversary	15,000	27.50
Alice in Wonderland Anniversary (Single issue)		
1981 Alice in Wonderland	7,500	17.50
Disney Anniversary (Single issue)		
1981 Pluto's 50th Birthday	7,500	17.50
Four Seasons of Love		
1982 Tickets on 50 Yard Line	10,000	17.50
1982 Let it Snow	10,000	17.50
1983 Spring Bouquet	10,000	17.50
1983 Shades of Summer	10,000	17.50
A Musician's Dream		
1982 Beat Goes On	10,000	17.50
1982 Knowing Score	10,000	17.50
1983 Perfect Harmony	10,000	17.50
1983 Tickling Ivory	10,000	17.50
World's Greatest Athlete		
1982 Go Deep	10,000	17.50
1982 Puck Stops Here	10,000	17.50
1983 Way You Play Game	10,000	17.50
1983 Crowd Went Wild	10,000	17.50
Disney Annual		
1983 Sneak Preview	20,000	22.50
1984 Command Performance	20,000	22.50
Paddington Bear Annual		
1983 Bear's Noel	10,000	22.50
1984 How Sweet It Is	10,000	22.50
Peanuts Annual		
1983 Peanuts in Concert	20,000	22.50
1984 Snoopy/Beaglescouts	20,000	22.50
See also: Addams Family (U.S.A.)		

MEXICO

	Edition Limit	Issue Price (US)
Bonita Silver		
Mother's Day		
1972 Mother and Baby	4,000	125.00
Roman Ceramica Excelsis		
Masterpiece Collection		
1979 Adoration	5,000	65.00
1980 Madonna with Grapes	5,000	87.50
1981 Holy Family	5,000	95.00
1982 Madonna of Streets	5,000	85.00
Ceramica Excelsis Collection		
1980 Little Children, Come to Me	15,000	45.00

NETHERLANDS

	Edition Limit	Issue Price (US)
Blue Delft (Schoonhaven)		
Christmas		
1970 Drawbridge Near Binnehof	Year	12.00
1971 St. Lauren's Church	Year	12.00
1972 Church at Bierkade	Year	12.00
1973 St. Jan's Church	Year	$ 12.00
1974 Dongeradeel	Year	13.00
1975 Maassluis	Year	15.00
1976 Montelbaanstower	Year	15.00
1977 Harbour Tower of Hoorn	Year	19.50
1978 Binnenpoort Gate	Year	21.00
Mother's Day		
1971 Mother & Daughter of 1600s	Year	12.00
1972 Mother & Daughter of Isle of Urk	Year	12.00
1973 Rembrandt's Mother	Year	12.00
Father's Day		
1971 Francisco Lana's Airship	Year	12.00
1972 Dr. Jonathon's Balloon	Year	12.00
Crown Delft		
Christmas		
1969 Man by Tree	Year	10.00
1970 Two Sleigh Riders	Year	10.00
1971 Christmas Tree on Market Square	Year	10.00
1972 Baking for Christmas	Year	10.00
Mother's Day		
1970 Sheep	Year	10.00
1971 Stork	Year	10.00
1972 Ducks	Year	10.00
1973 Mother's Day	1,000	10.00
Father's Day		
1970 Father's Day	Year	10.00
1971 Father's Day	Year	10.00
1972 Father's Day	1,000	10.00
1973 Father's Day	1,000	10.00
Kurz (Shuler International)		
Christmas		
1972 Christmas	500	60.00
1973 Christmas	500	70.00
1974 Christmas	500	65.00
Mother's Day		
1973 Mother's Day	500	65.00
Metawa		
Christmas		
1972 Skaters	3,000	30.00
1973 One-Horse Sleigh	1,500	30.00
1974 Sailboat	Year	35.00
Royal Delft		
Christmas		
1915 Glory to God, Christmas Bells (10″)	Year	NA
1915 Christmas Star (7″)	Year	NA
1916 Star—Floral Design (10″)	Year	NA
1916 Cradle of Child (10″)	Year	NA
1917 Shepherd with Sheep in Stable (10″)	Year	NA
1917 Christmas Star (10″)	Year	NA
1918 Shepherd with Sheep in Stable (10″)	Year	NA
1918 Christmas Star—Peace on Earth (10″)	Year	NA
1919 Church (10″)	Year	NA
1919 Christmas Star (10″)	Year	NA
1920 Holly Wreath (10″)	Year	NA
1920 Church Tower (10″)	Year	NA
1921 Canal Boatman (10″)	Year	NA
1921 Christmas Star (10″)	Year	NA
1922 Landscape (10″)	Year	NA
1922 Christmas Wreath (10″)	Year	NA
1923 Shepherd (10″)	Year	NA
1923 Christmas Star (10″)	Year	NA
1924 Christmas Star (10″)	Year	NA
1924 Town Gate with Shepherd (10″)	Year	NA
1925 Towngate in Delft (10″)	Year	NA
1925 Christmas Star (10″)	Year	NA
1926 Christmas Star (10″)	Year	NA
1926 Bell Tower (7″)	Year	NA
1926 Windmill Landscape (10″)	Year	NA
1927 Christmas Star (10″)	Year	NA
1927 Sailing Boat (10″)	Year	NA
1927 Church Tower (7″)	Year	NA
1928 Christmas Poinsettia (10″)	Year	NA
1928 Mill Christmas (7″)	Year	NA
1928 Lighthouse Christmas (10″)	Year	NA
1929 Christmas Bell (10″)	Year	NA
1929 Church Spire (7″)	Year	NA
1929 Small Dutch Town (10″)	Year	NA
1930 Church Entrance, Delft (10″)	Year	NA
1930 Christmas Rose (10″)	Year	NA
1930 Sailing Boat (7″)	Year	NA
1931 Christmas Star (10″)	Year	NA
1931 Snow Landscape (10″)	Year	NA
1931 Church Tower (7″)	Year	NA
1932 Bell Tower (7″)	Year	NA
1932 Fireplace (10″)	Year	NA
1932 Christmas Star (10″)	Year	NA
1933 Interior Scene with Exterior View (10″)	Year	NA
1934 Interior Scene (10″)	Year	NA
1934 Snowy Stable (10″)	Year	NA
1935 Interior Scene with Exterior View (10″)	Year	NA
1936 Interior Scene with Exterior View (10″)	Year	NA
1937 Interior Scene with Exterior View (10″)	Year	NA
1938 Interior Scene with Exterior View (10″)	Year	NA
1939 Interior Scene with Well-Staircase (10″)	Year	NA
1940 Interior with Christmas Tree (10″)	Year	NA
1941 Interior Scene Fireplace & Tree (10″)	Year	NA
1955 Christmas Star (9″)	Year	NA
1955 Church Tower (10″)	200	$ 20.00
1956 Two Christmas Bells in Floral (9″)	Year	NA
1956 Landscape (10″)	200	20.00
1956 Flower Design (9″)	Year	NA
1957 Christmas Star (9″)	Year	NA
1957 Landscape (10″)	225	22.00
1958 Christmas Star (9″)	Year	NA
1958 View of Village at Riverside (10″)	225	25.00
1959 View of Village at Riverside (10″)	250	25.00
1959 Landscape with Mill (7″)	400	10.00
1960 Landscape (7″)	400	10.00
1960 Street in Delft (10″)	250	25.00
1961 Snow Landscape (7″)	500	10.00
1961 Village Scene with Church Town (10″)	260	30.00
1962 Town View (7″)	500	10.00
1962 Tower in Leeuwarden (10″)	275	30.00
1963 Mill in Zeddam (7″)	500	15.00
1963 Tower in Enkhuisen (10″)	275	35.00
1964 Tower in Hoorn (10″)	300	35.00
1964 Mill in Poelenburg (7″)	600	15.00
1965 Towngate in Kampen (7″)	600	15.00
1965 Corn-Mill in Rhoon (10″)	300	35.00
1966 Towngate in Medemblik (7″)	600	20.00
1966 Snuff Mill in Rotterdam (10″)	325	40.00
1967 Mill in Hazerswoude (7″)	700	20.00
1967 Tower in Amsterdam (10″)	350	45.00
1968 Mill in Schiedam (7″)	700	25.00
1968 Tower in Amsterdam "Schreierstoren" (10″)	350	60.00
1969 Mill Near Gorkum (7″)	800	35.00
1969 Church in Utrecht (10″)	400	60.00
1970 Mill Near Haarlem (7″)	1,500	25.00
1970 Cathedral in Veere (10″)	500	60.00
1971 Towngate at Zierikzee (7″)	3,500	25.00
1971 "Dom" Tower in Utrecht (10″)	550	60.00
1972 Towngate at Elburg (7″)	3,500	40.00
1972 Church in Edam (10″)	1,500	70.00
1973 Towngate at Amersfoort (7″)	4,500	50.00
1973 DeWaag in Alkmaar (10″)	1,500	75.00
1974 Watergate at Sneek (7″)	4,500	80.00
1974 Kitchen in Hindeloopen (10″)	1,500	160.00
1975 Towngate at Amsterdam (7″)	1,000	140.00
1975 Farmer in Laren (10″)	1,500	250.00
1976 Towngate in Gorinehem (7″)	4,500	$115.00
1976 Farmer's Wife in Staphorst (10″)	1,500	220.00
1977 Dromedaris Tower (7″)	4,500	140.00
1977 Farm Family in Spakenburg (10″)	1,500	277.00
1978 Winter Skating Scene (10″)	1,000	277.00
1978 Christmas Fisherman (7″)	1,500	140.00
1978 Christmas Angels (7″)	1,500	140.00
Mother's Day		
1971 Mother & Daughter (Volendam)	2,500	50.00
1972 Mother & Daughter (Hindeloopen)	2,500	40.00
1973 Mother & Daughter (Marken)	3,000	50.00
1974 Mother & Daughter (Zuid-Beveland)	Year	80.00
1975 Mother & Daughter (Spakenburg)	Year	100.00
1976 Mother & Daughter (Scheveningen)	Year	115.00
Father's Day		
1972 Father & Son (Volendam)	1,500	40.00
1973 Father & Son (Hindeloopen)	2,000	40.00
1974 Father & Son (Marken)	1,000	80.00
1975 Father & Son (Zuid Beveland)	Year	80.00
1976 Father & Son (Spakenburg)	Year	140.00
Easter		
1973 Dutch Easter Palm (7″)	3,500	75.00
1973 Dutch Easter Palm (10″)	3,500	NA
1974 Dutch Easter Palm	1,000	110.00
1975 Dutch Easter Palm	1,000	125.00
1976 Dutch Easter Palm	1,000	175.00
Valentine		
1973 Enduring Beauty	1,500	75.00
1974 Valentine	1,000	125.00
1975 Valentine	1,000	125.00
1976 Valentine	1,000	175.00
Special Bicentenary		
1976 George Washington	2,500	350.00
1976 Eagle Plate	5,000	150.00
Schoonhaven		
See: Blue Delft (Neth.)		
Shuler International		
See: Kurz (Neth.)		
Zenith Delftware		
Hans Brinker		
1972 Skating	500	60.00
1973 Gretel Tending Geese	750	60.00
Anniversary		
1973 Autumn	500	45.00
1973 Spring	500	45.00
1973 Summer	500	45.00
1973 Winter	500	45.00
Birthday Boy		
1973 Monday's Child	3,000	15.00
1973 Tuesday's Child	3,000	15.00
1973 Wednesday's Child	3,000	15.00
1973 Thursday's Child	3,000	15.00
1973 Friday's Child	3,000	15.00
1973 Saturday's Child	3,000	15.00
1973 Sunday's Child	3,000	15.00
Birthday Girl		
1973 Monday's Child	3,000	15.00
1973 Tuesday's Child	3,000	15.00
1973 Wednesday's Child	3,000	15.00
1973 Thursday's Child	3,000	15.00
1973 Friday's Child	3,000	15.00
1973 Saturday's Child	3,000	15.00
1973 Sunday's Child	3,000	15.00

NORWAY

	Edition Limit	Issue Price (US)
Porsgrund		
(Single issue)		
1909 Christmas Flowers	Year	NA
Father's Day		
1971 Fishing	Year	10.00
1972 Cookout	Year	10.00
1973 Sledding	Year	10.00
1974 Father and Son	Year	10.00
1975 Skating	Year	12.50
1976 Skiing	Year	15.00
1977 Soccer	Year	16.50
1978 Canoeing	Year	17.50

	Edition Limit	Issue Price (US)
1979 Father and Daughter	Year	$ 19.50
1980 Sailing	Year	21.50
Easter		
1972 Ducks	Year	7.00
1973 Birds	Year	10.00
1974 Rabbits	Year	11.00
1975 Chicks	Year	16.00
1976 Sheep in Field	Year	18.00
1977 Butterflies	Year	23.00
Christmas		
1983 Christmas Night	Year	42.00

SPAIN

	Edition Limit	Issue Price (US)
Lladro		
Christmas		
1971 Caroling	Year	27.50
1972 Carolers	Year	35.00
1973 Boy and Girl	Year	45.00
1974 Carolers	Year	55.00
1975 Cherubs	Year	60.00
1976 Christ Child	Year	60.00
1977 Nativity Scene	Year	80.00
1978 Caroling Child	Year	80.00
1979 Snow Dance	Year	90.00
Santa Clara		
Christmas		
1970 Christmas Message	10,000	18.00
1971 Three Wise Men	10,000	18.00
1972 Children in Woods	10,000	20.00
1973 Archangel	5,000	25.00
1974 Spirit of Christmas	10,000	25.00
1975 Christmas Eve in Country	10,000	27.50
1976 Madonna and Child	10,000	25.00
1977 Mother and Child	10,000	27.50
1978 Angel with Flowers	10,000	32.00
1979 Madonna and Angels	10,000	34.50
Mother's Day		
1971 Mother and Child	10,000	15.00
1972 Mother and Children	12,000	15.00

SWEDEN

	Edition Limit	Issue Price (US)
Kosta		
Annual		
1971 Madonna & Child	Year	30.00
1972 St. George & Dragon	Year	30.00
1973 Viking Ship	Year	40.00
1974 Annual	Year	40.00
Orrefors		
Mother's Day		
1971 Flowers for Mother	2,500	45.00
1972 Mother and Children	2,500	45.00
1973 Mother and Child	2,500	50.00
1974 Mother and Child	5,000	50.00
1975 Mother and Child	2,500	60.00
1976 Children and Puppy	2,500	75.00
1977 Child and Dove	1,500	85.00
1978 Mother and Child	1,500	90.00
Rörstrand		
Christmas		
1904 Christmas Night in Stockholm	Year	.27
1905 Porridge Dish for Tomten	Year	.27
1906 Star Boys Singing to Lucia	Year	.27
1907 Christmas Eve in Lapland	Year	.27
1908 Christmas Eve with Christmas Roses	Year	.27
1909 Christmas Star over Jerusalem	Year	.27
1910 Christmas Tree	Year	.27
1911 Christmas Bells and Angel	Year	.56
1912 Christmas Service	Year	.56
1913 Christmas Day Early Service Trip	Year	.56
1914 Returning Home	Year	.56
1915 On Way to Church	Year	.56
1916 Kneeling Shepherd	Year	.56
1917 Three Kings Following Star	Year	.56
1918 Sleigh-ride in Dalecarlia	Year	.87
1919 Christmas on Snow Mountain	Year	.87
1920 Mary and Child Jesus	Year	.87
1921 Knight Offering Prayers	Year	.87
1922 Christmas Bells on Gotland	Year	.87
1923 Christmas Sheaf	Year	.87
1924 Tomtefar Bearing Gifts	Year	.87
1925 Christmas Star and Angels	Year	$ .87
Mother's Day		
1971 Mother & Child	Year	15.00
1972 Shelling Peas	Year	15.00
1973 Old Fashioned Picnic	Year	16.00
1974 Candle Lighting	Year	18.00
1975 Pontius on Floor	Year	20.00
1976 Apple Picking	Year	20.00
1977 Kitchen	Year	27.50
1978 Azalea	Year	27.50
1979 Studio Idyll	Year	31.50
1980 Lisbeth	Year	31.50
1981 Karin with Brita	Year	42.50
Father's Day		
1971 Father & Child	Year	15.00
1972 Meal at Home	Year	15.00
1973 Tilling Fields	Year	16.00
1974 Fishing	Year	18.00
1975 Painting	Year	20.00
1976 Plowing	Year	20.00
1977 Sawing	Year	27.50
1978 Self Portrait	Year	27.50
1979 Bridge	Year	31.50
1980 My Etch-Nook	Year	31.50
1981 Esbjorn with Playmate	Year	42.50
Christmas Poetry		
1979 Silent Night, Holy Night	NA	173.00
1980 Three Holy Kings	NA	180.00
1981 O Holy Night	NA	280.00
1982 Shepherds in Bethlehem	NA	280.00

UNITED STATES

	Edition Limit	Issue Price (US)
Abbey Press (Viletta)		
Mother's Day		
1979 Special Mothers are God's Creation	6,000	37.50
Christmas		
1979 Christmas Is a Gentle Season	6,000	37.50
Accent on Art		
Mother Goose		
1978 Jack & Jill	5,000	59.50
Nobility of Plains		
1978 Commanche	12,500	80.00
1979 Moving Day	3,500	80.00
Addams Family (Schmid)		
Mother's Day		
1972 On Tracks	Year	10.00
Christmas		
1972 Christmas Dinner	Year	10.00
Allison		
Nature's Beauty		
1981 Winter's Peace	7,500	70.00
1982 Summer's Joy	7,500	70.00
Late to Party		
1982 Piece of Cake	12,500	35.00
1983 Cheese Please	12,500	35.00
1983 Toast to a Mouse	12,500	35.00
American Archives (International Silver)		
(Single issue)		
1972 Christmas Rose	2,500	100.00
American Artists		
Famous Stallions		
1983 Black Stallion	19,500	49.50
1983 Andalusian	19,500	49.50
Feathered Friends		
1983 Parakeets	19,500	29.50
Mother and Child Cats		
1983 Kitty Love	19,500	29.50
Noble Tribes		
1983 Algonquin	19,500	49.50
Saturday Evening Post Covers		
1983 Santa's Computer	15 Days	29.50
American Arts Services (Viletta)		
Children		
1979 Last of Ninth	5,000	45.00
American Commemorative (Gorham)		
Southern Landmark		
1973 Monticello	9,800	35.00
1973 Williamsburg	9,800	40.00
1974 Beauvoir	9,800	40.00
1974 Cabildo	9,800	40.00
1975 Hermitage	9,800	40.00
1975 Oak Hill	9,800	40.00
1976 Governor Tryon's Palace	9,800	40.00
1976 Montpelier	9,800	40.00
1977 Elmscourt	9,800	40.00
1977 Ashland	9,800	$ 40.00
1978 Mt. Vernon	9,800	40.00
1978 White House	9,800	40.00
1979 Custis Lee	9,800	40.00
1979 Drayton Hall	9,800	40.00
1980 Fort Hall	9,800	40.00
1980 Liberty Hall	9,800	40.00
American Express (Gorham)		
Four Freedoms		
1976 Freedom to Worship	Year	37.50
1976 Freedom from Want	Year	37.50
1976 Freedom from Fear	Year	37.50
1976 Freedom of Speech	Year	37.50
Birds of North America		
1978 Saw Whet Owls	9,800	38.00
1978 Bobwhite Quail	9,800	38.00
1978 October Cardinals	9,800	38.00
1978 Long-Eared Owl	9,800	38.00
1978 Eastern Bluebirds	9,800	38.00
1978 American Woodcock	9,800	38.00
1978 Ruffed Grouse	9,800	38.00
1978 House Wren	9,800	38.00
American Express (Lenox)		
American Trees of Christmas		
1976 Douglas Fir	Year	60.00
1977 Scotch Pine	Year	60.00
American Heritage Art (Crown Parian)		
Battle Wagon		
1982 General Quarters	25,000	39.50
1983 Last Cruise	25,000	39.50
Celebrity Clowns		
1982 Emmett	12,500	50.00
1982 Judy	12,500	50.00
1982 Jimmy	12,500	50.00
1982 Shark	12,500	50.00
Early American Sail		
1982 Squall	5,000	39.50
1983 Young America	5,000	39.50
Lil Critters		
1982 Inquisitive	10,000	39.50
1982 Sassy	10,000	39.50
1983 Vigilance	10,000	39.50
1983 Chatty	10,000	39.50
Vanishing West		
1982 Hell Bent	5,000	60.00
1983 Cold Trail	5,000	60.00
1983 Horse Stick Medicine	5,000	60.00
1984 Letting 'Em Blow	5,000	60.00
1984 Eyeing Back Trail	5,000	60.00
Africa's Beauties		
1983 Elephant Family	5,000	65.00
1983 Zebra Family	5,000	65.00
America's Heritage of Flight		
1983 Kitty Hawk	5,000	39.50
1983 Jenny	5,000	39.50
1984 Race	5,000	39.50
1984 Corsair	5,000	39.50
Craftsman Heritage		
1983 Decoy Maker	5,000	39.50
1983 Sailmaker	5,000	39.50
1983 Farmer	5,000	39.50
1984 Platemaker	5,000	39.50
1984 Blacksmith	5,000	39.50
1984 Spinning Wheel	5,000	39.50
Equestrian Love		
1983 Arabian Destiny	5,000	39.50
1983 Quarterhorse Wrangler	5,000	39.50
Sawdust Antics		
1983 Emmett's 8 Ball	5,000	50.00
1983 Emmett with a Bang	5,000	50.00
1984 Emmett at Races	5,000	50.00
1984 Emmett at Plate	5,000	50.00
American Historial Plates (Castleton China)		
Aviation		
1972 Amelia Earhart	3,500	40.00
1972 Charles Lindberg	3,500	40.00
American Preservation Guild (Gorham)		
Catesby Collection		
1977 Cardinal	9,900	39.00
American Rose Society (Gorham)		
All-American Rose		
1975 Oregold	9,800	39.00
1975 Arizona	9,800	39.00
1975 Rose Parade	9,800	39.00
1976 America	9,800	39.00
1976 Cathedral	9,800	39.00
1976 Seashell	9,800	39.00
1977 Yankee Doodle	9,800	39.00
1977 Double Delight	9,800	39.00
1977 Prominent	9,800	39.00
1978 First Edition	9,800	39.00
1978 Color Magic	9,800	39.00
1978 Charisma	9,800	$ 39.00
1979 Paradise	9,800	39.00
1979 Sundowner	9,800	39.00
1979 Friendship	9,800	39.00
1980 Love	9,800	39.00
1980 Honor	9,800	39.00
1980 Cherish	9,800	39.00
1981 Bing Crosby	9,800	49.00
1981 White Lightnin'	9,800	49.00
1981 Marina	9,800	49.00
1982 Shreveport	9,800	49.00
1982 French Lace	9,800	49.00
1982 Brandy	9,800	49.00
1982 Mon Cheri	9,800	49.00
Antique Trader		
Currier & Ives		
1969 Baseball	2,000	9.00
1969 Franklin Experiment	2,000	9.00
1969 Haying Time	2,000	9.00
1969 Winter in Country	2,000	9.00
Easter		
1971 Child and Lamb	1,500	10.95
1972 Shepherd with Lamb	1,000	10.95
Mother's Day		
1971 Madonna and Child	1,500	10.95
1972 Mother Cat and Kittens	1,000	10.95
Father's Day		
1971 Pilgrim Father	1,500	10.95
1972 Deer Family	1,000	10.95
Thanksgiving		
1971 Pilgrims	1,500	10.95
1972 First Thanksgiving	1,000	10.95
Christmas		
1971 Christ Child	1,500	10.95
1972 Flight into Egypt	1,000	10.95
C. M. Russell		
1971 Bad One	2,000	11.95
1971 Discovery of Last Chance Gulch	2,000	11.95
1971 Doubtful Visitor	2,000	11.95
1971 Innocent Allies	2,000	11.95
1971 Medicine Man	2,000	11.95
Bible		
1973 David & Goliath	2,000	10.75
1973 Moses & Golden Idol	2,000	10.75
1973 Noah's Ark	2,000	10.75
1973 Samson	2,000	10.75
Arizona Artisan		
Christmas		
1974 Mexican Christmas	Year	20.00
1975 Navajo Christmas	Year	20.00
Thanksgiving		
1975 Navajo Thanksgiving Feast	Year	15.00
Arlington Mint		
Christmas		
1972 Hands in Prayer	Year	125.00
Armstrong		
Bicentennial		
1971 Calm Before Storm	250	250.00
1972 Gaspee Incident	175	250.00
Artists of the World		
Ruffin Annual		
1976 Navajo Lullaby	10,000	40.00
1977 Through Years	5,000	45.00
1978 Child of Pueblo	5,000	50.00
1979 Colima Madonna	5,000	50.00
1980 Sun Kachina	5,000	50.00
1981 Inner Peace	5,000	55.00
1982 Madonna of Cross	5,000	60.00
1983 Navajo Princess	5,000	60.00
World of Game Birds		
1977 Mallards	5,000	45.00
1978 Gambel Quail	5,000	45.00
1979 American Autumn Ring-necked Pheasant	5,000	50.00
1980 November Journey-Canada Geese	5,000	50.00
Don Ruffin Self-Portrait		
1979 Clown Also Cries	7,500	65.00
Children of Don Ruffin		
1980 Flowers for Mother	7,500	50.00
1981 Little Eagle	7,500	55.00
1982 Lost Moccasins	7,500	60.00
1983 Security	7,500	60.00
Prowlers of Clouds		
1981 Great Horned Owl	5,000	55.00
1981 Screech Owl	5,000	55.00
1982 Bald Eagle	5,000	60.00
1982 Golden Eagle	5,000	60.00

	Edition Limit	Issue Price (US)
Anthony Sidoni		
1982 Little Yankee	15,000	$ 35.00
1983 Little Satchmo	15,000	40.00
Vel Miller		
1982 Mama's Rose	15,000	35.00
1983 Papa's Boy	15,000	40.00
Woodland Friends		
1983 Whitetail Deer	5,000	60.00
1984 Black Bear	5,000	60.00
(Single issue)		
1983 DeGrazia and His Mountain	15,000	65.00
Audubon Crystal		
Endangered Birds		
1976 Kirtland's Warbler	5,000	195.00
1976 American Eagle	5,000	195.00
1977 Peregrine Falcon	5,000	200.00
Avondale		
Cameos of Childhood		
1978 Melissa	28,050	65.00
1979 First Born	12,000	70.00
1980 Melissa's Brother	Year	70.00
1981 Daddy and I	Year	75.00
Myths of Sea		
1979 Poseidon	15,000	70.00
1980 Maiden of Sea	15,000	75.00
Tribute to Ageless Art		
1979 Court Jesters	10,000	70.00
World of Dance		
1979 Prima Ballerina	15,000	70.00
Christmas		
1981 And Heavens Rejoiced	6,500	90.00
1982 And There Came Wise Men	6,500	90.00
1983 Shepherd	6,500	90.00
Growing Up		
1982 Ribbon for Her Hair	6,500	75.00
See also: Judaic Heritage Society (U.S.A.)		
B & J Art Designs		
Old Fashioned Christmas		
1983 Carol	15,000	45.00
Brantwood Collection		
Marian Carlsen Mother's Day		
1978 Jennifer and Jenny Fur	Year	45.00
1979 Football Brothers	5,000	45.00
Howe Christmas		
1978 Visit from Santa	Year	45.00
(Single issue)		
1978 Tribute to Rockwell	Year	35.00
John Falter Christmas		
1979 Christmas Morning	5,000	24.50
Rockwell Mother's Day		
1979 Homecoming	20,000	39.50
Little Clown		
1979 Going to Circus	5,000	29.50
Braymer Hall		
Childhood Sonatas		
1981 Serenade	15,000	28.50
1982 Prelude	15,000	28.50
1982 Caprice	15,000	28.50
American Folk		
1982 Spring Celebration	10,000	24.50
1982 Summer Bounty	10,000	24.50
Yesterday's Dreams		
1983 Swing Quartet	5,000	50.00
Brentwood Fine Arts (Fairmont)		
Nostalgic Memories		
1982 Amy	12,500	39.50
Briarcrest		
Good Ole Summertime		
1982 Watermelon Eater	10 Days	42.00
This Ole Bear		
1982 Chauncey James	5,000	45.00
(Single issue)		
1982 Carousel	10,000	35.00
John Brindle Fine Arts		
Fantasy in Motion		
1978 Little Blue Horse	3,000	75.00
1979 Horse of a Different Color	3,000	75.00
1980 Horse with Golden Horn	3,000	75.00
Moods of Orient		
1978 Softly, Sun Sets	4,000	75.00
1980 Tranquil Morn	4,000	75.00
Expressions		
1979 Quiet Eyes	3,000	60.00
(Single issue)		
1980 Homage	2,500	125.00

	Edition Limit	Issue Price (US)
Those Precious Years		
1980 Little Curt and Friend	3,000	$ 60.00
Cabochon		
Nancy Doyle's Candy Girls		
1983 Rebecca	15,000	50.00
1984 Shantelle	15,000	50.00
1984 Kelly Ann	15,000	50.00
Calhoun's Collectors Society		
Crystal Maidens		
1979 Spring—Strawberry Season	2,500	49.50
1979 Summer—Sunshine Season	2,500	49.50
1979 Autumn—Scenic Season	2,500	49.50
1979 Winter—Snowflake Season	2,500	49.50
Calhoun's Collectors Society (Schumann)		
Imperial Christmas		
1979 Liebling	10,000	65.00
1980 Hallelujah	10,000	65.00
1981 Stille Nacht	10,000	65.00
1982 Winter Melodie	10,000	75.00
California Porcelain and Bronze		
Best of Sascha		
1979 Flower Bouquet	7,500	65.00
Vanishing Animals		
1979 Asian Monarchs	7,500	40.00
1979 Snow Leopards	7,500	45.00
1980 Pandas	7,500	45.00
1981 Polar Bears	7,500	50.00
Carmel Collection		
Famous Parades		
1983 Thanksgiving Day Parade	Year	39.50
First Performances		
1983 Darling Diana	19,500	39.50
Joys of Christmas		
1983 Christmas Delight	19,500	39.50
Carson Mint (Viletta)		
Yesterday's Children		
1978 Lisa and Jumeau Doll	5,000	60.00
1979 Adrianne and Bye-Lo Baby	5,000	60.00
1980 Lydia and Shirley Temple Doll	5,000	60.00
1981 Melanie and Scarlett O'Hara Doll	5,000	60.00
Hollywood Squares		
1979 Peter Marshall	100 Days	28.50
1980 George Gobel	100 Days	28.50
Moment in Time		
1979 Freedom Flight	5,000	55.00
Old Fashioned Mother's Day		
1979 Daisies from Mary-Beth	20 Days	37.50
1980 Daisies from Jimmy	20 Days	37.50
1981 Daisies from Meg	20 Days	37.50
1982 Daisies for Mommie	20 Days	37.50
America Has Heart		
1980 My Heart's Desire	Year	24.50
1981 Hearts and Flowers	Year	24.50
1982 Hearty Sailer	Year	28.50
1983 Shannon's Sweetheart	Year	28.50
Magic Afternoon		
1980 Enchanted Garden	5,000	39.50
1981 Delightful Tea Party	5,000	39.50
Big Top		
1981 White Face	60 Days	28.50
1982 Tramp	60 Days	28.50
Littlest Christmas		
1982 Littlest Stocking	12,500	29.50
1983 Littlest Santa	12,500	29.50
Nature's Children		
1982 Candice	12,500	29.50
1983 Cory	12,500	29.50
Bear Feats		
1983 Teddy Bear Picnic	15,000	37.50
To Mom with Love		
1983 A Basket of Love	15,000	37.50
Castleton China		
Natural History		
1973 Painted Lady	1,500	40.00
1973 Roseate Spoonbill	1,500	40.00
(Single issue)		
1976 Gen. Douglas MacArthur	1,000	30.00
Castleton China (Shenango)		
Bicentennial		
1972 New Dawn	7,600	60.00

	Edition Limit	Issue Price (US)
1972 Turning Point	7,600	$ 60.00
1973 Valley Forge	7,600	60.00
1973 Declaration	7,600	60.00
1973 Star Spangled Banner	7,600	60.00
1973 U.S.S. Constitution	7,600	60.00
1974 One Nation	7,600	60.00
1974 Westward Ho	7,600	60.00
See also: American Historical Plates (U.S.A.)		
Caverswall		
See: Ghent Collection (U.S.A.)		
Certified Rarities		
Indian Dancer		
1978 Eagle Dancer	2,500	300.00
1979 Hoop Dancer	2,500	300.00
Postal Artists		
1978 Colias Eurydice	15,000	60.00
1979 Euphydryas Phaeton	7,500	60.00
Renaissance Masters		
1978 Alba Madonna	15,000	55.00
1979 Pieta	5,000	55.00
Chilmark		
Family Christmas		
1978 Trimming Tree	10,000	65.00
In Appreciation		
1979 Flowers of Field	10,000	65.00
Holy Night		
1979 Wisemen	10,000	65.00
Twelve Days of Christmas		
1979 Partridge in Pear Tree	10,000	89.50
Cleveland Mint		
Da Vinci		
1972 Last Supper	5,000	125.00
Collector Creations (Reed & Barton)		
Thomas Nast Christmas		
1973 Christmas	750	100.00
(Single issue)		
1973 Alice in Wonderland	750	100.00
Collector's Heirlooms (Fairmont)		
Children at Play		
1979 Maple Leaf Noses	7,500	60.00
Passing of Plains Indians		
1979 Cheyenne Chieftain	5,000	65.00
Collector's Heirlooms (Viletta)		
Childhood Memories		
1978 Jennifer by Candlelight	5,000	60.00
1979 Brian's Birthday	5,000	60.00
Joys of Motherhood		
1978 Crystal's Joy	7,500	60.00
Collectors Weekly		
American		
1971 Miss Liberty	500	12.50
1972 Miss Liberty	900	12.50
1973 Eagle	900	9.75
Continental Mint		
Tom Sawyer		
1976 Taking His Medicine	5,000	60.00
1977 Painting Fence	5,000	60.00
1978 Lost in Cave	5,000	60.00
1979 Smoking Pipe	5,000	60.00
(Single issue)		
1979 Butter Girl	7,000	60.00
Creative World		
Pearl Buck (Single issue)		
1972 Good Earth	10,000	NA
Four Seasons		
1972 Fall (Silverplate)	2,000	75.00
1972 Fall (Sterling)	2,000	125.00
1973 Winter (Silverplate)	2,000	75.00
1973 Winter (Sterling)	250	125.00
1973 Spring (Silverplate)	300	75.00
1973 Spring (Sterling)	750	125.00
1974 Summer (Silverplate)	300	75.00
1974 Summer (Sterling)	750	125.00
Brown's Rockwells		
1977 Looking Out to Sea	15,000	50.00
1978 Yankee Doodle	15,000	50.00
1979 Girl at Mirror	15,000	55.00
Immortals of Early American Literature		
1978 Village Smithy	15,000	50.00
1979 Rip Van Winkle	15,000	55.00
Aesop's Fables		
1979 Fox & Grapes	9,750	85.00
Living Dolls		
1982 Eriko and Noriko	9,500	49.50
1983 Ingrid and Ingemar	9,500	49.50
Prize Collection		
1982 Family Cares	12,500	45.00
1983 Wind in a Frolic	12,500	45.00

	Edition Limit	Issue Price (US)
Wags to Riches		
1982 Benji Movie Star	100 Days	$ 29.50
1982 Benji and Tiffany	100 Days	29.50
1983 Merry Christmas Benji	19,500	35.00
Help My Friends		
1983 Corky's Dream	100 Days	35.00
Crown Parian		
Rosemary Calder		
1978 Affection	7,500	60.00
James Daly		
1978 Sweet Dreams	7,500	55.00
Beautiful Cats of World		
1979 Sheena	5,000	60.00
1979 Sheena and Sheena's Cubs	5,000	60.00
1980 Elisheba	5,000	60.00
1980 Elisheba's Cubs	5,000	60.00
1981 Atarah	5,000	60.00
1981 Atarah's Cubs	5,000	60.00
1982 Tamar	5,000	60.00
1982 Tamar's Cubs	5,000	60.00
Penni Anne Cross		
1979 Crow Baby	7,500	55.00
1981 Paiute Pals	7,500	55.00
1982 Big Sister's Buckskins	7,500	55.00
Julian Ritter		
1979 Reve de Ballet	7,500	55.00
Western		
1979 Under Surveillance	10,000	65.00
1979 Promised Land	10,000	65.00
1979 Winter Song	10,000	65.00
1979 Boomtown and Wildcatters	10,000	65.00
Sporting Dogs		
1980 Decoy	5,000	55.00
1981 Dusty	5,000	55.00
1982 Rummy	5,000	55.00
1983 Scarlet	5,000	55.00
Happy Art		
1981 Woody's Triple Self Portrait	10,000	39.50
Portraits of Childhood		
1981 Miss Murray	7,500	65.00
Children to Love		
1982 Wendy	10,000	60.00
1983 Jake	10,000	60.00
Owl Family		
1982 Saw-Whet Owl Family	5,000	55.00
1982 Great Horned Owl Family	5,000	55.00
1983 Snowy Owl Family	5,000	55.00
1983 Barred Owl Family	5,000	55.00
Reflections of Seasons		
1982 Winter's Dream	7,500	39.50
(Single issue)		
1982 Buon Natale	1,000	300.00
Special Heart		
1983 Reaching Together	40,000	35.00
1983 Love in Your Heart	40,000	35.00
See also: American Heritage Art (U.S.A.)		
Curator Collection		
Masterpieces of Impressionism		
1980 Woman with a Parasol	17,500	35.00
1981 Young Mother Sewing	17,500	35.00
1982 Sara in Green Bonnet	17,500	35.00
1983 Margot in Blue	17,500	35.00
Masterpieces of West		
1980 Texas Night Herder	17,500	35.00
1981 Indian Trapper	17,500	35.00
1982 Cowboy Style		
1982 Indian Style (Set of two)	17,500	70.00
Masterpieces of Rockwell		
1980 After Prom	17,500	35.00
1981 Challenger	17,500	42.50
1981 Girl at Mirror	17,500	50.00
1982 Missing Tooth	17,500	50.00
Jesse's World		
1981 This Simple Faith	17,500	39.95
Magical Moments		
1981 Happy Dreams	NA	29.95
1981 Harmony	NA	29.95
1982 His Majesty	NA	29.95
1982 Waiting for Daddy	NA	29.95
1983 Thank You, God	NA	29.95
1983 Lullaby	NA	29.95
Rockwell Americana		
1981 Shuffleton's Barbershop	17,500	75.00
1982 Breaking Home Ties	17,500	75.00
1983 Walking to Church	17,500	75.00

	Edition Limit	Issue Price (US)
Special Occasions		
1981 Bubbles	NA	$ 29.95
1982 Butterflies	NA	29.95
Stockbridge Trilogy		
1981 Stockbridge in Winter, Part I	NA	45.00
1982 Stockbridge in Winter, Part II	NA	45.00
1983 Stockbridge in Winter, Part III	NA	45.00
Classic Circus		
1982 Favorite Clown	17,500	39.95
Legends		
1982 Paul Bunyan	10,000	45.00
1983 Rip Van Winkle	10,000	45.00
Melodies of Childhood		
1982 Twinkle, Twinkle	25,000	35.00
1983 Row Your Boat	25,000	39.95
Playful Pets		
1982 Curiosity	10,000	45.00
1982 Master's Hat	10,000	45.00
Tribute		
1982 I Want You	NA	29.95
1982 Gee! I Wish I Were a Man	NA	29.95
1983 Soldier's Farewell	NA	29.95
Becker Babies		
1983 Snowpuff	NA	35.00
Nursery		
1983 In Slumberland	NA	35.00
1983 Awakening	NA	35.00
Danbury Mint		
Currier & Ives (Silver)		
1972 Road Winter	7,500	125.00
1973 Central Park Winter	7,500	125.00
1974 Winter in Country	7,500	125.00
1975 American Homestead	7,500	125.00
1976 American Winter-Evening	7,500	135.00
1977 Winter Morning	7,500	135.00
Christmas		
1975 Silent Night	NA	24.50
1976 Joy to World	NA	27.50
1977 Away in Manger	NA	27.50
1978 First Noel	NA	29.50
Bicentennial (Silver)		
1973 Boston Tea Party	7,500	125.00
1974 First Continental Congress	7,500	125.00
1975 Paul Revere's Ride	7,500	125.00
1976 Declaration of Independence	7,500	125.00
1977 Washington at Valley Forge	7,500	125.00
1978 Molly Pitcher	7,500	125.00
1979 Bon Homme Richard	7,500	125.00
Michelangelo (Silver)		
1973 Creation of Adam	7,500	125.00
1973 Pieta	7,500	125.00
1973 Moses	7,500	125.00
1973 Holy Family	7,500	125.00
Great Art Masterpieces (Silver)		
1975 Mona Lisa	7,500	125.00
1975 Last Supper	7,500	125.00
1976 Sunflower	7,500	125.00
1976 Blue Boy	7,500	125.00
Stuart Devlin Silver		
Americana		
1972 Gaspee Incident	1,000	130.00
Ebeling & Reuss		
Christmas		
1981 Waiting for Christmas	7,000	15.00
1982 Time of Song and Caroling	7,500	15.00
(Single issue)		
1983 Love One Another	12,500	17.50
R.J. Ernst Enterprises (Viletta)		
Performance		
1979 Act I	5,000	65.00
Women of West		
1979 Expectation	10,000	39.50
1979 Silver Dollar Sal	10,000	39.50
1980 School Marm	10,000	39.50
1980 Dolly	10,000	39.50
Love Is		
1980 Rufus and Roxanne	19,000	14.95
A Beautiful World		
1981 Tahitian Dreamer	27,500	27.50
1982 Flirtation	27,500	27.50
1983 Elke of Oslo	27,500	27.50
Hollywood Greats		
1980 John Wayne	27,500	29.95

	Edition Limit	Issue Price (US)
1981 Gary Cooper	27,500	$ 29.95
1982 Clark Gable	27,500	29.95
1983 Alan Ladd	27,500	29.95
Classy Cars		
1981 '26 T	20 Days	24.50
1982 Model A	20 Days	24.50
1982 Model A Pickup	20 Days	24.50
1983 Panel Van	20 Days	24.50
Commemoratives		
1981 John Lennon	30 Days	39.50
1981 Elvis Presley	30 Days	39.50
1982 Marilyn Monroe	30 Days	39.50
1983 Judy Garland	30 Days	39.50
A Love Story		
1981 Chapter One	20 Days	24.50
Pinups		
1981 Stars and Stripes Forever	20 Days	24.50
So Young, So Sweet		
1981 Girl with Straw Hat	10 Days	39.50
1982 My Favorite Necklace	10 Days	39.50
1983 Breakfast Time	10 Days	39.50
Turn of Century		
1981 Riverboat Honeymoon	10 Days	35.00
1982 Children's Carousel	10 Days	35.00
1982 Flower Market	10 Days	35.00
1983 Ballroom Race	10 Days	35.00
Little Misses Young and Fair		
1982 Heart of a Child	29,000	60.00
1983 Where Wild Flowers Grow	29,000	60.00
Mommie and Me		
1982 First Tea	10 Days	35.00
1983 Baby's Sleeping	10 Days	35.00
My Fair Ladies		
1982 Lady Sabrina	29,000	50.00
1983 Lady Victoria	29,000	50.00
(Single issue)		
1982 Henry Fonda	100 Days	45.00
Fondest Memories		
1983 A Touching Moment	NA	60.00
1984 Mother's Pearls	NA	60.00
Liebchen		
1983 Winter Liebchen	30 Days	19.50
1983 Spring Liebchen	30 Days	19.50
1984 Summer Liebchen	30 Days	19.50
1984 Autumn Liebchen	30 Days	19.50
Narrow Gauge		
1983 Halfway to Alamosa	10 Days	29.50
1984 Down from Rico	10 Days	29.50
Star Trek		
1983 Spock	90 Days	29.50
Yesterdays		
1983 Amber	10 Days	24.50
1983 Elmer	10 Days	24.50
Americana		
1984 Somewhere in Autumn	20 Days	29.50
Childhood Memories		
1984 Sometimes an Angel	20 Days	24.50
Days Ago		
1984 Blue Belle	20 Days	24.50
Fishing Boats		
1984 Sunset at Monterey	10 Days	24.50
1984 Blue Sea	10 Days	24.50
Friends		
1984 I Love You Orville	20 Days	24.50
Romantic Memories		
1984 Sunday Afternoon	14,400	60.00
Fairmont		
Carousel Horses		
1977 (Set of two)	3,000	80.00
Spencer Annual		
1977 Patient Ones	10,000	42.50
1978 Yesterday, Today and Tomorrow	10,000	47.50
Irene Spencer's Special Requests		
1978 Hug Me	10,000	55.00
1978 Sleep Little Baby	10,000	65.00
Olaf Wieghorst		
1978 Sioux Warrior	5,000	65.00
1979 Indian Scout	5,000	65.00
Rural America		
1978 Fence	5,000	45.00
Timeless Moments		
1978 Tenderness	5,000	45.00
1979 Renaissance	5,000	50.00
1980 Coming in Glory	5,000	39.95
Children of America		
1979 Eskimo Girl	3,000	48.00
Lords of Plains		
1979 Sitting Bull	5,000	60.00

	Edition Limit	Issue Price (US)
Rockwell Early Works		
1979 Old Man Winter	15,000	$ 19.95
1980 Inventor	15,000	19.95
1980 Ready for School	15,000	19.95
1980 Music Master	15,000	19.95
1981 Tinkerer	15,000	19.95
Gnome Holiday		
1980 Gnome Bliss	5,000	24.50
1981 Gift of Love	5,000	29.95
Gnomes Four Seasons		
1980 Little Swinger (Spring)	15,000	29.50
1980 Gnome de Bloom (Summer)	15,000	29.50
1980 Lookouts (Fall)	15,000	29.50
1980 First Skater (Winter)	15,000	29.50
1981 Spring Sharing (Spring)	15,000	29.95
1981 Fun and Games (Summer)	15,000	29.95
1981 Up Up and Away (Fall)	15,000	29.95
1981 First Skier (Winter)	15,000	29.95
1982 Gnome Knowledge (Spring)	15,000	29.95
1982 Summer Harvest (Summer)	15,000	29.95
1982 Gnome Family Tailors (Fall)	15,000	29.95
1982 Keep Gnome Fires Burning (Winter)	15,000	29.95
American's Most Beloved (Single issue)		
1980 John Wayne	5,000	13.95
Long Road West		
1981 Trailblazers	20,000	40.00
1981 Prairie Schooner	20,000	40.00
1981 Pony Express	20,000	40.00
1981 Peacemakers	20,000	40.00
1981 Cowboys of West	20,000	40.00
1981 Lawmen of West	20,000	40.00
When I Grow Up		
1981 I'll Be Loved	7,500	29.95
1981 I'll Be Like Mommy	7,500	29.95
1982 I'll Be First Lady	7,500	29.95
1982 I'll Be a Star	7,500	29.95
Jansen's International Beauties		
1982 Lisa	7,500	55.00
1983 Ingrid	7,500	55.00
Vanishing Americana		
1983 American Eagle	15,000	13.50
1984 Country Doctor	15,000	13.50
(Single issue)		
1983 I Love Teddy Bears	NA	39.50
(Single issue)		
1983 My Little Sheltie	5,000	39.95
(Single issue)		
1983 Organ Grinder	5,000	19.95
Legends of Gnomes		
1984 Gnome Home	15,000	29.95
See also:		
Brentwood Fine Arts (U.S.A.)		
Collector's Heirlooms (U.S.A.)		
Ghent Collection (U.S.A.)		
Mistwood Designs (U.S.A.)		
Fenton Glass		
American Craftsman		
1970 Glassmaker	Year	10.00
1971 Printer	Year	10.00
1972 Blacksmith	Year	10.00
1973 Shoemaker	Year	10.00
1974 Cooper	Year	11.00
1975 Silversmith	Year	13.50
1976 Gunsmith	Year	13.50
1977 Potter	Year	15.00
1978 Wheelwright	Year	15.00
1979 Cabinetmaker	Year	15.00
1980 Tanner	Year	16.50
1981 Housewright	Year	17.50
Christmas in America		
1970 Little Brown Church (Blue Satin)	Year	12.50
1970 Little Brown Church (Carnival)	Year	12.50
1970 Little Brown Church (Brown)	Year	17.50
1971 Old Brick Church (Blue Satin)	Year	12.50
1971 Old Brick Church (Brown)	Year	17.50
1971 Old Brick Church (Carnival)	Year	12.50
1971 Old Brick Church (White Satin)	Year	12.50
1972 Two Horned Church (Blue Satin)	Year	12.50
1972 Two Horned Church (Brown)	Year	17.50

	Edition Limit	Issue Price (US)
1972 Two Horned Church (Carnival)	Year	$ 12.50
1972 Two Horned Church (White Satin)	Year	12.50
1973 St. Mary's (Blue Satin)	Year	12.50
1973 St. Mary's (Carnival)	Year	12.50
1973 St. Mary's (White Satin)	Year	12.50
1973 St. Mary's (Brown)	Year	17.50
1974 Nation's Church (Blue Satin)	Year	13.50
1974 Nation's Church (Carnival)	Year	13.50
1974 Nation's Church (White Satin)	Year	13.50
1974 Nation's Church (Brown)	Year	18.50
1975 Birthplace of Liberty (Blue Satin)	Year	13.50
1975 Birthplace of Liberty (Carnival)	Year	13.50
1975 Birthplace of Liberty (White Satin)	Year	13.50
1975 Birthplace of Liberty (Brown)	Year	20.00
1976 Old North Church (Blue Satin)	Year	15.00
1976 Old North Church (Carnival)	Year	15.00
1976 Old North Church (White Satin)	Year	15.00
1976 Old North Church (Brown)	Year	25.00
1977 San Carlos (Blue Satin)	Year	15.00
1977 San Carlos (Carnival)	Year	15.00
1977 San Carlos (White Satin)	Year	15.00
1978 Church of Holy Trinity (Blue Satin)	Year	15.00
1978 Church of Holy Trinity (Carnival)	Year	15.00
1978 Church of Holy Trinity (White Satin)	Year	15.00
1979 San Jose y Miguel de Aguayo (Blue Satin)	Year	15.00
1979 San Jose y Miguel de Aguayo (Carnival)	Year	15.00
1979 San Jose y Miguel de Aguayo (White Satin)	Year	15.00
1980 Christ Church (Blue Satin)	Year	16.50
1980 Christ Church (Carnival)	Year	16.50
1980 Christ Church (White Satin)	Year	16.50
1981 Mission of San Xavier del Bac (Blue Satin)	Year	18.50
1981 Mission of San Xavier del Bac (Carnival)	Year	18.50
1981 Mission of San Xavier del Bac (White Satin)	Year	18.50
Mother's Day		
1971 Madonna, Sleeping Child (Blue Satin)	Year	12.50
1971 Madonna, Sleeping Child (Carnival)	Year	12.50
1972 Madonna of Goldfinch (Blue Satin)	Year	12.50
1972 Madonna of Goldfinch (Carnival)	Year	12.50
1972 Madonna of Goldfinch (White Satin)	Year	12.50
1973 Cowper Madonna (Blue Satin)	Year	12.50
1973 Cowper Madonna (Carnival)	Year	12.50
1973 Cowper Madonna (White Satin)	Year	12.50
1974 Madonna of Grotto (Blue Satin)	Year	12.50
1974 Madonna of Grotto (Carnival)	Year	12.50
1974 Madonna of Grotto (White Satin)	Year	12.50
1975 Taddei Madonna (Blue Satin)	Year	13.50
1975 Taddei Madonna (Carnival)	Year	13.50
1975 Taddei Madonna (White Satin)	Year	13.50
1976 Holy Night (Blue Satin)	Year	13.50
1976 Holy Night (Carnival)	Year	13.50
1976 Holy Night (White Satin)	Year	13.50

	Edition Limit	Issue Price (US)
1977 Madonna & Child (Blue Satin)	Year	$ 15.00
1977 Madonna & Child (Carnival)	Year	15.00
1977 Madonna & Child (White Satin)	Year	15.00
1978 Madonnina (Blue Satin)	Year	15.00
1978 Madonnina (Carnival)	Year	15.00
1978 Madonnina (White Satin)	Year	15.00
1979 Madonna of Rose Hedge (Blue Satin)	Year	15.00
1979 Madonna of Rose Hedge (Carnival)	Year	15.00
1979 Madonna of Rose Hedge (White Satin)	Year	15.00
Valentine's Day		
1972 Romeo and Juliet (Blue Satin)	Year	15.00
1972 Romeo and Juliet (Carnival)	Year	15.00
Bicentennial		
1974 Eagle (Blue Satin)	Year	15.00
1975 Eagle (Red Satin)	Year	15.00
1976 Eagle (Chocolate)	Year	17.50
1976 Eagle (White Satin)	Year	15.00
Alliance		
1975 Lafayette and Washington (Blue Satin)	Year	15.00
1975 Lafayette and Washington (Red Satin)	Year	17.50
1975 Lafayette and Washington (White Satin)	Year	15.00
1976 Lafayette and Washington (Blue Satin)	Year	15.00
1976 Lafayette and Washington (Chocolate)	Year	17.50
1976 Lafayette and Washington (White Satin)	Year	15.00
Christmas Classics		
1978 Christmas Morn	Year	25.00
1979 Nature's Christmas	Year	30.00
1980 Going Home	Year	38.50
1981 All Is Calm	Year	42.50
1982 Country Christmas	Year	42.50
Currier & Ives		
1980 Old Grist Mill	NA	25.00
1981 Harvest	NA	25.00
Mother's Day Classics		
1980 New Born	Year	28.50
1981 Gentle Fawn	Year	32.50
1982 Nature's Awakening	Year	35.00
Christmas Fantasy		
1983 Anticipation	7,500	45.00
Firehouse		
This Ole Bear		
1982 Emma Louise	5,000	39.50
1983 Buster and Sam	5,000	39.50
Fleetwood Collection (Gorham)		
Birds and Flowers of Meadow and Garden		
1980 Robin and Crab Apple Blossom	*	39.00
1980 Goldfinch and Bull Thistle	*	39.00
1980 Cardinal and Wild Lupine	*	39.00
1980 Chickadee and New England Aster	*	39.00
1980 Baltimore Oriole and Morning Glory	*	39.00
1980 Blue Bird and Black-Eyed Susan	*	39.00
1980 Painted Bunting and Blackberry	*	39.00
1980 Golden-Crowned Kinglet and Downey Phlox	*	39.00
1980 Red-Breasted Nuthatch and Japanese Honeysuckle	*	39.00
1980 Magnolia Warbler and Day Lily	*	39.00
1980 Ruby-Throated Hummingbird and Fire Pink	*	39.00
1980 Scarlet Tanager and Blue Columbine	*	39.00

*Subscription period

	Edition Limit	Issue Price (US)
Christmas		
1980 Magi	7,500	$ 49.50
1981 Holy Child	7,500	49.50
1982 Shepherds	7,500	49.50
Blossoms of China		
1981 Azalea	7,500	49.50
1981 Camelia	7,500	49.50
1981 Herbaceous Peony	7,500	49.50
1981 Chrysanthemum	7,500	49.50
1981 Lotus	7,500	49.50
1981 Magnolia	7,500	49.50
1981 Narcissus	7,500	49.50
1981 Orchid	7,500	49.50
1981 Peony	7,500	49.50
1981 Plum Blossom	7,500	49.50
1981 Rose	7,500	49.50
1981 Winter Jasmine	7,500	49.50
Golden Age of Sail		
1982 Flying Cloud	5,000	39.00
1982 New World	5,000	39.00
1982 Young America	5,000	39.00
1982 Courier	5,000	39.00
1982 Sea Witch	5,000	39.00
1982 Great Republic	5,000	39.00
(Single issue)		
1983 Mom's Apple Pie	NA	29.00
Fostoria		
American Milestones		
1971 Betsy Ross Flag	5,000	12.50
1972 National Anthem	8,000	12.50
1973 Washington Crossing Delaware	Year	12.50
1974 Spirit of '76	Year	13.00
1975 Mount Rushmore	Year	16.00
State Plates		
1971 California	6,000	12.50
1971 New York	12,000	12.50
1971 Ohio	3,000	12.50
1972 Florida	Year	12.50
1972 Hawaii	Year	12.50
1972 Pennsylvania	Year	12.50
1972 Massachusetts	Year	13.00
1972 Texas	Year	13.00
1973 Michigan	Year	13.50
Franklin Crystal		
Historical		
1976 Liberty Tree	10,317	120.00
Seven Seas		
1976 Atlantic Ocean	2,799	120.00
1976 Caribbean	2,799	120.00
1976 Indian Ocean	2,799	120.00
1976 Mediterranean	2,799	120.00
1976 Pacific	2,799	120.00
1976 South China Sea	2,799	120.00
1976 Arctic	2,799	120.00
Annual		
1977 Snowflake	3,428	185.00
1978 Snowbird	798	185.00
Rockwell's American Sweethearts		
1977 Youngsters at Play	1,004	120.00
1977 Teenagers Together	1,004	120.00
1978 Bride and Groom	1,004	120.00
1978 Proud Parents	1,004	120.00
1978 Graduation Day	1,004	120.00
1978 Retirement Kiss	1,004	120.00
Franklin Mint		
American West		
1972 Horizon's West (Silver)	5,860	150.00
1972 Horizon's West (Gold)	67	2200.00
1973 Mountain Man (Silver)	5,860	150.00
1973 Mountain Man (Gold)	67	2200.00
1973 Prospector (Silver)	5,860	150.00
1973 Prospector (Gold)	67	2200.00
1973 Plains Hunter (Silver)	5,860	150.00
1973 Plains Hunter (Gold)	67	2200.00
Audubon Society		
1972 Goldfinch	10,193	125.00
1972 Wood Duck	10,193	125.00
1973 Cardinal	10,193	125.00
1973 Ruffed Grouse	10,193	125.00
Mother's Day		
1972 Mother and Child	21,987	125.00
1973 Mother and Child	6,154	125.00
1974 Mother and Child	5,116	150.00
1975 Mother and Child	2,704	175.00
1976 Mother and Child	1,858	180.00
Presidential		
1972 George Washington	10,304	150.00
1972 John Adams	4,859	150.00
1972 Thomas Jefferson	4,933	150.00
1972 James Madison	3,058	150.00
1972 James Monroe	2,722	150.00

	Edition Limit	Issue Price (US)
1972 John Quincy Adams	2,501	$150.00
1972 Andrew Jackson	2,408	150.00
1973 Martin Van Buren	2,291	150.00
1973 William H. Harrison	2,182	150.00
1973 John Tyler	2,144	150.00
1973 James Polk	2,083	150.00
1973 Zachary Taylor	2,023	150.00
1973 Millard Fillmore	1,967	150.00
1974 Franklin Pierce	1,907	150.00
1974 James Buchanan	1,841	150.00
1974 Abraham Lincoln	2,955	150.00
1974 Andrew Johnson	1,777	150.00
1974 Ulysses S. Grant	1,754	150.00
1975 Rutherford B. Hayes	1,705	150.00
1975 James A. Garfield	1,675	150.00
1975 Chester A. Arthur	1,604	150.00
1975 Grover Cleveland	1,644	150.00
1976 Benjamin Harrison	1,619	150.00
1976 William McKinley	1,571	150.00
1976 Theodore Roosevelt	1,555	150.00
1976 William H. Taft	1,592	150.00
1976 Woodrow Wilson	1,563	150.00
1977 Warren G. Harding	1,544	150.00
1977 Calvin Coolidge	1,527	150.00
1977 Herbert Hoover	1,520	150.00
1977 Franklin D. Roosevelt	1,770	150.00
1977 Harry S. Truman	1,493	150.00
1978 Dwight D. Eisenhower	1,494	150.00
1978 John F. Kennedy	1,494	150.00
1978 Lyndon B. Johnson	1,483	150.00
1978 Richard M. Nixon	1,475	150.00
1978 Gerald R. Ford	NA	150.00
1978 Jimmy Carter	NA	150.00
James Wyeth		
1972 Along Brandywine	19,670	125.00
1973 Winter Fox	10,394	125.00
1974 Riding to Hunt	10,751	150.00
1975 Skating on Brandywine	8,058	175.00
1976 Brandywine Battlefield	6,968	180.00
Younger's Bird		
1972 Cardinal	13,939	125.00
1972 Bobwhite	13,939	125.00
1972 Mallards	13,939	125.00
1972 American Bald Eagle	13,939	125.00
John James Audubon		
1973 Wood Thrush	5,273	150.00
1973 Bald Eagle	3,005	150.00
1974 Night Heron	3,040	150.00
1974 Audubon's Warbler	3,034	150.00
Bernard Buffet		
1973 Gazelle	570	150.00
1974 Panda	570	150.00
1975 Giraffe	570	150.00
1976 Lion	570	150.00
1977 Rhinoceros	570	150.00
Bicentennial		
1973 Jefferson Drafting Declaration of Independence	8,556	175.00
1974 John Adams Champions Cause of Independence	8,442	175.00
1975 Caesar Rodney Decides Vote on Independence	8,319	175.00
1976 John Hancock Signs Declaration of Independence	10,166	175.00
Easter		
1973 Resurrection	7,116	175.00
1974 He Is Risen	3,719	185.00
1975 Last Supper	2,004	200.00
1976 Crucifixion	3,904	250.00
1977 Resurrection	1,206	250.00
Presidential Inaugural		
1973 Nixon/Agnew	10,483	150.00
1974 Ford (Silver)	1,141	200.00
1974 Ford (Gold)	11	3500.00
1977 Carter	928	225.00
Thanksgiving—by Dohanos		
1972 First Thanksgiving	10,142	125.00
1973 American Wild Turkey	3,547	125.00
1974 Thanksgiving Prayer	5,150	150.00
1975 Family Thanksgiving	3,025	175.00
1976 Home from Hunt	3,474	175.00
Four Seasons		
1975 Spring Blossoms	2,648	240.00
1975 Summer Bouquet	2,648	240.00
1976 Autumn Garland	2,648	240.00
1976 Winter Spray	2,648	240.00
American Revolution Bicentennial		
1976 Boston Tea Party	3,596	75.00
1976 Patrick Henry Urges Armed Resistance	3,596	75.00
1976 Paul Revere's Ride	3,596	75.00

	Edition Limit	Issue Price (US)
1976 Battle of Concord Bridge	3,596	$ 75.00
1976 Capture of Fort Ticonderoga	3,596	75.00
1976 Battle of Bunker Hill	3,596	75.00
1977 Signing of Declaration	3,596	75.00
1977 Washington Crosses Delaware	3,596	75.00
1977 Burgoyne Defeated at Saratoga	3,596	75.00
1977 Winter at Valley Forge	3,596	75.00
1977 Alliance with France	3,596	75.00
1977 Bonhomme Richard Defeats Serapis	3,596	75.00
1977 Victory at Yorktown	3,596	75.00
Annual		
1977 Tribute to Arts	1,901	280.00
1978 Tribute to Nature	435	280.00
Belskie		
1977 Mother's Day	290	210.00
Freedom		
1977 Lafayette Joins Washington	546	275.00
Rockwell Thanksgiving		
1977 Old Fashioned Thanksgiving	2,361	85.00
Christmas		
1977 Skating Party	908	55.00
Franklin Porcelain		
Hans Christian Andersen		
1976 Princess and Pea	16,875	38.00
1976 Ugly Duckling	16,875	38.00
1976 Little Mermaid	16,875	38.00
1976 Emperor's New Clothes	16,875	38.00
1976 Steadfast Tin Soldier	16,875	38.00
1976 Little Match Girl	16,875	38.00
1977 Snow Queen	16,875	38.00
1977 Red Shoes	16,875	38.00
1977 Tinder Box	16,875	38.00
1977 Nightingale	16,875	38.00
1977 Thumbelina	16,875	38.00
1977 Shepherdess & Chimney Sweep	16,875	38.00
Christmas Annual		
1976 Silent Night	19,286	65.00
1977 Deck Halls	9,185	65.00
1978 We Three Kings	Year	75.00
1979 Hark, Herald Angels Sing	Year	75.00
1980 Joy to World	Year	125.00
1981 O, Holy Night	Year	125.00
Flowers of Year		
1976 January	27,394	50.00
1976 February	27,394	50.00
1977 March	27,394	50.00
1977 April	27,394	50.00
1977 May	27,394	50.00
1978 June	27,394	50.00
1978 July	27,394	50.00
1978 August	27,394	50.00
1978 September	27,394	50.00
1979 October	27,394	50.00
1979 November	27,394	50.00
1979 December	27,394	50.00
Mother's Day		
1977 A Mother's Love	Year	65.00
1978 A Mother's Joy	Year	65.00
1979 A Mother's Gift	Year	75.00
Grimm's Fairy Tales		
1978 Sleeping Beauty	27,006	42.00
1978 Twelve Dancing Princesses	27,006	42.00
1978 Brementown Musicians	27,006	42.00
1979 Golden Goose	27,006	42.00
1979 Hansel and Gretel	27,006	42.00
1979 Rapunzel	27,006	42.00
1980 Snow White/Seven Dwarfs	27,006	42.00
1980 Frog Prince	27,006	42.00
1980 Red Riding Hood	27,006	42.00
1981 Rumpelstilskin	27,006	42.00
1981 Cinderella	27,006	42.00
1981 Shoemaker and Elves	27,006	42.00
Songbirds of World		
1977 Baltimore Oriole	20,225	55.00
1978 Bohemian Waxwing	20,225	55.00
Mark Twain		
1977 Whitewashing Fence	2,645	38.00
1977 Stealing a Kiss	2,645	38.00
1977 Traveling River	2,645	38.00
1977 Trading Lives	2,645	38.00
1977 Rafting Down River	2,645	38.00
1978 Riding Bronc	2,645	38.00

	Edition Limit	Issue Price (US)
1978 Jumping Frog Race	2,645	$ 38.00
1978 Facing Charging Knight	2,645	38.00
1978 Disguising Huck	2,645	38.00
1978 Living Along River	2,645	38.00
1978 Learning to Smoke	2,645	38.00
1978 Finger Printing Pays Off	2,645	38.00
Hometown Memories		
1979 Country Fair	Year	29.00
1980 Little Red School House	Year	29.00
1981 Sunday Picnic	Year	29.00
1982 Skating Party	Year	29.00
Country Year Collection		
1980 Woodlands in April	*	55.00
1980 Country Path in May	*	55.00
1980 June in Country Garden	*	55.00
1980 July Beside River	*	55.00
1980 Wheatfields in August	*	55.00
1980 September on Moors	*	55.00
1980 Colors of Autumn in October	*	55.00
1980 Country Lane in December	*	55.00
*Subscription period		
Calendar		
1981 Calendar	Year	55.00
1982 Calendar	Year	58.00

Frankoma

	Edition Limit	Issue Price (US)
Christmas		
1965 Goodwill Toward Man	Year	5.00
1966 Bethlehem Shepherds	Year	5.00
1967 Gifts for Christ Child	Year	5.00
1968 Flight into Egypt	Year	5.00
1969 Laid in a Manger	Year	5.00
1970 King of Kings	Year	5.00
1971 No Room in Inn	Year	5.00
1972 Seeking Christ Child	Year	5.00
1973 Annunciation	Year	5.00
1974 She Loved & Cared	Year	5.00
1975 Peace on Earth	Year	5.00
1976 Gift of Love	Year	6.00
1977 Birth of Eternal Life	Year	6.00
1978 All Nature Rejoiced	Year	6.00
1979 Stay of Hope	Year	6.00
1980 Unto Us a Child Is Born	Year	10.00
1981 O Come Let Us Adore Him	Year	12.00
1982 Wise Men Rejoice	Year	12.00
1983 Wise Men Bring Gifts	Year	12.00
Bicentennial		
1972 Provocations	Year	6.00
1973 Patriots & Leaders	Year	6.00
1974 Battles, Independence	Year	5.00
1975 Victories for Independence	Year	6.00
1976 Symbols of Freedom	Year	6.00
Teenagers of Bible		
1973 Jesus, Carpenter	Year	5.00
1974 David, Musician	Year	5.00
1975 Jonathan, Archer	Year	5.00
1976 Dorcas, Seamstress	Year	5.00
1977 Peter, Fisherman	Year	5.00
1978 Martha, Homemaker	Year	7.50
1979 Daniel, Courageous	Year	7.50
1980 Ruth, Devoted	Year	8.00
1981 Joseph, Dreamer	Year	8.00
1982 Mary, Mother	Year	8.00
Madonnas		
1977 Grace Madonna	Year	12.50
1978 Madonna of Love	Year	12.50

Ghent Collection

	Edition Limit	Issue Price (US)
Christmas Wildlife		
1974 Cardinals in Snow	10,135	20.00
1975 We Three Kings	12,750	29.00
1976 Partridge and Pear Tree	12,750	32.00
1977 Foxes and Evergreen	12,750	32.00
1978 Snowy Owls	12,750	32.00
Mother's Day		
1975 Cotton Tail	12,750	20.00
1976 Mallard Family	12,750	29.00
1977 Chipmunks & Trillium	12,750	32.00
1978 Raccoon Family	12,750	32.00
1979 Maytime	12,750	32.00
American Bicentennial Wildlife		
1976 American Bald Eagle	2,500	95.00
1976 American White-Tailed Deer	2,500	95.00
1976 American Bison	2,500	95.00
1976 American Wild Turkey	2,500	95.00

	Edition Limit	Issue Price (US)
Fausett Mural (Single issue)		
1976 From Sea to Shining Sea	1,976	$ 76.00
(Single issue)		
1978 Pilgrim of Peace	15 Days	29.50
Lands of Fable		
1981 Xanadu	17,500	55.00
1982 Atlantis	17,500	55.00
Man's Dream of Flight		
1981 Flight of Icarus	19,500	37.50
1981 Vision of Leonardo	19,500	37.50
1981 First Lighter-than-Air Flight	19,500	37.50
1981 Wright Brothers	19,500	37.50
1981 Lindbergh Flies Atlantic	19,500	37.50
1981 Barnstormers	19,500	37.50
1981 Jet Age	19,500	37.50
1981 Giant Leap for Mankind	19,500	37.50
Hans Brinker Delft		
1982 Hero of Haarlem	17,500	29.50
1982 Race	17,500	29.50
1982 Thousand Guilders	17,500	29.50
1982 On Canal	17,500	29.50
1982 Shadows in Home	17,500	29.50
1982 Mysterious Watch	17,500	29.50

Ghent Collection (Bing & Grøndahl)

	Edition Limit	Issue Price (US)
Hans Christian Andersen		
1979 Thumbelina	7,500	42.50
1979 Princess and Pea	7,500	42.50
1979 Wild Swans	7,500	42.50
1979 Emperor's New Clothes	7,500	42.50
1980 Little Mermaid	7,500	42.50
1980 Nightingale	7,500	42.50

Ghent Collection (Caverswall)

	Edition Limit	Issue Price (US)
Christmas Annual		
1979 Good King Wenceslaus	2,500	350.00
Country Diary of an Edwardian Lady		
1979 April	10,000	80.00
1979 June	10,000	80.00

Ghent Collection (Fairmont)

	Edition Limit	Issue Price (US)
Legends of Christmas		
1979 Bringing in Tree	5,000	65.00
Memory Annual		
1978 1977 Memory Plate	1,977	77.00
1979 1978 Memory Plate	1,978	78.00
1980 1979 Memory Plate	1,979	78.00
Israeli Commemorative (Single issue)		
1978 Promised Land	5,738	79.00
Spirit of America		
1978 Making of a Nation	1,978	78.00
1979 Growing Years	1,978	78.00

Ghent Collection (Gorham)

	Edition Limit	Issue Price (US)
April Fool Annual		
1978 April Fool's Day	10,000	35.00
1979 April Fool's Day	10,000	35.00
1980 April Fool's Day	10,000	37.50

Ghent Collection (Kaiser)

	Edition Limit	Issue Price (US)
Treasures of Tutankhamun		
1978 Golden Mask	3,247	90.00
1978 Golden Throne	3,247	90.00
1978 Horus Falcon	3,247	90.00
1978 Ivory Chest	3,247	90.00

Ghent Collection (Viletta)

	Edition Limit	Issue Price (US)
Olympics		
1980 1980 Winter Olympics	13 Days	24.50
1980 1980 Summer Olympics	13 Days	29.50

Gnomes United

	Edition Limit	Issue Price (US)
Gnomes		
1979 Gnome on Range	10,000	23.00
Gnome Patrol		
1979 Dr. Kwik	5,000	45.00

Golf Digest

	Edition Limit	Issue Price (US)
Second Hole (Single issue)		
1973 Dorado Beach Club	2,000	45.00
Twelfth Hole (Single issue)		
1973 Spyglass Hill	2,000	45.00
Freedom		
1977 Lafayette Joins Washington	546	275.00

Gorham

	Edition Limit	Issue Price (US)
(Single issue)		
1970 American Family Tree	5,000	17.00
Lionel Barrymore		
1971 Quiet Waters	15,000	25.00
1972 San Pedro Harbor	15,000	25.00
1972 Little Boatyard (Silver)	1,000	100.00

	Edition Limit	Issue Price (US)
1972 Nantucket (Silver)	1,000	$100.00
Bicentennial		
1971 Burning of Gaspee (Pewter)	5,000	35.00
1972 Burning of Gaspee (Silver)	750	550.00
1972 1776 (China)	18,500	17.50
1972 1776 (Vermeil)	500	500.00
1972 1776 (Silver)	750	250.00
1972 Boston Tea Party (Pewter)	5,000	35.00
1973 Boston Tea Party (Silver)	750	550.00
Gallery of Masters		
1971 Man in Gilt Helmet	10,000	50.00
1972 Self-Portrait Rembrandt, with Saskia	10,000	50.00
1973 Honorable Mrs. Graham	7,500	50.00
Moppets Mother's Day		
1973 Flowers for Mother	20,000	10.00
1974 Mother's Hat	20,000	12.00
1975 In Mother's Clothes	20,000	13.00
1976 Flowers	20,000	13.00
1977 Gift for Mother	18,500	13.00
1978 Moppet's Mother's Day	18,500	10.00
Moppets Christmas		
1973 Christmas March	20,000	10.00
1974 Trimming Tree	20,000	12.00
1975 Carrying Tree	20,000	13.00
1976 Asleep under Tree	18,500	13.00
1977 Star for Treetop	18,500	13.00
1978 Presents	18,500	10.00
1979 Moppet's Christmas	18,500	12.00
1980 Happy Merry Christmas Tree	Year	12.00
1981 Happy Merry Christmas Tree	Year	12.00
1982 Happy Merry Christmas Tree	Year	12.00
Remington Western		
1973 Aiding a Comrade	Year	25.00
1973 New Year on Cimarron	Year	25.00
1973 Fight for Waterhole	Year	25.00
1973 Flight	Year	25.00
1974 Old Ramond	Year	20.00
1974 Breed	Year	20.00
1975 Cavalry Officer	5,000	37.50
1975 Trapper	5,000	37.50
Irene Spencer Annual		
1974 Dear Child	10,000	37.50
1975 Promises to Keep	10,000	40.00
(Single issue)		
1974 Streakers	Year	19.50
(Single issue)		
1974 Golden Rule	Year	19.50
(Single issue)		
1974 Big Three	10,000	17.50
(Single issue)		
1974 Weigh-In	10,000	17.50
(Single issue)		
1975 Benjamin Franklin	18,500	19.50
Boy Scouts of America		
1975 Our Heritage	18,500	19.50
1976 Scout Is Loyal	18,500	19.50
1977 Scoutmaster	18,500	19.50
1977 Good Sign	18,500	19.50
1978 Pointing Way	18,500	19.50
1978 Campfire Story	18,500	19.50
American Artists		
1976 Apache Mother & Child	9,800	25.00
1976 Black Regiment	7,500	25.00
America's Cup Plates (Set of five)		
1976 America, 1861		
1976 Puritan		
1976 Reliance		
1976 Ranger		
1976 Courageous	1,000	200.00
Omnibus Muralis		
1976 200 Years with Old Glory	5,000	60.00
1977 Life of Christ	5,000	65.00
First Lady		
1977 Amy and Rosalynn	Year	24.95
Presidential		
1977 John F. Kennedy	9,800	30.00
1977 Eisenhower	9,800	30.00
Julian Ritter Annual		
1977 Christmas Visit	9,800	24.50
1978 Fluttering Heart	9,800	24.50

	Edition Limit	Issue Price (US)
Ritter's Four Seasons Clowns		
1977 Falling in Love (Set of four)	5,000	$100.00
1978 To Love a Clown (Set of four)	5,000	120.00
Santa Fe Railway Collection		
1977 Navajo Silversmith	7,500	37.50
1978 Turquoise Bead Maker	7,500	37.50
1979 Basketweaver	7,500	42.50
1980 Arrow Maker	7,500	45.00
Borsato Masterpiece Collection		
1977 Serenity	5,000	75.00
1978 Titian Madonna	5,000	75.00
1979 Ballerina	5,000	75.00
Little Men		
1977 Come Ride with Me	9,500	50.00
Moppets Anniversary		
1979 Moppet Couple	20,000	13.00
(Single issue)		
1978 Triple Self-Portrait	Year	37.50
Wild West		
1980 Bronc to Breakfast	9,800	38.00
1981 In Without Knocking	9,800	38.00
Four Seasons Landscape		
1980 Summer Respite	15,000	45.00
1980 Autumn Reflections	15,000	45.00
1981 Winter Delights	15,000	45.00
1981 Spring Recess	15,000	45.00
Rockwell Four Seasons		
1981 Old Timers (Set of four)	Year	100.00
1982 Life with Father (Set of four)	Year	100.00
1983 Old Buddies (Set of four)	Year	115.00
1984 Traveling Salesman (Set of four)	Year	115.00
(Single issue—Set of two)		
1981 Day in Life of Boy		
1981 Day in Life of Girl	Year	50.00
Four Ages of Love		
1981 Sweet Song So Young	10,000	100.00
1982 Flowers in Tender Bloom	10,000	100.00
Masterpieces of Rockwell		
1981 Girl at Mirror	17,500	50.00
Young Love		
1981 Beguiling Buttercup	17,500	62.50
1982 Flying High	17,500	62.50
Encounters, Survivals and Celebrations		
1982 A Fine Welcome	7,500	50.00
1983 Winter Trails	7,500	50.00
Pastoral Symphony		
1982 When I Was a Child	7,500	42.50
1983 Gather Children	7,500	42.50
A Merry Mouse		
1983 A Merry Mouse Christmas	5,000	15.00
Museum Doll		
1983 Lydia	5,000	29.00
1983 Belton Bebe Doll	5,000	29.00
Heaven Mother's Day		
1984 Mother Is Love	5,000	24.95

See also:
American Commemorative (U.S.A.)
American Express (U.S.A.)
American Preservation Guild (U.S.A.)
American Rose Society (U.S.A.)
Fleetwood Collection (U.S.A.)
Ghent Collection (U.S.A.)
Lincoln Mint (U.S.A.)
Volair (U.S.A.)

Greentree Potteries

	Edition Limit	Issue Price (US)
Grant Wood		
1971 Studio	2,000	10.00
1972 Antioch School	2,000	10.00
1973 At Stone City	2,000	10.00
1974 Adolescence	2,000	10.00
1975 Birthplace	2,000	10.00
1976 American Gothic	2,000	10.00
Kennedy		
1972 Center for Performing Arts	2,000	20.00
1973 Birthplace, Brookline, Mass.	2,000	12.00
Motorcar		
1972 1929 Packard Dietrich Convertible	2,000	20.00
1973 Model "A" Ford	2,000	20.00
Mississippi River		
1973 Delta Queen	2,000	10.00
1973 Tri-Centennial	2,000	10.00

	Edition Limit	Issue Price (US)
Dave Grossman Designs		
Margaret Keane		
1976 Balloon Girl	5,000	$ 25.00
1977 My Kitty	5,000	25.00
1978 Bedtime	5,000	25.00
Tom Sawyer		
1975 Whitewashing Fence	10,000	24.00
1976 First Smoke	10,000	24.00
1977 Take Your Medicine	10,000	24.00
1978 Lost in Cave	10,000	25.00
Looney Tunes Mother's Day		
1976 Bugs Bunny	10,000	13.00
Looney Tunes Christmas		
1977 Christmas	10,000	13.00
1978 Christmas	5,000	14.00
Children of Week		
1978 Monday's Child	5,000	30.00
1979 Tuesday's Child	5,000	30.00
1979 Wednesday's Child	5,000	30.00
1980 Thursday's Child	5,000	30.00
1980 Friday's Child	5,000	30.00
1981 Saturday's Child	5,000	30.00
1981 Sunday's Child	5,000	30.00
Annual Fall		
1978 Peace	5,000	55.00
1979 Santa	5,000	55.00
Annual		
1979 Leapfrog	Year	50.00
1980 Lovers	Year	60.00
1981 Dreams of Long Ago	Year	60.00
Rockwell		
1979 Butter Boy	5,000	40.00
Huckleberry Finn		
1979 Secret	10,000	40.00
1980 Listening	10,000	40.00
1981 No Kings Nor Dukes	10,000	40.00
1982 Snake Escapes	10,000	40.00
(Single issue)		
1980 Norman Rockwell Back to School	10,000	24.00
Rockwell Christmas		
1980 Christmas Trio	Year	75.00
1981 Santa's Good Boys	Year	75.00
1982 Faces of Christmas	Year	75.00
Rockwell Boy Scout Annual		
1981 Can't Wait	10,000	30.00
1982 A Guiding Hand	10,000	30.00
1983 Tomorrow's Leader	10,000	30.00
Magic People		
1982 Music for a Queen	9,500	65.00
1982 Fantasy Festival	10,000	65.00
1983 Bubble Chariot	10,000	65.00
1983 Kite Carriage	10,000	65.00
Milk Glass		
1983 Dreamboats	15,000	24.00
Hackett American Collectors		
Corita Kent Annual		
1979 I Love You Very	30,000	19.95
1980 You Bring Spring	10,000	21.95
1981 Love	10,000	30.00
1982 Cheers	10,000	32.50
Endangered Species		
1980 California Sea Otters	7,500	35.00
1981 Asian Pandas	7,500	37.50
1982 Australian Koala Bears	7,500	39.50
1982 River Otters	7,500	39.50
Ocean Moods		
1980 Sunset Tide	5,000	50.00
1981 Moonlight Flight	5,000	50.00
1982 Morning Surf	5,000	50.00
1983 Afternoon Surf	5,000	50.00
Save Whales		
1980 Trust and Love	10,000	30.00
Snow Babies		
1980 Canadian Harp Seals	7,500	39.50
1981 Polar Bear Cubs	7,500	39.50
1982 Snow Leopards	7,500	42.50
Friends of Forest		
1981 Forest Alert	7,500	50.00
1982 Brookside Protection	7,500	50.00
1982 Mountain Guardian	7,500	50.00
1983 Lookouts	7,500	50.00
Horses in Action		
1981 Challenge	7,500	39.50
1982 Country Days	7,500	50.00
1983 Family Portrait	7,500	50.00
1983 All Grown Up	7,500	50.00
Parkhurst Christmas		
1981 Christmas Tear	7,500	39.50
1982 Christmas Morning	7,500	39.50
1983 Night Before Christmas	7,500	39.50
Wonderful World of Clowns		
1981 Kiss for a Clown	7,500	39.50

	Edition Limit	Issue Price (US)
1981 Rainbow's End	7,500	$ 39.50
1982 Happy Days	7,500	42.50
1982 Filling Pop's Shoes	7,500	42.50
Wonderous Years		
1981 After Rains	5,000	39.50
1982 I Got One	5,000	42.50
1982 Fascination	5,000	42.50
(Single issue)		
1981 John Lennon	90 Days	25.00
Crazy Cats		
1982 Primping Time	10,000	42.50
Daisy Cats		
1982 Daisy Kitten	10,000	42.50
1982 Daisy Cat	10,000	42.50
Days Remembered		
1982 First Birthday	19,500	29.50
Early Discoveries		
1982 Let's Play	10,000	42.50
Escalera Christmas		
1982 Special Delivery	19,500	32.50
1983 Especially for You	19,500	35.00
Everyone's Friends		
1982 Springtime	10,000	42.50
1982 Autumn Bandit	10,000	42.50
1983 Snowtime Bunnies	10,000	42.50
Family Portraits		
1982 Mother's Joy	7,500	85.00
Fashions by Irene		
1982 Elegant Lady	15,000	45.00
Escalera Father's Day		
1982 Daddy's Rose	10,000	42.50
1983 Daddy's Wish	10,000	42.50
Impressions by Joanne Mix		
1982 Windy Day	10,000	42.50
1982 Sunny Day	10,000	42.50
1983 Summer's Day	10,000	42.50
Joanne Mix Christmas		
1982 Christmas Love	7,500	39.50
Kelly's Stable		
1982 My Champion	15,000	42.50
1983 Glory Bound	15,000	42.50
1983 Arabian Spring	15,000	42.50
Landfalls		
1982 San Francisco Bay	7,500	39.50
1983 Newport Harbor	7,500	39.50
1983 Miami Beach	7,500	39.50
Little Orphans		
1982 Surprise Package	19,500	29.50
1983 Castaway	19,500	32.50
Mother and Child		
1982 Mother's Love	10,000	42.50
1982 Tenderness	10,000	42.50
1983 Serenity	10,000	42.50
Parkhurst Mother's Day		
1982 Daisies for Mother	10,000	42.50
Ocean Stars		
1982 Sea Horses	10,000	42.50
1982 Dolphins	10,000	42.50
1983 Whales	10,000	42.50
Parkhurst Diamond		
1982 Chance Encounter	1,500	300.00
Peaceful Retreat		
1982 Refuge	19,500	29.50
1983 Solitude	19,500	32.50
1983 Tranquility	19,500	35.00
Prairie Children		
1982 Young Pioneers	19,500	32.50
1983 Adam	19,500	35.00
Side by Side		
1982 My Hero	19,500	32.50
1983 Sippin' Soda	19,500	35.00
Special Moments		
1982 April	10,000	42.50
1982 Rachel	10,000	42.50
Sunday Best		
1982 Stacey	10,000	42.50
1982 Laurie	10,000	42.50
Waterbird Families		
1982 Marsh Venture	10,000	42.50
1982 Afternoon Swim	10,000	42.50
1983 Nesting Wood Ducks	10,000	42.50
1983 Returning Home	10,000	42.50
World of Ozz Franca		
1982 Images	10,000	42.50
1982 Lost and Found	10,000	42.50
1983 Best Friends	10,000	42.50
(Single issue)		
1982 Hog Heaven	15,000	42.50
(Single issue)		
1982 Henry Fonda	10,000	39.50
(Single issue)		
1982 Reggie Jackson	10,000	60.00

	Edition Limit	Issue Price (US)
(Single issue)		
1982 John Wayne	10,000	$ 39.50
Classic Cars		
1983 '57 Chevy	5,000	39.50
Costume Party		
1983 Belinda	7,500	39.50
Famous Planes of Yesterday		
1983 Spirit of St. Louis	5,000	39.50
Favorite Dreams		
1983 Daddy's Sailor	7,500	39.50
Golfing Greats		
1983 Arnold Palmer	100 Days	45.00
Huggable Moments		
1983 Naptime	10,000	39.50
1983 Playtime	10,000	39.50
Joan Horton Christmas		
1983 Moonlight Sleighride	5,000	39.50
Jungle Babies		
1983 Baby Bengals	5,000	39.50
Memorable Impressions		
1983 Beachcomber	7,500	39.50
1983 Beach Girl	7,500	39.50
Puzzling Moments		
1983 Problem Solver	7,500	39.50
1983 Practice Makes Perfect	7,500	39.50
Reflections of Sea		
1983 Golden Shores	5,000	42.50
Sadako's Helpers		
1983 Artist's Pal	7,500	39.50
Sensitive Moments		
1983 Sharing Beauty	5,000	39.50
Snow Babies		
1982 Arctic Foxes	7,500	42.50
Summer Fun		
1983 Fishing Together	7,500	39.50
Yesterday's Expressions		
1983 Gloria	5,000	39.50
(Single issue-set of two)		
1983 Bjorn Borg		
1983 Martina Navratilova	15,000	39.50
(Single issue)		
1983 Frog Heaven	5,000	39.50
(Single issue)		
1983 Hopalong Cassidy	7,500	42.50
(Single issue)		
1983 Laurel and Hardy	15,000	42.50
(Single issue)		
1983 Other Heaven	5,000	39.50
(Single issue)		
1983 Steve Garvey	10,000	60.00
(Single issue)		
1984 Nolan Ryan	8,402	42.50
(Single issue)		
1984 Tom Seaver	6,728	42.50
Hamilton Collection		
Japanese Floral Calendar		
1981 New Year's Day	10 Days	32.50
1982 Early Spring	10 Days	32.50
1982 Spring	10 Days	32.50
1982 Girl's Day	10 Days	32.50
1982 Buddah's Birthday	10 Days	32.50
1983 Herald's of Spring	10 Days	32.50
1983 Boy's Doll Day	10 Days	32.50
1983 Summer	10 Days	32.50
1983 Autumn	10 Days	32.50
1983 Festival of Full Moon	10 Days	32.50
1983 Late Autumn	10 Days	32.50
1983 Winter	10 Days	32.50
Legends of Camelot		
1981 Secret Romance	12,500	62.50
1982 Merlin Magician	12,500	62.50
1982 I Knight Thee Sir Lancelot	12,500	62.50
Story of Heidi		
1981 Heidi	14,750	45.00
1981 Grandfather	14,750	45.00
1981 Heidi and Peter	14,750	45.00
1981 Grandmother	14,750	45.00
1982 Kittens	14,750	45.00
1982 Mountain Cure	14,750	45.00
Story of Noah's Ark		
1981 Two by Two . . .	12,500	45.00
1982 In Divine Harmony	12,500	45.00
Treasures of Chinese Mandarins		
1981 Bird of Paradise	2,500	75.00
1982 Guardians of Heaven	2,500	75.00
1982 Tree of Immortality	2,500	75.00
1982 Dragon of Eternity	2,500	75.00
Tribute to Ballet		
1981 Nutcracker	15,000	62.50
Fairies of Fields and Flowers		
1982 Willow Fairy	NA	45.00

	Edition Limit	Issue Price (US)
Gardens of Orient		
1982 Flowering of Spring	10 Days	$ 19.50
1983 Festival of May	10 Days	19.50
1983 Cherry Blossom Brocade	10 Days	19.50
Lewis & Clark Expedition		
1982 In Bitteroots	NA	55.00
1982 Sacajawea at Big Water	NA	55.00
1982 Lewis Crossing	NA	55.00
1982 Buffalo Gangue	NA	55.00
1982 Salt Makers	NA	55.00
1982 Up Jefferson	NA	55.00
1982 Arrival of Sgt. Pryor	NA	55.00
1982 Visitors at Fort Clatsop	NA	55.00
Eternal Wishes of Good Fortune		
1983 Friendship	10 Days	34.95
1983 Love	10 Days	34.95
1983 Fertility	10 Days	34.95
1983 Purity and Perfection	10 Days	34.95
1983 Illustrious Offspring	10 Days	34.95
1983 Peace	10 Days	34.95
1983 Longevity	10 Days	34.95
1983 Immortality	10 Days	34.95
1983 Marital Bliss	10 Days	34.95
1983 Beauty	10 Days	34.95
1983 Fortitude	10 Days	34.95
1983 Youth	10 Days	34.95
Majestic Birds of Prey		
1983 Golden Eagle	12,500	55.00
1983 Cooper's Hawk	12,500	55.00
Utz Mother's Day		
1983 A Gift of Love	Year	27.50
(Single issue)		
1983 Princess Grace	NA	40.00
A Garden of Verses		
1984 Picture Books in Winter	NA	24.50
Hamilton Collection (Boehm Studios)		
Rose Collection		
1979 Peace Rose	15,000	45.00
1979 Queen Elizabeth Rose	15,000	45.00
1979 White Masterpiece Rose	15,000	45.00
1979 Angel Face Rose	15,000	45.00
1979 Tropicana Rose	15,000	45.00
1979 Elegance Rose	15,000	45.00
1979 Royal Highness Rose	15,000	45.00
1979 Mister Lincoln Rose	15,000	45.00
Boehm Owl Collection		
1980 Snowy Owl	15,000	45.00
1980 Boreal Owl	15,000	45.00
1980 Barn Owl	15,000	45.00
1980 Saw Whet Owl	15,000	45.00
1980 Great Horned Owl	15,000	45.00
1980 Screech Owl	15,000	45.00
1980 Short Eared Owl	15,000	45.00
1980 Barred Owl	15,000	45.00
Hummingbird Collection		
1980 Calliope Hummingbird	15,000	55.00
1980 Broadtail Hummingbird	15,000	55.00
1980 Rufous Flame Bearer Hummingbird	15,000	55.00
1980 Broad-Billed Hummingbird	15,000	55.00
1980 Streamer-Tail Hummingbird	15,000	55.00
1980 Blue-Throated Hummingbird	15,000	55.00
1980 Crimson-Topaz Hummingbirds	15,000	55.00
1980 Brazilian Ruby	15,000	55.00
Roses of Excellence Collection		
1981 Love Rose	Year	60.00
1982 White Lightnin'	Year	62.50
Water Bird Collection		
1981 Canadian Geese	15,000	55.00
1981 Wood Ducks	15,000	55.00
1981 Common Mallards	15,000	55.00
1981 Green-Winged Teals	15,000	55.00
1981 Ross' Geese	15,000	55.00
1981 Canvas-Backs	15,000	55.00
1981 Hooded Mergansers	15,000	55.00
1981 American Pintails	15,000	55.00
Life's Best Wishes		
1982 Longevity	15,000	75.00
1982 Happiness	15,000	75.00
Miniature Roses		
1982 Toy Clown	Year	39.50
Tribute to Award-Winning Roses		
1983 Irish Gold	15,000	62.50

	Edition Limit	Issue Price (US)
Hamilton Collection (Hutschenreuther)		
Roses of Redouté		
1983 China Rose	17,500	$ 32.50
Hamilton Collection (Kaiser)		
Summer Days of Childhood		
1983 Garden Magic	10 Days	29.50
1983 Mountain Friends	10 Days	29.50
Hamilton Collection (Porcelaine Ariel)		
A Tribute to Love		
1980 Shaft of Light	17,500	45.00
1980 Jug of Wine	17,500	45.00
1981 Sultan After Sultan	17,500	45.00
1981 Bird Is on Wing	17,500	45.00
1982 If Today Be Sweet	17,500	45.00
1982 Flower Once Has Blown	17,500	45.00
Greatest Show on Earth		
1981 Clowns-Heart of Circus	10 Days	30.00
1981 Elephants	10 Days	30.00
1981 Aerialists	10 Days	30.00
1981 Great Parade	10 Days	30.00
1982 Midway	10 Days	30.00
1982 Equestrians	10 Days	30.00
1982 Lion Tamer	10 Days	30.00
1982 Grande Finale	10 Days	30.00
Hamilton Collection (Royal Devon)		
Rockwell Home of Brave		
1981 Reminiscing	18,000	35.00
1982 Hero's Welcome	18,000	35.00
Hamilton Collection (Viletta)		
Coppelia Ballet		
1980 Franz's Fantasy Love	28 Days	25.00
1980 Creation of a Doll	28 Days	25.00
1981 Secret Is Unlocked	28 Days	25.00
1981 Swanhilda's Deception	28 Days	25.00
1981 An Uneasy Sleep	28 Days	25.00
1981 Coppelia Awakens	28 Days	25.00
1982 A Shattered Dream	28 Days	25.00
1982 Wedding	28 Days	25.00
Portraits of Childhood		
1981 Butterfly Magic	28 Days	24.95
1982 Sweet Dreams	28 Days	24.95
1983 Turtle Talk	28 Days	24.95
Waltzes of Johann Strauss		
1981 Emperor's Waltz	28 Days	25.00
1981 Blue Danube	28 Days	25.00
1981 Voices of Spring	28 Days	25.00
1981 Vienna Life	28 Days	25.00
1982 Roses of South	28 Days	25.00
1982 Wine, Women and Song	28 Days	25.00
1982 Artist's Life	28 Days	25.00
1982 Tales of Vienna Woods	28 Days	25.00
Carefree Days		
1982 Autumn Wanderer	10 Days	24.50
1982 Best Friends	10 Days	24.50
1982 Feeding Time	10 Days	24.50
1983 Bathtime Visitor	10 Days	24.50
1983 First Catch	10 Days	24.50
1983 Monkey Business	10 Days	24.50
1984 Touchdown	10 Days	24.50
Hamilton Mint		
Picasso		
1972 Le Gourmet	5,000	125.00
1972 Tragedy	5,000	125.00
1973 Lovers	5,000	125.00
Kennedy		
1974 (Gold on Pewter)	Year	40.00
1974 (Pewter)	Year	25.00
Man's Best Friend		
1978 Hobo	9,500	40.00
1978 Doctor	9,500	40.00
1979 Making Friends	9,500	40.00
1979 Gone Fishing	9,500	40.00
1980 Thief	9,500	40.00
1980 Puppy Love	9,500	40.00
Historic Providence Mint		
(Single issue)		
1979 Children's Year	3,000	95.00
Children of Seasons		
1980 Children of Spring	3,000	107.50
America Beautiful		
1981 Spacious Skies	17,500	37.50
1981 Amber Waves of Grain	17,500	37.50
1981 Purple Mountain Majesties	17,500	37.50
1981 God Shed His Grace	17,500	37.50
1981 Crown Good with Brotherhood	17,500	37.50
1981 From Sea to Shining Sea	17,500	37.50

	Edition Limit	Issue Price (US)
Vanishing American Barn		
1983 Bucks County Barn	14,500	$ 39.50
1983 Victorian Barn	14,500	39.50
1983 New England Barn	14,500	39.50
1983 Southern Tobacco Barn	14,500	39.50
1983 Forebay Barn	14,500	39.50
1983 Appalachian Barn	14,500	39.50
1983 Connected Barn	14,500	39.50
1983 Hudson River Barn	14,500	39.50
1983 Log Barn	14,500	39.50
1983 Thatched Barn	14,500	39.50
1983 Lancaster Barn	14,500	39.50
1983 Round Barn	14,500	39.50
Ralph Homan Studios (Viletta)		
Seasons of Oak		
1979 Lazy Days	5,000	55.00
1980 Come Fly with Me	5,000	55.00
Home Plates (Mingolla)		
Christmas (Enamel on Copper)		
1973 Christmas	1,000	95.00
1974 Christmas	1,000	110.00
1975 Christmas	1,000	125.00
1976 Christmas	1,000	125.00
1977 Scene from Childhood	2,000	200.00
Christmas (Porcelain)		
1974 Christmas	5,000	35.00
1975 Christmas	5,000	35.00
1976 Christmas	5,000	35.00
1977 Winter Wonderland	7,000	45.00
Four Seasons (Enamel on Copper)		
1978 Dashing Thru Snow	2,000	150.00
1979 Spring Flowers	2,000	150.00
1980 Beach Fun	2,000	150.00
1981 Balloon Breeze	2,000	150.00
Christmas in Country (Enamel on Copper)		
1979 Dear Santa	1,000	70.00
1980 Country Cousin	1,000	90.00
Hoyle Products		
Clown		
1977 Runaway	7,500	45.00
1978 It's Your Move	7,500	45.00
1979 Understudy	7,500	45.00
1980 Idol	7,500	45.00
Traveling Salesman		
1977 Traveling Salesman	7,500	35.00
1978 Country Pedlar	7,500	40.00
1979 Horse Trader	7,500	40.00
1980 Expert Salesman	7,500	45.00
Wilderness Wings		
1978 Gliding In	5,000	35.00
1979 Taking Off	5,000	40.00
1980 Joining Up	5,000	45.00
1981 Canvasbacks	5,000	47.50
Four Seasons		
1978 Gay Blades	Year	55.00
1979 Boy Meets Dog	Year	55.00
1980 Chilly Reception	Year	65.00
Rockwell Four Seasons (Bronze)		
1979 Adventurers Between Adventures	9,500	55.00
Cowboy		
1977 Sharing an Apple	5,000	35.00
1978 Split Decision	5,000	35.00
1979 Hiding Out	5,000	35.00
1980 In Trouble	5,000	35.00
Mother's Day		
1980 Family Circus	5,000	25.00
Rare Rockwells		
1980 Mrs. O'Leary's Cow	7,500	30.00
1981 Come and Get It	7,500	30.00
Hilda		
1981 Toasting Marshmallows	5,000	25.00
Nostalgia		
1981 Pepsi Cola Girl	5,000	25.00
1982 Olympia Girl	5,000	30.00
1982 Savannah Beer Girl	5,000	30.00
1983 Dr. Pepper Girl	5,000	30.00
Wings of Wild		
1982 Cinnamon Teal	5,000	30.00
1982 Moment of Rest	5,000	30.00
1983 Mourning Doves	5,000	30.00
Gothic Romance		
1982 Moonlight Romance	5,000	30.00
By-Gone Days		
1983 Breakfast with Teddy	12,500	35.00
Nostalgia Magazines		
1983 Ladies Home Journal	12,500	35.00
Hudson Pewter		
Bicentennial		
1975 Spirit of '76	10,000	45.00

	Edition Limit	Issue Price (US)
Mother's Day		
1979 Cherished	10,000	$ 35.00
Songbirds of Four Seasons		
1979 Hummingbird	7,500	35.00
America's Sailing Ships		
1979 U.S.S. Constitution	5,000	35.00
A Child's Christmas		
1979 Littlest Angels	10,000	35.00
1980 Heaven's Christmas Tree	10,000	42.50
Twas Night Before Christmas		
1982 Not a Creature Was Stirring	10,000	47.50
1983 Visions of Sugar Plums	10,000	47.50
Imperial		
America Beautiful		
1969 U.S. Capitol	500	17.50
1970 Mount Rushmore	500	17.50
1971 Statue of Liberty	500	17.50
1972 Monument Valley, Arizona	500	17.50
1973 Liberty Bell	500	17.50
1974 Golden Gate	500	19.95
1975 Mt. Vernon	500	19.95
Christmas		
1970 Partridge (Carnival)	Year	12.00
1970 Partridge (Crystal)	Year	15.00
1971 Two Turtle Doves (Carnival)	Year	12.00
1971 Two Turtle Doves (Crystal)	Year	16.50
1972 Three French Hens (Carnival)	Year	12.00
1972 Three French Hens (Crystal)	Year	16.50
1973 Four Colly Birds (Carnival)	Year	12.00
1973 Four Colly Birds (Crystal)	Year	16.50
1974 Five Golden Rings (Carnival)	Year	12.00
1974 Five Golden Rings (Crystal)	Year	16.50
1975 Six Geese A-Laying (Carnival)	Year	14.00
1975 Six Geese A-Laying (Crystal)	Year	19.00
1976 Seven Swans (Carnival)	Year	16.00
1976 Seven Swans (Crystal)	Year	21.00
1977 Eight Maids A-Milking (Carnival)	Year	18.00
1977 Eight Maids A-Milking (Crystal)	Year	23.00
1978 Nine Ladies Dancing (Carnival)	Year	20.00
1978 Nine Ladies Dancing (Crystal)	Year	25.00
1979 Ten Lords A-Leaping (Carnival)	Year	22.00
1979 Ten Lords A-Leaping (Crystal)	Year	27.00
1980 Eleven Pipers Piping (Carnival)	Year	24.00
1980 Eleven Pipers Piping (Crystal)	Year	29.00
1981 Twelve Drummers Drumming (Carnival)	Year	28.00
1981 Twelve Drummers Drumming (Crystal)	Year	34.00
Coin Crystal		
1971 1964 Kennedy Half Dollar	Year	15.00
1972 Eisenhower Dollar	Year	15.00
(Single issue)		
1976 Bicentennial	Year	20.00
Incolay Studios		
Life's Interludes		
1979 Uncertain Beginning	Year	95.00
1980 Finally Friends	12,000	95.00
Four Elements		
1983 Air	9,170	25.00
International Museum		
Christmas Stamp Art		
1979 Gingerbread Santa	Year	29.00
1980 Madonna and Child	Year	37.50
1981 Botticelli's Madonna and Child	9,900	45.00
1982 Madonna of Goldfinch	9,900	45.00
Dance, Ballerina, Dance		
1982 First Slippers	14,500	47.50
1982 At Barre	14,500	47.50

	Edition Limit	Issue Price (US)
1982 Recital	14,500	$ 47.50
1982 Pirouette	14,500	47.50
1982 Swan Lake	14,500	47.50
1982 Opening Night	14,500	47.50
Letter Writers		
1982 Portrait of Michelangelo	15,000	45.00
1982 Mrs. John Douglas	15,000	45.00
1983 Don Antonio de Noriega	15,000	45.00
1983 Lovely Reader	15,000	45.00
Super Heroes		
1983 Superman	NA	29.50
International Silver		
We Are One		
1972 Declaration of Independence	7,500	40.00
1973 Midnight Ride of Paul Revere	7,500	40.00
1973 Stand at Concord Bridge	7,500	40.00
1974 Crossing Delaware	7,500	50.00
1974 Battle of Valley Forge	7,500	50.00
1975 Surrender at Yorktown	7,500	50.00
Christmas		
1974 Tiny Tim	7,500	75.00
1975 Caught	7,500	75.00
1976 Bringing Home Tree	7,500	75.00
1977 Fezziwig's Christmas Ball	7,500	75.00
1978 Alleluia	7,500	75.00
1979 Rejoice	7,500	100.00
1980 Adoration	7,500	125.00
Presidential		
1975 Washington	7,500	75.00
1976 Jefferson	7,500	75.00
1976 Lincoln	7,500	75.00
1976 F. Roosevelt	7,500	75.00
1977 Eisenhower	7,500	75.00
1977 Kennedy	7,500	75.00
Seasons American Past		
1976 Autumn	7,500	60.00
1976 Spring	7,500	60.00
1976 Summer	7,500	60.00
1976 Winter	7,500	60.00
See also: American Archives (U.S.A.)		
Interpace		
Modigliani (Single issue)		
1972 Caryatid	10,000	60.00
Architects of Democracy (Set of four)		
1974 George Washington		
1974 John Adams		
1974 Thomas Jefferson		
1974 Alexander Hamilton	1,776	225.00
JM Company		
Competitive Sports		
1979 Downhill Racing Slalom	10,000	25.00
Oriental Birds		
1979 Window at Tiger Spring Temple	10,000	39.00
Love		
1980 Love's Serenade	5,000	50.00
Joys (Viletta)		
Precious Moments		
1979 Friend in Sky	28 Days	21.50
1980 Sand in Her Shoe	28 Days	21.50
1980 Snow Bunny	28 Days	21.50
1980 Seashells	28 Days	21.50
1981 Dawn	28 Days	21.50
1981 My Kitty	28 Days	21.50
Judaic Heritage Society		
Jewish Holidays		
1972 Chanukah (Silver)	2,000	150.00
1972 Chanukah (Gold)	25	1900.00
1972 Pesach (Silver)	2,000	150.00
1972 Pesach (Gold)	25	1900.00
1972 Purim (Silver)	2,000	150.00
(Single issue)		
1974 Purim (Silver)	1,000	150.00
Great Jewish Women		
1976 Golda Meir	4,000	35.00
1976 Henrietta Szold	4,000	35.00
1976 Emma Lazarus	4,000	35.00
Heritage Plates		
1976 Rabbi	4,000	35.00
1976 Hasidim	4,000	35.00
1976 Shtetl	4,000	35.00
(Single issue)		
1977 Jacob and Angel	5,000	45.00
(Single issue)		
1977 Hatikvah (Copper)	5,000	55.00

	Edition Limit	Issue Price (US)
(Single issue)		
1977 Hatikvah (Gold Plated)	1,000	$ 75.00
(Single issue)		
1977 Hatikvah (Sterling Silver)	500	180.00
Jewish Holidays		
1979 Chanukah	2,500	50.00
1979 Purim	2,500	50.00
1979 Shavouth	2,500	50.00
1979 Rosh Hashanah	2,500	50.00
1979 Simchat Torah	2,500	50.00
1979 Pesach	2,500	50.00
Jerusalem Wedding		
1979 Bride of Jerusalem	6,000	65.00
1979 Hasidic Dancers	6,000	65.00
Judaic Heritage Society (Avondale)		
(Single issue)		
1980 Shalom—Peace	6,000	95.00
Judaic Heritage Society (Viletta)		
Israel's 30th Anniversary (Single issue)		
1979 L'Chayim to Israel	10,000	59.50
Israel's 30th Anniversary (Single issue)		
1979 Prophecy of Isaiah	4,000	59.50
David Kaplan Studio		
Fiddler's People		
1978 Fiddler on Roof	7,500	60.00
1979 Tevya	7,500	60.00
1980 Miracle of Love	7,500	60.00
1981 Wedding	7,500	60.00
Loveables		
1982 Little Angel	12,500	40.00
Keller & George (Reed & Barton)		
Bicentennial		
1972 Monticello (Damascene)	1,000	75.00
1972 Monticello (Silver Plate)	200	200.00
1973 Mt. Vernon (Damascene)	Year	75.00
Kensington		
Children of Week		
1980 Wednesday's Child	27,500	28.50
Kern Collectibles		
Linda's Little Loveables		
1977 Blessing	7,500	30.00
1978 Appreciation	7,500	37.50
1979 Adopted Burro	7,500	42.50
Runci Mother's Day		
1977 Darcy	5,000	50.00
1978 A Moment to Reflect	5,000	55.00
1979 Fulfillment	5,000	45.00
1980 A Renewal of Faith	5,000	45.00
Christmas of Yesterday		
1978 Christmas Call	5,000	45.00
1979 Woodcutter's Christmas	5,000	50.00
1980 Making Christmas Goodies	5,000	55.00
1981 Singing Christmas Carols	5,000	55.00
Adventures of Old West		
1981 Grizzly Ambush	7,500	65.00
1982 Train Robbers	7,500	65.00
1983 Bank Holdup	7,500	65.00
My Favorite Pets		
1981 Schnauzers	7,500	39.95
1982 Cocker Spaniels	7,500	39.95
1983 Pointers	7,500	42.50
Horses of Harland Young		
1982 Quarterhorses	10,000	55.00
1983 Arabians	10,000	55.00
School Days		
1982 Apple for My Teacher	7,500	65.00
This Little Pig		
1982 Pig Went to Market	9,800	39.95
1983 Pig Stayed Home	9,800	42.50
A Child's World		
1983 Kathie	9,800	45.00
1983 Meredith	9,800	45.00
1984 Freddie	9,800	45.00
Kitty Cats		
1983 Morrie	7,500	39.00
1984 Tattoo	7,500	39.00
North American Game Birds		
1983 Canadian Geese	7,500	60.00
Portraits of Innocence		
1983 Sarah	7,500	55.00
Zoological Garden		
1983 Elephants	5,000	55.00
(Single issue)		
1984 Champ	7,500	$ 39.50
Kern Collectibles (Haviland & Parlon)		
Patti Canaris Songbird		
1980 Cardinals	5,000	65.00
1981 Blue Birds	5,000	70.00
1982 Orioles	5,000	70.00
1983 Goldfinches	5,000	70.00
Patti Canaris Butterfly		
1982 Monarchs	7,500	75.00
Kern Collectibles (Pickard)		
Cowboy Artists (Sets of two)		
1976 Out There		
1976 Cutting Out a Stray	3,000	130.00
1977 Broken Cinch		
1977 No Place to Cross	1,000	130.00
Companions		
1977 Cubs	5,000	40.00
1978 Mighty Sioux	5,000	40.00
1979 Nature Girl	5,000	50.00
1980 Buffalo Boy	5,000	50.00
1981 Shepherds	5,000	55.00
Kern Collectibles (Rosenthal)		
John Falter Harvest Time		
1976 Gathering Pumpkins	5,000	70.00
1977 Honest Day's Work	4,000	70.00
Runci Classic		
1977 Summertime	5,000	95.00
1978 Springtime	5,000	95.00
Kern Collectibles (Royal Bayreuth)		
Christmas		
1972 Carriage in Village	4,000	15.00
1973 Snow Scene	5,000	16.50
1974 Old Mill	4,000	24.00
1975 Forest Chalet "Serenity"	4,000	27.50
1976 Christmas in Country	5,000	40.00
1977 Peace on Earth	5,000	40.00
1978 Peaceful Interlude	5,000	45.00
1979 Homeward Bound	5,000	50.00
Sun Bonnet Babies (Set of seven)		
1974 Monday (Washing Day)		
1974 Tuesday (Ironing Day)		
1974 Wednesday (Mending Day)		
1974 Thursday (Scrubbing Day)		
1974 Friday (Sweeping Day)		
1974 Saturday (Baking Day)		
1974 Sunday (Fishing Day)	15,000	120.00
Antique American Art		
1976 Farmyard Tranquility	3,000	50.00
1977 Half Dome	3,000	55.00
1978 Down Memory Lane	3,000	65.00
(Single issue)		
1976 Sun Bonnet Babies Composite	15,000	75.00
L. Henry		
1976 Just Friends	5,000	50.00
1977 Interruption	4,000	55.00
Anniversary		
1980 Young Americans	5,000	125.00
Sun Bonnet Babies Playtime		
1981 Swinging	5,000	60.00
1981 Round Dance	5,000	60.00
1982 Marbles	5,000	60.00
1982 Playing Catch	5,000	60.00
Kern Collectibles (Sango)		
Living American Artist		
1976 Sweethearts (Rockwell)	10,000	30.00
1977 Apache Girl (Perillo)	5,000	35.00
1978 Natural Habitat	5,000	40.00
Great Achievements in Art		
1980 Arabian	3,000	65.00
1981 Texas Longhorns	3,000	70.00
Kilkelly		
St. Patrick's Day		
1975 Pipe and Shamrock	Year	16.50
1976 Third Look in Logan	Year	20.00
Kirk		
DeGrazia		
1972 Heavenly Blessing	200	75.00
Mother's Day		
1972 Mother and Child	3,500	75.00
1973 Mother and Child	2,500	80.00
Bicentennial		
1972 U.S.S. Constellation	825	75.00
1972 Washington	5,000	75.00
Thanksgiving		
1972 Thanksgiving Ways and Means	3,500	$150.00
Christmas		
1972 Flight into Egypt	3,500	150.00
Lake Shore Prints		
Rockwell		
1973 Butter Girl	9,433	14.95
1974 Truth about Santa	15,141	19.50
1975 Home from Fields	8,500	24.50
1976 A President's Wife	2,500	70.00
Lapsys		
Crystal Christmas		
1977 Snowflake	5,000	47.50
1978 Peace on Earth	5,000	47.50
Lenox		
Boehm Birds		
1972 Bird of Peace (Mute Swan)	5,000	150.00
1973 Young America, 1776 (Eaglet)	6,000	175.00
Colonial Christmas Wreath		
1981 Virginia	Year	65.00
1982 Massachusetts	Year	65.00
1983 Maryland	Year	70.00
Nature's Nursery		
1983 Snow Leopards	15,000	65.00
1983 Koalas	15,000	65.00
1984 Llamas	15,000	70.00
Butterflies and Flowers		
1983 Question Mark Butterfly and New England Aster	25,000	65.00
1983 Sonoran Blue Butterfly and Mariposa Lily	25,000	65.00
1983 Malachite Butterfly and Orchid	25,000	65.00
1984 Ruddy Daggerwing Butterfly and Lantana	25,000	70.00
See also: American Express (U.S.A.)		
Lincoln Mint		
Great Artists (Dali)		
1971 Unicorn Dyonisiaque (Gold)	100	1500.00
1971 Unicorn Dyonisiaque (Silver)	5,000	100.00
1972 Dyonisiaque et Pallas Athens (Gold)	300	2000.00
1972 Dyonisiaque et Pallas Athens (Gold Plate)	2,500	150.00
1972 Dyonisiaque et Pallas Athens (Silver)	7,500	125.00
Easter		
1972 Christ (Silver)	20,000	150.00
1972 Christ (Gold Plate)	10,000	200.00
1974 Christ (Pewter)	Year	45.00
Mother's Day		
1972 Collies (Silver)	3,000	125.00
Christmas		
1972 Madonna Della Seggiola (Gold Plate)	125	150.00
1972 Madonna Della Seggiola (Silver)	3,000	125.00
Dali Cross Plate		
1977 Gold Cross	5,000	225.00
1977 Silver Cross	10,000	175.00
Lincoln Mint (Gorham)		
Christmas		
1978 Santa Belongs to All Children	7,500	29.50
Litt		
Christmas		
1978 Madonna & Child	1,000	200.00
1979 O Holy Night	1,000	200.00
Annual		
1979 Apache Sunset	1,250	275.00
Lynell Studios		
Little Traveler		
1978 On His Way	4,000	45.00
1979 On Her Way	4,000	45.00
American Adventure		
1979 Whaler	7,500	50.00
1979 Trapper	7,500	50.00
1980 Forty-Niner	7,500	50.00
1981 Pioneer Woman	7,500	50.00
1981 Wagon Master	7,500	50.00
1982 Wagon Ho!	7,500	50.00
All-American Soap Box Derby		
1979 Last Minute Changes	Year	24.50
1980 At Gate	Year	24.50
1981 In Stretch	Year	$ 29.50
Rockwell Legendary Art Christmas		
1979 Snow Queen	60 Days	24.50
1980 Surprises for All	60 Days	24.50
1981 Grandpop and Me	60 Days	29.50
1982 Santa's Secret	10,000	35.00
1983 Looking for Santa	10,000	35.00
John Wayne		
1979 Man of Golden West	Year	45.00
RCA Victor Nipper Plate		
1980 His Master's Voice	NA	24.50
Rockwell Legendary Art Annual		
1980 Artist's Daughter	Year	65.00
Rockwell Legendary Art Mother's Day		
1980 Cradle of Love	60 Days	29.50
1981 A Mother's Blessing	60 Days	29.50
1982 Memories	60 Days	29.50
Rockwell Legendary Art Rare Rockwell Paintings		
1980 Poor Richard	17,500	45.00
Popeye's 50th Anniversary (Single issue)		
1980 Happy Birthday Popeye	Year	22.50
Great Chiefs of Canada		
1980 Chief Joseph Brant	7,500	65.00
1981 Crowfoot	7,500	65.00
1982 Tecumseh	7,500	65.00
Betsey Bates Christmas		
1979 Olde Country Inn	7,500	38.50
1980 Village School House	7,500	38.50
1981 Village Blacksmith	7,500	38.50
1982 Christmas Village	7,500	38.50
Children's World		
1981 Official Babysitter	15,000	24.50
1981 Cowboy Capers	15,000	29.50
1982 Nurse Nancy	15,000	29.50
Eyes of Seasons		
1981 Winter	19,500	38.50
1981 Spring	19,500	38.50
1981 Summer	19,500	38.50
1981 Autumn	19,500	38.50
Hagel Christmas		
1981 Shhh!	17,500	29.50
1982 Kiss for Santa	10,000	35.00
How West Was Won		
1981 Pony Express	19,500	38.50
1982 Oregon Trail	19,500	38.50
1982 California Gold Rush	19,500	38.50
1982 Cattle Drive	19,500	38.50
1983 Peace Pipe	19,500	38.50
1983 Driving Golden Spike	19,500	38.50
North American Wildlife		
1981 Snuggling Cougars	7,500	65.00
Oriental Dreams		
1981 Tranquility	15,000	55.00
Rockwell's Scotty		
1981 Scotty Stowaway	17,500	45.00
1982 Scotty Strikes Bargain	17,500	45.00
(Single issue)		
1981 Reagan Bush Inaugural	17,500	45.00
Best of Times		
1982 Candy Shop	15,000	38.50
Children's World		
1982 Pet Shop	17,500	29.50
Circus Dreams		
1982 Two for Show	19,500	24.50
Greatest Clowns of Circus		
1982 Emmett Kelly	NA	45.00
1982 Lou Jacobs	NA	45.00
1982 Felix Adler	NA	45.00
1982 Otto Griebling	NA	45.00
Hagel Mother's Day		
1982 Once Upon a Time	60 Days	29.50
Hobo Joe		
1982 Hold Onions	10,000	50.00
1982 Do Not Disturb	10,000	50.00
1983 No Camping or Fishing	10,000	50.00
1983 Traveling in Style	10,000	50.00
Little House on Prairie		
1982 Welcome to Walnut Creek	NA	45.00
1982 Country Girls	NA	45.00
(Single issue)		
1982 Betty Boop	15,000	24.50
(Single issue)		
1982 I Love Lucy	100 Days	45.00
(Single issue)		
1982 Norman Rockwell Tribute	5,000	55.00
(Single issue)		
1982 Thanks for Memories	100 Days	45.00
(Single issue)		
1982 Young at Heart	100 Days	45.00

	Edition Limit	Issue Price (US)
Lionel Barrymore		
1983 Nantucket	7,500	$ 45.00
(Single issue)		
1984 Wayne Gretzky	Year	39.95
Mallek Studios		
Navajo Christmas		
1971 Indian Wise Men	1,000	15.00
1972 On Reservation	2,000	17.00
1973 Hoke Denetsosie	2,000	17.00
1974 Monument Valley	2,000	18.00
1975 Coming Home for Christmas	2,000	18.00
1976 Deer with Rainbow	2,000	20.00
1977 Goat Herders	2,000	20.00
1978 Hogan Christmas	2,000	20.00
1979 Navajo Madonna	3,000	25.00
1980 Children's Playmates	3,500	25.00
Chinese Lunar Calendar		
1972 Year of Rat	1,000	15.00
1973 Year of Ox	1,000	15.00
1974 Year of Rabbit	1,000	15.00
Christmas Game Birds		
1972 Gambel Quail	1,000	15.00
1973 Partridge	1,000	15.00
1974 Owl and Cactus	1,000	15.00
1975 Chinese Wood Duck	1,000	15.00
1976 Wild Turkey	1,000	15.00
1977 Mallard	1,000	15.00
1978 Canadian Geese	1,000	15.00
1979 American Woodcock	1,000	15.00
Mexican Christmas		
1972 Manger	1,000	15.00
1973 Madonna	1,000	15.00
1974 Corona	1,000	18.00
1975 Pinata	1,000	18.00
1976 Procession	1,000	20.00
1977 Wisemen	1,000	20.00
Navidad (Single issue)		
1972 Navidad en Mexico	500	15.00
(Single issue)		
1972 Amish Harvest	1,000	17.00
A.B.C.'s		
1974 A.B.C. Rabbit	1,000	15.00
1975 A.B.C. Mice	1,000	15.00
1976 A.B.C. Ducklings	1,000	15.00
1977 A.B.C. Elephant	1,000	15.00
1978 A.B.C. Owls	1,000	15.00
(Single issue)		
1976 Kewpie Doll	1,000	15.00
(Single issue)		
1982 Barnyard Serenade	5,000	25.00
(Single issue)		
1982 Beep, Beep	2,000	25.00
Master Engravers of America		
Indian Dancers		
1979 Eagle Dancer	2,500	300.00
1980 Hoop Dancer	2,500	300.00
McCalla Enterprises (Viletta)		
Making Friends		
1978 Feeding Neighbor's Pony	5,000	45.00
1979 Cowboys 'n' Indians	5,000	47.50
1980 Surprise for Christy	5,000	47.50
Love Letters		
1980 Mail Order Bride	5,000	60.00
Metal Arts		
America's First Family (Single issue)		
1977 Carters	9,500	40.00
Freedom (Single issue)		
1977 Washington at Valley Forge (Sterling)	500	225.00
Freedom (Single issue)		
1977 Washington at Valley Forge (Pewter)	1,000	95.00
Winslow Homer's Sea		
1977 Breezing Up	9,500	29.95
Rockwell Copper Christmas		
1978 Christmas Gift	Year	48.00
1979 Big Moment	Year	48.00
Metlox Potteries		
See: Vernonware (U.S.A.)		
Metropolitan Museum of Art		
Treasures of Tutankhamun		
1977 King Tut	2,500	150.00
Mingolla		
See: Home Plates (U.S.A.)		
Mistwood Designs (Fairmont)		
American Wildlife		
1981 Desperado at Waterhole	5,000	45.00

	Edition Limit	Issue Price (US)
1981 Bayou Bunnies	5,000	$ 50.00
Woodland Game Birds		
1981 After Flight	5,000	60.00
Modern Concepts		
Special Moments		
1982 David's Dilemma	12,500	35.00
1983 Secrets	12,500	35.00
Signs of Love		
1983 When Hearts Touch	17,500	39.00
Modern Masters		
Through Eyes of Love		
1981 Enchanted Eyes	9,500	55.00
1982 Summer Secrets	9,500	55.00
1983 Garden Gathering	9,500	55.00
Babes in Woods		
1982 Newborn Fawn	9,500	45.00
1983 First Outing	9,500	45.00
1983 Bandy Bandit	9,500	50.00
Floral Felines		
1982 Baron	9,500	55.00
1983 Her Majesty	9,500	55.00
Will Moses America		
1982 September Fair	7,500	45.00
1983 Spring Recess	7,500	45.00
Litter Basket		
1983 Last of Litter	15 Days	35.00
Little Ladies		
1983 When Mommy's Away	15 Days	29.50
(Single issue)		
1983 Twelve Days of Christmas	12 Days	45.00
Modern Masters/GBS		
Horses of Fred Stone		
1981 Patience	9,500	55.00
1982 Arabian Mare and Foal	9,500	55.00
1982 Safe and Sound	9,500	55.00
1983 Contentment	9,500	55.00
A Child's Best Friend		
1982 Christi's Kitty	15 Days	29.50
1982 Patrick's Puppy	15 Days	29.50
Moussalli		
Birds of Four Seasons		
1978 Cardinal (Winter)	1,000	375.00
1979 Indigo Bunting (Fall)	1,000	375.00
1979 Hummingbird (Summer)	1,000	375.00
1980 Wren (Spring)	1,000	375.00
Mother's Day		
1979 Chickadee	500	450.00
Museum Editions (Ridgewood)		
Colonial Heritage		
1974 Tidewater, Virginia	9,900	40.00
1975 Pennsbury Manor	9,900	40.00
1975 Old New York	9,900	40.00
1976 Hammond-Harwood House	9,900	40.00
1976 Joseph Webb House	9,900	40.00
1977 Old Court House	9,900	40.00
1977 Mulberry Plantation	9,900	40.00
Museum Editions (Viletta)		
Christmas Annual		
1978 Expression of Faith	7,400	49.95
1979 Skating Lesson	7,400	49.95
Colonial Heritage		
1978 Moffatt-Ladd House	9,900	40.00
1978 Trent House	9,900	40.00
1979 Cupola House	9,900	40.00
1979 Nicholas House	9,900	40.00
1980 Derby House	9,900	40.00
1980 Davenport House	9,900	40.00
Nostalgia Collectibles		
Shirley Temple		
1982 Baby Take a Bow	25,000	35.00
1983 Curly Top	25,000	35.00
1983 Stand Up and Cheer	25,000	35.00
1983 Captain January	25,000	35.00
Ohio Arts		
Norman Rockwell		
1979 Looking Out to Sea	20,000	19.50
OK Collectibles		
Fantasy Farm		
1984 Lowena	3,000	39.95
Meadow		
1984 Chester	5,000	55.00
Pacific Art		
Just Like Daddy's Hats		
1983 Jessica	10,000	29.00
(Single issue)		
1983 Guardian Angel	7,500	29.50

	Edition Limit	Issue Price (US)
Paramount Classics (Pickard)		
(Single issue)		
1977 Coronation Plate	5,000	$ 95.00
(Single issue)		
1977 Queen Victoria	5,000	95.00
(Single issue)		
1977 King George III	5,000	95.00
Pemberton & Oakes (Viletta)		
Moments Alone		
1980 Dreamer	15 Days	28.80
1981 Reverie	15 Days	28.80
1982 Gentle Thoughts	15 Days	28.80
1983 Wheat Field	4,800	28.80
Nutcracker II		
1981 Nutcracker Grand Finale	28 Days	24.40
1982 Arabian Dancers	28 Days	24.40
1983 Dewdrop Fairy	28 Days	24.40
Swan Lake		
1983 Swan Queen	15,000	35.00
Children and Pets		
1984 Tender Moment	19,500	19.00
Pickard		
Presidential		
1971 Truman	3,000	35.00
1973 Lincoln	5,000	35.00
(Single issue)		
1982 Great Seal of United States	10,000	95.00
Children of Christmas Past		
1983 Sledding on Christmas Day	7,500	60.00
Children of Mary Cassatt		
1983 Simone in a White Bonnet	7,500	60.00
1983 Children Playing on Beach	7,500	60.00
See also:		
Kern Collectibles (U.S.A.)		
Paramount Classics (U.S.A.)		
Porcelain Limited		
Children of Seasons		
1982 Spring Joy	9,800	49.95
1982 Summer Love	9,800	49.95
1982 Fall's Adventure	9,800	49.95
1982 Winter's Dreamer	9,800	49.95
Ram		
Boston 500		
1973 Easter	500	30.00
1973 Mother's Day	500	30.00
1973 Father's Day	500	30.00
1973 Christmas	500	30.00
Great Bird Heroes		
1973 Cher Ami	1,000	7.95
1973 Mocker	1,000	7.95
Reco International		
Americana (Single issue)		
1972 Gaspee	1,000	130.00
Four Seasons (Set of four)		
1973 Fall		
1973 Spring		
1973 Summer		
1973 Winter	2,500	200.00
Western (Single issue)		
1974 Mountain Man	1,000	165.00
Christmas (Single issue)		
1977 Old Mill in Valley	5,000	28.00
Games Children Play		
1979 Me First	10,000	45.00
1980 Forever Bubbles	10,000	45.00
1981 Skating Pals	10,000	45.00
1982 Join Me	10,000	45.00
Grandparents		
1981 Grandma's Cookie Jar	Year	37.50
1981 Grandpa and Doll House	Year	37.50
Arabelle and Friends		
1982 Ice Delight	15,000	35.00
1983 First Love	15,000	35.00
Little Professionals		
1982 All is Well	10,000	39.50
1983 T.L.C.	10,000	39.50
Reed & Barton		
Audubon		
1970 Pine Siskin	5,000	60.00
1971 Red-Shouldered Hawk	5,000	60.00
1972 Stilt Sandpiper	5,000	60.00
1973 Red Cardinal	5,000	60.00
1974 Boreal Chickadee	5,000	60.00
1975 Yellow-Breasted Chat	5,000	65.00

	Edition Limit	Issue Price (US)
1976 Bay-Breasted Warbler	5,000	$ 65.00
1977 Purple Finch	5,000	65.00
(Single issue)		
1970 Zodiac	1,500	75.00
California Missions		
1971 San Diego	1,500	75.00
1972 Carmel	1,500	75.00
1973 Santa Barbara	1,500	60.00
1974 Santa Clara	1,500	60.00
1976 San Gabriel	1,500	65.00
Annual		
1972 Free Trapper	2,500	65.00
1973 Outpost	2,500	65.00
1974 Toll Collector	2,500	65.00
1975 Indians Discovering Lewis & Clark	2,500	65.00
Currier & Ives		
1972 Village Blacksmith	1,500	85.00
1972 Western Migration	1,500	85.00
1973 Oaken Bucket	1,500	85.00
1973 Winter in Country	1,500	85.00
1974 Preparing for Market	1,500	85.00
Kentucky Derby		
1972 Nearing Finish	1,000	75.00
1973 Riva Ridge	1,500	75.00
1974 100th Running	1,500	75.00
(Single issue)		
1972 Delta Queen	2,500	75.00
(Single issue)		
1972 Road Runner	1,500	65.00
Founding Father		
1973 Ben Franklin	2,500	65.00
1974 George Washington	2,500	65.00
1975 Thomas Jefferson	2,500	65.00
1976 Patrick Henry	2,500	65.00
1976 John Hancock	2,500	65.00
1976 John Adams	2,500	65.00
(Single issue)		
1975 Chicago Fire	Year	60.00
(Single issue)		
1975 Mississippi Queen	2,500	75.00
See also:		
Collector Creations (U.S.A.)		
Keller & George (U.S.A.)		
Ridgewood		
Bicentennial		
1974 First in War	12,500	40.00
Tom Sawyer (Set of four)		
1974 Trying a Pipe		
1974 Lost in Cave		
1974 Painting Fence		
1974 Taking Medicine	3,000	39.95
Wild West (Set of four)		
1975 Discovery of Last Chance Gulch		
1975 Doubtful Visitor		
1975 Bad One		
1975 Cattleman	15,000	65.00
Leyendecker Christmas		
1975 Christmas Morning	10,000	24.50
1976 Christmas Surprise	10,000	24.50
Leyendecker Mother's Day		
1976 Grandma's Apple Pie	5,000	24.50
1977 Tenderness	10,000	35.00
Little Women		
1976 Sweet Long Ago	5,000	45.00
1976 Song of Spring	5,000	45.00
1977 Joy in Morning	5,000	45.00
See also: Museum Editions (U.S.A.)		
River Shore		
Baby Animals Collection		
1979 Akiku	20,000	65.00
1980 Roosevelt	20,000	65.00
1981 Clover	20,000	65.00
1982 Zuela	20,000	65.00
Della Robbia Annual		
1979 Adoration	5,000	550.00
1980 Virgin and Child	5,000	450.00
Remington Bronze		
1977 Bronco Buster	15,000	55.00
1978 Coming Thru Rye	15,000	60.00
1979 Cheyenne	15,000	60.00
1980 Mountain Man	15,000	60.00
(Single issue)		
1979 Spring Flowers	17,000	75.00
(Single issue)		
1980 Looking Out to Sea	17,000	75.00
Grant Wood		
1981 American Gothic	17,000	80.00
Rockwell's Four Freedoms		
1981 Freedom of Speech	17,000	65.00

		Edition Limit	Issue Price (US)
Vignette			
1981	Broken Window	22,500	$ 19.50
1982	Sunday Best	22,500	19.50
(Single issue)			
1981	Grandpa's Guardian	17,000	80.00
Christmas After Christmas			
1982	Kay's Doll	9,500	75.00
Rockwell Collectors Club			
Christmas			
1978	Christmas Story	15,000	24.50
Rockwell Museum			
American Family			
1978	Baby's First Step	9,900	28.50
1978	Happy Birthday Dear Mother	9,900	28.50
1978	Sweet Sixteen	9,900	28.50
1978	First Haircut	9,900	28.50
1979	First Prom	9,900	28.50
1979	Student	9,900	28.50
1979	Wrapping Christmas Presents	9,900	28.50
1979	Birthday Party	9,900	28.50
1979	Little Mother	9,900	28.50
1980	Washing Our Dog	9,900	28.50
1980	Mother's Little Helper	9,900	28.50
1980	Bride & Groom	9,900	28.50
American Family II			
1980	New Arrival	22,500	35.00
1980	Sweet Dreams	22,500	35.00
1980	Little Shaver	22,500	35.00
1980	We Missed You Daddy	22,500	35.00
1980	Home Run Slugger	22,500	35.00
1980	Giving Thanks	22,500	35.00
1980	Space Pioneers	22,500	35.00
1980	Little Salesman	22,500	35.00
1980	Almost Grown Up	22,500	35.00
1980	Courageous Hero	22,500	35.00
1980	At Circus	22,500	35.00
1980	Good Food, Good Friends	22,500	35.00
Christmas			
1979	Day After Christmas	25,000	75.00
1980	Checking His List	Year	75.00
1981	Ringing in Good Cheer	Year	75.00
1982	Waiting for Santa	Year	75.00
1983	High Hopes	Year	75.00
1984	Space Age Santa	Year	75.00
(Single issue)			
1979	Norman Rockwell Remembered	Year	45.00
Classic			
1981	Puppy Love	60 Days	24.50
1981	While Audience Waits	60 Days	24.50
1981	Off to School	60 Days	24.50
1982	Country Doctor	60 Days	24.50
1982	Spring Fever	60 Days	24.50
1982	Dollhouse for Sis	60 Days	24.50
Mother's Day			
1982	A Tender Moment	5,000	70.00
(Single issue)			
1983	A Tribute to J.F.K.	NA	39.50
(Single issue)			
1983	With This Ring	NA	45.00
Roman			
A Child's Play			
1982	Kite Flying	30 Days	29.95
1982	Breezy Day	30 Days	29.95
Child's World			
1982	Baby Blossoms	15,000	24.95
1982	I Wish, I Wish	15,000	24.95
1982	Trees So Tall	15,000	24.95
1982	Daisy Dreamer	15,000	24.95
Ice Capades Clown			
1983	Presenting Freddie Trenkler		24.50
Petty Girls of Ice Capades			
1983	Ice Princess	30 Days	24.50
Cats			
1984	Grizabella	NA	29.50
(Single issue)			
1984	Carpenter	NA	100.00
Royal Cornwall			
Bethlehem Christmas			
1977	First Christmas Eve	10,000	29.95
1978	Glad Tidings	10,000	34.50
1979	Gift Bearers	10,000	34.50
1980	Great Joy	10,000	39.95
Creation			
1977	In Beginning	19,500	45.00
1977	In His Image	19,500	45.00
1977	Adam's Rib	19,500	45.00
1977	Banished from Eden	19,500	45.00

		Edition Limit	Issue Price (US)
1977	Noah and Ark	19,500	$ 45.00
1977	Tower of Babel	19,500	45.00
1978	Sodom & Gomorrah	19,500	45.00
1978	Jacob's Wedding	19,500	45.00
1978	Rebekah at Well	19,500	45.00
1978	Jacob's Ladder	19,500	45.00
1978	Joseph's Coat of Many Colors	19,500	45.00
1978	Joseph Interprets Pharaoh's Dream	19,500	45.00
Classic Christmas			
1978	Child of Peace	17,500	55.00
1978	Silent Night	17,500	55.00
1978	Most Precious Gift	17,500	55.00
1978	We Three Kings	17,500	55.00
Four Seasons			
1978	Warmth	17,500	60.00
1978	Voices of Spring	17,500	60.00
1978	Fledgling	17,500	60.00
1978	We Survive	17,500	60.00
Golden Age of Cinema			
1978	King & His Ladies	22,500	45.00
1978	Fred & Ginger	22,500	45.00
1978	Judy & Mickey	22,500	45.00
1979	Philadelphia Story	22,500	45.00
1979	Thin Man	22,500	45.00
1979	Gigi	22,500	45.00
Mother's Day			
1978	God Bless Mommy	10,000	35.00
Alice in Wonderland			
1979	Alice and White Rabbit	27,500	45.00
1979	Advice from a Caterpillar	27,500	45.00
1979	Cheshire Cat's Grin	27,500	45.00
1979	Mad Hatter's Tea Party	27,500	45.00
1979	Queen's Croquet Match	27,500	45.00
1979	Who Stole Tarts?	27,500	45.00
Kitten's World			
1979	Just Curious	27,500	45.00
1979	Hello, World	27,500	45.00
1979	Are You a Flower?	27,500	45.00
1979	Talk to Me	27,500	45.00
1979	My Favorite Toy	27,500	45.00
1979	Purr-Fect Pleasure	27,500	45.00
Promised Land			
1979	Pharaoh's Daughter Finds Moses	24,500	45.00
1979	Burning Bush	24,500	45.00
1979	Let My People Go	24,500	45.00
1979	Parting of Red Sea	24,500	45.00
1979	Miriam's Song of Thanksgiving	24,500	45.00
1979	Manna from Heaven	24,500	45.00
1979	Water from Rock	24,500	45.00
1979	Battle of Amalek	24,500	45.00
1979	Ten Commandments	24,500	45.00
1979	Golden Calf	24,500	45.00
1979	Moses Smashes Tablets	24,500	45.00
1979	Glorious Tabernacle	24,500	45.00
Treasures of Childhood			
1979	My Cuddlies Collection	19,500	45.00
1979	My Coin Collection	19,500	45.00
1979	My Shell Collection	19,500	45.00
1979	My Stamp Collection	19,500	45.00
1979	My Doll Collection	19,500	45.00
1979	My Rock Collection	19,500	45.00
Beauty of Bouguereau			
1980	Lucie	19,500	35.00
1980	Madelaine	19,500	35.00
1980	Frere et Soeur	19,500	35.00
1980	Solange et Enfant	19,500	35.00
1980	Colette	19,500	35.00
1980	Jean et Jeanette	19,500	35.00
Four Faces of Love			
1980	Romeo & Juliet	17,500	55.00
1980	Young Galahad	17,500	55.00
1980	At Locksley Hall	17,500	55.00
1980	St. Agnes Eve	17,500	55.00
Dorothy's Day			
1980	Brand New Day	15,000	55.00
1980	All by Myself	15,000	55.00
1981	Off to School	15,000	55.00
1981	Best Friends	15,000	55.00
1981	Helping Mommy	15,000	55.00
1981	Bless Me Too	15,000	55.00
Legendary Ships of Seas			
1980	Flying Dutchman	19,500	49.50
1980	Refanu	19,500	49.50
1980	Palatine	19,500	49.50
1980	Gaspé Bay	19,500	49.50
1980	Roth Ramhach	19,500	49.50
1980	Pride	19,500	49.50
1980	Copenhagen	19,500	49.50

		Edition Limit	Issue Price (US)
1980	Frigorifique	19,500	$ 49.50
1980	Foochow Sea Junk	19,500	49.50
1980	Rescue	19,500	49.50
Little People			
1980	Off to Picnic	19,500	34.50
1980	Decorating Tree	19,500	34.50
1980	Cruising Down River	19,500	34.50
1980	Sweetest Harvest	19,500	34.50
1980	Happy Chorus	19,500	34.50
1980	Painting Leaves	19,500	34.50
Memories of America			
1980	Bringing in Maple Sugar	5,000	120.00
1980	Old Automobile	5,000	120.00
1981	Halloween	5,000	120.00
1981	Rainbow	5,000	120.00
Windows on World			
1980	Golden Gate of San Francisco	19,500	45.00
1981	Snow Village/ Madulain	19,500	45.00
1981	Rainy Day in London	19,500	45.00
1981	Water Festival/Venice	19,500	45.00
1981	Harvesting in Ukraine	19,500	45.00
1981	Serengeti Plain	19,500	45.00
1982	Springtime in Paris	19,500	45.00
1982	Lunch in Michelstadt	19,500	45.00
1982	Flamenca of Madrid	19,500	45.00
1982	Tokyo at Cherry Time	19,500	45.00
1982	Palace of Winds, Jaipur	19,500	45.00
1982	Carnival Time in Rio	19,500	45.00
Exotic Birds of Tropique			
1981	Scarlet Macaws	19,500	49.50
1981	Toco Toucan	19,500	49.50
1981	Rosy Flamingos	19,500	49.50
1982	Greater Cockatoo	19,500	49.50
1982	Ultramarine King	19,500	49.50
1982	Red Fan Parrot	19,500	49.50
1982	Bird of Paradise	19,500	49.50
Love's Precious Moments			
1981	Love's Sweet Vow	17,500	55.00
1981	Love's Sweet Verse	17,500	55.00
1981	Love's Sweet Offering	17,500	55.00
1981	Love's Sweet Embrace	17,500	55.00
1981	Love's Sweet Melody	17,500	55.00
1981	Love's Sweet Kiss	17,500	55.00
Most Precious Gifts of Shen-Lung			
1981	Fire	19,500	49.50
1981	Water	19,500	49.50
1981	Sun	19,500	49.50
1982	Moon	19,500	49.50
1982	Earth	19,500	49.50
1982	Sky	19,500	49.50
Puppy's World			
1981	1st Birthday	19,500	49.50
1981	Beware of Dog	19,500	49.50
1981	Top Dog	19,500	49.50
1981	Need a Friend?	19,500	49.50
1981	Double Trouble	19,500	49.50
1981	Just Clowning	19,500	49.50
1981	Guest for Dinner	19,500	49.50
1981	Gift Wrapped	19,500	49.50
Courageous Few			
1982	Fall of Jericho	24,500	59.50
1982	Gideon's Three Hundred	24,500	59.50
1982	Strength of Samson	24,500	59.50
Impressions of Yesteryear			
1982	Moon Mist	19,500	59.50
1982	Fall Flowers	19,500	59.50
1982	Wishing Well	19,500	59.50
Legend of Peacock Maidens			
1982	Dance of Peacock Maiden	19,500	69.50
1982	Promise of Love	19,500	69.50
1982	Betrayal	19,500	69.50
1982	Prince and Python	19,500	69.50
Noble Flower Maidens			
1982	Iris Maiden	19,500	65.00
1982	Plum Blossom	19,500	65.00
1982	Quince Maiden	19,500	65.00
America's Golden Years			
1983	County Fair	NA	49.50
Memories of Western Prairies			
1983	Picking Daisies	Year	49.50
1984	Feeding Colt	Year	49.50
2000 Years of Sailing Ships			
1983	Cutty Sark and Thermopylae	NA	49.50
Royal Devon			
See: Hamilton Collection (U.S.A.)			
Royal Oaks Limited			
Love's Labor			
1982	Intruder	15,000	50.00

		Edition Limit	Issue Price (US)
1982	It's My Turn!	15,000	$ 50.00
1983	Look! I Can Fly!	15,000	50.00
1983	Just Like Your Own!	15,000	50.00
Royal Orleans			
Pink Panther Christmas			
1982	Sleigh Ride	13,000	25.00
1983	Happy Landings	13,000	18.50
1984	Down Chimney	13,000	18.50
(Single issue)			
1982	M*A*S*H	Year	25.00
In Trompe L'Oeil			
1984	Up to Mischief	10,000	25.00
Wuthering Heights			
1984	Yorkshire Brontës	NA	35.00
Royal Worcester			
Birth of a Nation			
1972	Boston Tea Party	10,000	45.00
1973	Ride of Paul Revere	10,000	45.00
1974	Incident at Concord Bridge	10,000	50.00
1975	Declaration of Independence	10,000	65.00
1976	Washington Crossing Delaware	10,000	65.00
Currier & Ives			
1974	Road-Winter	10,000	59.50
1975	Old Grist Mill	10,000	59.50
1976	Winter Pastime	10,000	59.50
American History			
1977	Washington's Inauguration	1,250	65.00
Annual			
1977	Home to Thanksgiving	500	59.50
Royalwood			
(Single issue)			
1977	Doctor and Doll	Year	21.50
Leyendecker			
1978	Cornflake Boy	10,000	25.00
1978	Cornflake Girl	10,000	25.00
John A. Ruthven			
Moments of Nature			
1977	Screech Owls	5,000	37.50
1979	Chickadees	5,000	39.50
1980	California Quail	5,000	39.50
Sebastian			
American's Favorite Scenes			
1978	Motif #1	10,000	75.00
1979	Grand Canyon	10,000	75.00
Seeley's Doll Plates			
Antique French Dolls			
1979	Bru	5,000	39.00
1979	E.J.	5,000	39.00
1979	A.T.	5,000	39.00
1980	Alexandre	5,000	39.00
1980	Schmitt	5,000	39.00
1980	Marque	5,000	39.00
Old German Dolls			
1981	Lucy	7,500	39.00
1981	Whistler	7,500	39.00
1982	April	7,500	39.00
1982	Elise	7,500	39.00
(Single issue)			
1981	Dear Googly	7,500	39.00
Old Baby Dolls			
1982	Hilda	9,500	43.00
1982	Goldie	9,500	43.00
1982	Lori	9,500	43.00
1982	Bye-Lo	9,500	43.00
1982	Laughing Baby	9,500	43.00
French Dolls II			
1983	Snow Angel	5,000	39.00
1983	"H's" Bébé Halo	5,000	39.00
1983	Bru's Faith	5,000	39.00
1984	Steiner's Easter	5,000	39.00
1984	Marque's Alyce	5,000	39.00
1984	Jumeau's Gaynell	5,000	39.00
Seven Seas			
Historical Event			
1969	Moon Landing, No Flag	2,000	13.50
1969	Moon Landing, with Flag	25,000	13.50
1970	Year of Crisis	4,000	15.00
1971	First Vehicular Travel	3,000	15.00
1972	Last Moon Journey	2,000	15.00
1973	Peace	3,000	15.00
Mother's Day			
1970	Girl of All Nations	5,000	15.00
1971	Sharing Confidence	1,400	15.00
1972	Scandinavian Girl	1,600	15.00
1973	All-American Girl	1,500	15.00

	Edition Limit	Issue Price (US)
Christmas Carols		
1970 I Heard Bells	4,000	$ 15.00
1971 Oh Tannenbaum	4,000	15.00
1972 Deck Halls	1,500	18.00
1973 O Holy Night	2,000	18.00
1974 Jingle Bells	1,200	25.00
1975 Winter Wonderland	1,500	25.00
1976 Twelve Days of Christmas	1,200	25.00
1977 Up on Housetop	1,500	25.00
1978 Little Town of Bethlehem	1,500	25.00
1979 Santa Claus Is Coming to Town	1,500	25.00
1980 Frosty Snowman	1,500	25.00
New World		
1970 Holy Family	3,500	15.00
1971 Three Wise Men	1,500	15.00
1972 Shepherds Watched	1,500	18.00
Passion Play (Single issue)		
1970 Oberammergau	2,500	18.00
Shenango		
See: Castleton China (U.S.A.)		
Signature Collection		
Carnival		
1982 Knock 'em Down	19,500	39.95
1982 Carousel	19,500	39.95
1983 Fortune Teller	19,500	39.95
1983 Ring Bell	19,500	39.95
How Do I Love Thee		
1982 Alaina	24,000	39.95
1982 Taylor	24,000	39.95
1983 Rendezvous	24,000	39.95
1983 Embrace	24,000	39.95
Baker Street Duo		
1983 Sherlock Holmes	9,800	55.00
1983 Watson	9,800	55.00
Childhood Delights		
1983 Amanda	10,000	45.00
Grandma's Scrapbook		
1983 Courting	12,500	45.00
1983 Sunday Drive	12,500	45.00
Unicorn Magic		
1983 Morning Encounter	10,000	50.00
1983 Afternoon Outing	10,000	50.00
Silver Creations		
Churchillian Heritage		
1972 Hour of Decision	NA	150.00
1973 Yalta Conference	NA	150.00
1973 Clydesdales	NA	150.00
Smith Glass		
Americana		
1971 Morgan Silver Dollar	5,000	10.00
Christmas		
1971 Family at Christmas	NA	10.00
1972 Flying Angel	NA	10.00
1973 St. Mary's in Mountains	NA	10.00
Famous Americans		
1971 Kennedy	2,500	10.00
1971 Lincoln	2,500	10.00
1972 Jefferson Davis	5,000	11.00
1972 Robert E. Lee	5,000	11.00
Southern Living Gallery		
Wildflowers of South		
1981 Wild Honeysuckle	19,500	49.50
1981 Flowering Dogwood	19,500	49.50
1981 Buttercup	19,500	49.50
1981 Regal Lily	19,500	49.50
1981 Queen Anne's Lace	19,500	49.50
1981 Bluebonnet	19,500	49.50
1981 Southern Magnolia	19,500	49.50
1981 Bee Balm	19,500	49.50
1981 Lady Slipper Orchid	19,500	49.50
1981 Birdsfoot Violet	19,500	49.50
1981 Frost Aster	19,500	49.50
1981 Black-Eyed Susan	19,500	49.50
Game Birds of South		
1982 Bobwhite Quail	19,500	39.95
1982 Wild Turkey	19,500	39.95
1982 Mourning Dove	19,500	39.95
1982 Mallard Duck	19,500	39.95
1982 Wood Duck	19,500	39.95
1982 Ruffed Grouse	19,500	39.95
1982 Pintail Duck	19,500	39.95
1982 Ring-necked Pheasant	19,500	39.95
1982 American Woodcock	19,500	39.95
1982 American Coot	19,500	39.95
1982 Canada Goose	19,500	39.95
1982 Green-winged Teal	19,500	39.95

	Edition Limit	Issue Price (US)
Sterling America		
Christmas Customs		
1970 England	2,500	$ 18.00
1971 Holland	2,500	18.00
1972 Norway	2,500	18.00
1973 Germany	2,500	20.00
1974 Mexico	2,500	24.00
Twelve Days of Christmas		
1970 Partridge	2,500	18.00
1971 Turtle Doves	2,500	18.00
1972 French Hens	2,500	18.00
1973 Colly Birds	2,500	18.00
1974 Five Rings	2,500	24.00
1975 Six Geese	2,500	24.00
1976 Seven Swans	2,500	24.00
1977 Eight Maids	2,500	28.00
Mother's Day		
1971 Mare & Foal	2,500	18.00
1972 Horned Owl	2,500	18.00
1973 Raccoons	2,500	20.00
1974 Deer	2,500	24.00
1975 Quail	2,500	24.00
Stieff		
Bicentennial		
1972 Declaration of Independence	10,000	50.00
1974 Betsy Ross	10,000	50.00
1975 Crossing Delaware	10,000	50.00
1976 Serapio & Bon Homme	10,000	50.00
Stratford Collection		
Real Children		
1982 Michael's Miracle	24,500	45.00
1983 Susan's World	24,500	45.00
Stuart International		
Childhood Secrets		
1983 Billy's Treasure	19,500	39.50
Syracuse China		
Grandma Moses (Sets of four)		
1972 Old Checkered House in Winter		
1972 Mary and Little Lamb		
1972 In Harvest Time		
1972 Sugaring Off	NA	80.00
1972 Hoosick Valley from Window		
1972 Taking in Laundry		
1972 It Snows, Oh it Snows		
1972 Joy Ride	NA	80.00
Towle Silversmiths		
Valentines		
1972 Single Heart	Year	10.00
1973 Entwined Hearts	Year	10.00
Christmas		
1972 Three Wise Men	2,500	250.00
U.S. Historical Society		
Annual Historical		
1977 Great Events	5,000	60.00
1978 Great Events	10,000	75.00
Stained Glass Cathedral Christmas		
1978 Canterbury Cathedral	10,000	87.00
1979 Flight into Egypt (St. John Divine)	10,000	97.00
1980 Madonna and Child	10,000	125.00
1981 Magi	10,000	150.00
1982 Flight into Egypt	10,000	150.00
1983 Shepherds at Bethlehem	10,000	150.00
American Christmas Carols		
1982 Deck Halls	10,000	55.00
1983 O Christmas Tree	10,000	55.00
Great American Sailing Ships		
1983 Old Ironsides—U.S.S. Constitution	10,000	150.00
Stained Glass Flowers		
1983 Spring Flowers	10,000	135.00
200 Years of Flight		
1983 Man's First Flight	5,000	85.00
(Single issue)		
1984 Robert E. Lee	10,000	150.00
Vague Shadows		
Plainsmen		
1979 Buffalo Hunt	2,500	300.00
1979 Proud One	2,500	300.00
Professionals		
1979 Big Leaguer	15,000	29.95
1980 Ballerina's Dilemma	15,000	32.50
1981 Quarterback	15,000	32.50
1982 Rodeo Joe	15,000	35.00
1983 Major Leaguer	15,000	35.00
1983 Hockey Player	15,000	35.00

	Edition Limit	Issue Price (US)
Santa		
1980 Santa's Joy	Year	$ 29.95
1981 Santa's Bundle	Year	29.95
Storybook Collection		
1980 Little Red Riding Hood	18 Days	29.95
1981 Cinderella	18 Days	29.95
1981 Hansel and Gretel	18 Days	29.95
1982 Goldilocks and Three Bears	18 Days	29.95
Arctic Friends (Set of two)		
1981 Siberian Love		
1981 Snow Pals	7,500	100.00
Four Princesses		
1981 Lily of Mohawks	7,500	50.00
1981 Pocahontas	7,500	50.00
1982 Minnehaha	7,500	50.00
1982 Sacajawea	7,500	50.00
(Single issue)		
1981 Apache Boy	5,000	95.00
Child Life		
1982 Siesta	12,500	45.00
Legends of West		
1982 Daniel Boone	10,000	65.00
1982 Davy Crockett	10,000	65.00
1983 Kit Carson	10,000	65.00
1983 Buffalo Bill	10,000	65.00
Nature's Harmony		
1982 Peaceable Kingdom	12,500	100.00
1982 Zebra	12,500	50.00
1982 Tiger	12,500	50.00
1983 Black Panther	12,500	50.00
1983 Elephant	12,500	50.00
War Ponies		
1982 Sioux War Pony	7,500	60.00
1983 Nez Perce War Pony	7,500	60.00
1983 Apache War Pony	7,500	60.00
Motherhood		
1983 Madre	12,500	50.00
Perillo Chieftain		
1983 Chief Pontiac	7,500	70.00
Perillo Masterpiece Collection		
1983 Papoose	3,000	100.00
Vernonware (Metlox Potteries)		
Songs of Christmas		
1971 Twelve Days	9,000	15.00
1972 Jingle Bells	9,000	17.50
1973 First Noel	9,000	20.00
1974 Upon a Midnight Clear	9,000	20.00
1975 O Holy Night	10,000	20.00
1976 Hark! Herald Angels	10,000	20.00
1977 Away in Manger	10,000	30.00
1978 White Christmas	10,000	30.00
1979 Little Drummer Boy	10,000	30.00
Viletta		
Disneyland		
1976 Betsy Ross	3,000	15.00
1976 Crossing Delaware	3,000	15.00
1976 Signing Declaration	3,000	15.00
1976 Spirit of '76	3,000	15.00
Bicentennial		
1977 Patriots	15,000	37.00
In Tribute to America's Great Artists		
1978 DeGrazia by Don Marco	5,000	65.00
Days of West		
1978 Cowboy Christmas	5,000	55.00
Alice in Wonderland		
1980 Alice and White Rabbit	28 Days	25.00
1981 Mad Hatter's Tea Party	28 Days	25.00
1981 Alice and Cheshire Cat	28 Days	25.00
1981 Alice and Croquet Match	28 Days	25.00

See also:
Abbey Press (U.S.A.)
American Arts Services (U.S.A.)
Carson Mint (U.S.A.)
Collector's Heirlooms (U.S.A.)
R. J. Ernst Enterprises (U.S.A.)
Ghent Collection (U.S.A.)
Hamilton Collection (U.S.A.)
Ralph Homan Studios (U.S.A.)
Joys (U.S.A.)
Judaic Heritage Society (U.S.A.)
McCalla Enterprises (U.S.A.)
Museum Editions (U.S.A.)
Pemberton & Oakes (U.S.A.)
Warwick (U.S.A.)
Westbury (U.S.A.)
Edward Weston Editions (U.S.A.)

	Edition Limit	Issue Price (US)
Volair (Gorham)		
Audubon American Wildlife Heritage		
1977 House Mouse	2,500	90.00
1977 Royal Louisiana Heron	2,500	$ 90.00
1977 Virginia Deer	2,500	90.00
1977 Snowy Owl	2,500	90.00
Warwick (Viletta)		
Great Comedians		
1978 Little Tramp	7,500	35.00
1978 Outrageous Groucho	7,500	35.00
George Washington Mint		
American Indian		
1972 Curley (Gold)	100	2000.00
1972 Curley (Proof)	100	1000.00
1972 Curley (Sterling)	7,300	150.00
1973 Two Moons (Gold)	100	2000.00
1973 Two Moons (Proof)	100	1000.00
1973 Two Moons (Sterling)	7,300	150.00
Mother's Day		
1972 Whistler's Mother (Sterling)	9,800	150.00
1972 Whistler's Mother (Proof)	100	1000.00
1972 Whistler's Mother (Gold)	100	2000.00
1974 Motherhood (Sterling)	2,300	175.00
1974 Motherhood (Proof)	100	1000.00
1974 Motherhood (Gold)	100	2000.00
Picasso		
1972 Don Quixote (Gold)	100	2000.00
1972 Don Quixote (Proof)	100	1000.00
1972 Don Quixote (Sterling)	9,800	125.00
Remington		
1972 Rattlesnake (Gold)	100	2000.00
1972 Rattlesnake (Proof)	100	1000.00
1972 Rattlesnake (Sterling)	800	250.00
Da Vinci		
1972 Last Supper	NA	125.00
N. C. Wyeth		
1972 Uncle Sam's America (Gold)	100	2000.00
1972 Uncle Sam's America (Proof)	100	1000.00
1972 Uncle Sam's America (Sterling)	9,800	150.00
1973 Massed Flags (Gold)	100	2000.00
1973 Massed Flags (Proof)	100	1000.00
1973 Massed Flags (Sterling)	2,300	150.00
Israel Anniversary (Single issue)		
1973 Struggle	10,000	300.00
Picasso (Single issue)		
1974 Rites of Spring (Sterling)	9,800	125.00
Remington (Single issue)		
1974 Coming Through Rye (Sterling)	2,500	300.00
Wendell August Forge		
Great Americans		
1971 J.F.K. (Pewter)	5,000	40.00
1971 J.F.K. (Silver)	500	200.00
1972 Lincoln (Pewter)	5,000	40.00
1972 Lincoln (Silver)	500	200.00
Great Moments		
1971 Columbus (Pewter)	5,000	40.00
1971 Columbus (Silver)	500	200.00
1972 Landing of Pilgrims (Pewter)	5,000	40.00
1972 Landing of Pilgrims (Silver)	500	200.00
1973 First Thanksgiving (Pewter)	5,000	40.00
1973 First Thanksgiving (Silver)	500	200.00
1974 Patrick Henry (Pewter)	5,000	40.00
1974 Patrick Henry (Silver)	500	200.00
1975 Paul Revere (Pewter)	5,000	45.00
1975 Paul Revere (Silver)	500	200.00
1976 Signing of Declaration (Pewter)	5,000	50.00
1976 Signing of Declaration (Silver)	500	200.00
Wings of Man		
1971 Columbus' Ships (Pewter)	5,000	40.00
1971 Columbus' Ships (Silver)	500	200.00
1972 Conestoga Wagon (Pewter)	5,000	40.00
1972 Conestoga Wagon (Silver)	500	200.00
Peace (Single issue)		
1973 Facing Doves (Silver)	2,500	250.00
Christmas		
1974 Caroler (Bronze)	2,500	25.00
1974 Caroler (Pewter)	2,500	30.00

	Edition Limit	Issue Price (US)
1975 Christmas in Country (Bronze)	2,500	$ 30.00
1975 Christmas in Country (Pewter)	2,500	35.00
1976 Lamplighter (Bronze)	2,500	35.00
1976 Lamplighter (Pewter)	2,500	40.00
1977 Covered Bridge (Bronze)	2,500	40.00
1977 Covered Bridge (Pewter)	2,500	45.00
Wildlife		
1977 On Guard (Aluminum)	1,900	35.00
1977 On Guard (Bronze)	1,500	45.00
1977 On Guard (Pewter)	1,500	55.00
1977 On Guard (Silver)	100	250.00
1978 Thunderbird (Aluminum)	1,900	40.00
1978 Thunderbird (Bronze)	1,500	50.00

	Edition Limit	Issue Price (US)
1978 Thunderbird (Pewter)	1,500	$ 60.00
1978 Thunderbird (Silver)	100	250.00
Westbury (Viletta)		
Tender Moments		
1978 Old Fashioned Persuasion	7,500	40.00
1979 Dandelions	7,500	45.00
Westminster Collectibles		
Holidays		
1976 All Hallows Eve	5,000	38.50
1977 Christmas	5,000	38.50
Westmoreland		
Christmas		
1972 Holy Birth	2,500	35.00
1973 Manger Scene	3,500	35.00
1974 Gethsemane	1,500	35.00

	Edition Limit	Issue Price (US)
1975 Christ Is Risen	1,500	$ 45.00
Edward Weston Editions (Viletta)		
Unicorn Fantasies		
1979 Follower of Dreams	5,000	55.00
1980 Twice Upon a Time	5,000	55.00
1981 Familiar Spirit	5,000	60.00
1982 Noble Gathering	5,000	65.00
Weddings Around World		
1979 Hawaiian Wedding	5,000	75.00
1980 Dutch Wedding	5,000	75.00
Wheaton		
Presidential		
1971 Adams	9,648	5.00
1971 Eisenhower	8,856	5.00
1971 Hoover	10,152	5.00

	Edition Limit	Issue Price (US)
1971 Kennedy	11,160	$ 5.00
1971 Lincoln	9,648	5.00
1971 Madison	9,504	5.00
1971 Monroe	9,792	5.00
1971 F. D. Roosevelt	9,432	5.00
1971 Taft	9,648	5.00
1971 Van Buren	9,576	5.00
1971 Washington	10,800	5.00
1971 Wilson	8,712	5.00
Whitehall China		
Raphael Soyer		
1979 Model on Bed	10,000	39.95
Wildlife Internationale		
Water Fowl		
1983 Wood Ducks	5,000	65.00

INDEX OF BRADEX-LISTED
PLATE MAKERS AND SPONSORS

NOTE: "Maker" is a general term for the name under which a plate is issued and is not necessarily the actual "manufacturer."
A Maker can be a distributor, manufacturer, or occasionally a "sponsor." See GLOSSARY OF COMMONLY USED TERMS.

INDEX OF PLATE TITLES AND SERIES BY TYPE

NOTE: Plate titles listed in alphabetical order and enclosed in quotation marks:
"Aabenraa Marketplace"..........**14-R59-1.14**

Types of series are listed in bold face with individual makers indented and listed below:
Anniversary
Goebel *(Hummel)*.........**22-G54-3.1 to 22-G54-3.2**

INDEX OF PLATE ARTISTS

Jensen, Oluf............. 14-R59-1.4; 14-R59-1.10; 14-R59-1.11; 14-R59-1.12; 14-R59-1.14; 14-R59-1.16; 14-R59-1.18; 14-R59-1.22; 14-R59-1.25; 14-R59-1.27
Johnson, Robert 84-R18-2.1; 84-R18-2.2; 84-R18-2.3
Jorgensen, J. Bloch ... 14-B36-1.22
Jorgensen, Povl 14-B36-1.14

K

Karl, Prof................. 22-R55-1.40
Karner, Theo 22-R55-1.15; 22-R55-1.21
Keller, Hedi 22-K46-1.1; 22-K46-1.2; 22-K46-1.3; 22-K46-1.4; 22-K46-1.5; 22-K46-1.6
Kjolner, Th. 14-R59-1.34; 14-R59-1.41; 14-R59-1.46
Koch, Otto 22-R55-1.23
Krog, Arnold 14-R59-1.8
Krumeich, Thaddeus............. 22-A3-5.1; 22-A3-5.2; 22-A3-5.3; 22-A3-5.4
Kuck, Sandra........... 84-R60-8.1; 84-R60-8.2; 84-R60-8.3
Kursár, Raymond 84-K41-3.1; 84-K41-3.2; 84-K41-3.3; 84-K41-3.4; 84-K41-3.5; 84-K41-3.6; 84-K41-3.7
Küspert, Georg........ 22-R55-1.55; 22-R55-1.56; 22-R55-1.57; 22-R55-1.58; 22-R55-1.59; 22-R55-1.60; 22-R55-1.61; 22-R55-1.62; 22-R55-1.63; 22-R55-1.64; 22-R55-1.65

L

Lalique, Marie-Claude 18-L3-1.1; 18-L3-1.2; 18-L3-1.3; 18-L3-1.4; 18-L3-1.5; 18-L3-1.6; 18-L3-1.7; 18-L3-1.8; 18-L3-1.9; 18-L3-1.10; 18-L3-1.11; 18-L3-1.12
Lambert, Georgia..... 84-K41-8.1; 84-K41-8.2
Lamincia, Franco...... 38-V22-15.1
Lange, Kai 14-R59-1.33; 14-R59-1.40; 14-R59-1.45; 14-R59-1.47; 14-R59-1.48; 14-R59-1.49; 14-R59-1.54; 14-R59-1.56; 14-R59-1.57; 14-R59-1.58; 14-R59-1.59; 14-R59-1.60; 14-R59-1.61; 14-R59-1.62; 14-R59-1.63; 14-R59-1.64; 14-R59-1.65; 14-R59-1.66; 14-R59-1.67; 14-R59-1.68; 14-R59-1.70; 14-R59-1.71; 14-R59-1.72; 14-R59-1.73; 14-R59-1.74; 14-R59-1.75; 14-R59-1.76; 14-R59-1.77
Larsen, Ove............. 14-B36-1.41; 14-B36-1.42; 14-B36-1.43; 14-B36-1.46; 14-B36-1.47; 14-B36-1.48; 14-B36-1.49; 14-B36-1.50; 14-B36-1.51
Larsen, Th. 14-B36-1.19; 14-B36-1.20
Licea, Eve 84-K41-6.1; 84-K41-6.2
Lippi, Fra 84-R18-2.5; 84-R18-2.7
Lochner, Steven 84-R18-2.6
Lockhart, James 84-P29-1.1; 84-P29-1.2; 84-P29-1.3; 84-P29-1.4; 84-P29-1.5; 84-P29-1.6; 84-P29-1.7; 84-P29-1.8; 84-P29-1.9; 84-P29-1.10; 84-P29-1.11
Lotto, Lorenzo 84-P29-2.2

M

McClelland, John 84-R60-1.1; 84-R60-1.2; 84-R60-1.3; 84-R60-1.4; 84-R60-2.1; 84-R60-2.2; 84-R60-2.3; 84-R60-2.4; 84-R60-2.5; 84-R60-2.6; 84-R60-3.1; 84-R60-3.2; 84-R60-3.3; 84-R60-3.4

Malfertheiner, Joseph 38-A54-1.1; 38-A54-1.2; 38-A54-1.3; 38-A54-1.4; 38-A54-1.5; 38-A54-1.6; 38-A54-1.7; 38-A54-1.8
Maratti, Carlo 22-K4-1.7
Masseria, Francisco............... 26-R62-11.1; 26-R62-11.2; 26-R62-11.3; 26-R62-11.4
Mays, Maxwell......... 84-R18-2.7; 84-R18-2.8; 84-R18-2.9
Memling, Hans 84-P29-2.6
Mermagen, Prof...... 22-R55-1.8
Moltke, H. 14-B36-1.17
Money, Rusty 84-E74-1.1; 84-E74-1.2; 84-E74-1.3; 84-E74-1.4; 84-E74-1.5; 84-E74-1.6
Mueller, Hans 22-B7-1.1; 22-B7-1.2; 22-B7-1.3; 22-B7-1.4; 22-B7-1.6; 22-B7-1.7; 22-B7-1.8; 22-B7-1.9; 22-B7-1.10; 22-B7-1.11; 22-B7-1.12; 22-B7-1.13; 22-B7-1.14; 22-B7-1.15; 22-B7-1.16; 22-B7-1.17; 22-B7-1.18; 22-B7-2.1; 22-B7-2.2; 22-B7-2.3; 22-B7-2.4; 22-B7-2.5; 22-B7-2.6; 22-B7-2.7; 22-B7-2.8; 22-B7-2.9; 22-B7-2.10; 22-B7-2.11; 22-B7-2.12; 22-B7-2.13; 22-B7-2.14; 22-B7-2.15; 22-B7-2.16
Mundel, Alfred 22-R55-1.36
Murillo 18-H8-2.4
Mutze, Walter.......... 22-R55-1.31; 22-R55-1.32; 22-R55-1.33

N

Nast, Thomas........... 84-R18-2.10
Neiman, LeRoy 26-R62-3.1; 26-R62-3.2; 26-R62-3.3; 26-R62-3.4
Neubacher, Gerda 22-K4-5.1; 22-K4-5.2; 22-K4-5.3; 22-K4-5.4; 22-K4-5.5
Ng, Kee Fung 84-A72-1.1; 84-A72-1.2; 84-A72-1.3; 84-A72-1.4; 84-A72-1.5; 84-A72-1.6
Nicolai, Friedrich 22-R55-1.13
Nielsen, Herne........ 14-R59-1.31
Nielsen, Sv. Nic 14-R59-1.32
Nightingale, Sandy................... 18-B61-1.1; 18-B61-1.2; 18-B61-1.3; 18-B61-1.4; 18-B61-1.5; 18-B61-1.6
Nitschke, Detlev 22-B20-4.1; 22-B20-4.2
Northcott, Joann 22-K4-1.6; 22-K4-2.7; 22-K4-2.10
Nylund, Gunnar 76-R54-1.1; 76-R54-1.2; 76-R54-1.3; 76-R54-1.4; 76-R54-1.5; 76-R54-1.6; 76-R54-1.7; 76-R54-1.8; 76-R54-1.9; 76-R54-1.10; 76-R54-1.11; 76-R54-1.12; 76-R54-1.13; 76-R54-1.14; 76-R54-1.15; 76-R54-1.16

O

Olsen, Benjamin 14-R59-1.17; 14-R59-1.20; 14-R59-1.23; 14-R59-1.26; 14-R59-1.28
Olsen, Cathinka....... 14-B36-1.10
Olsen, Ib Spang 14-R59-2.8; 14-R59-2.9; 14-R59-2.10; 14-R59-2.11; 14-R59-2.12
Olsen, Viggo 14-R59-1.37; 14-R59-1.43

P

Perillo, Gregory 84-V3-2.1; 84-V3-2.2; 84-V3-2.3; 84-V3-2.4; 84-V3-2.5
Peter, Nori 22-K4-2.9

GLOSSARY OF COMMONLY USED TERMS

A

Aftermarket. See *Market*.

Alabaster. A dense, fine-grained form of gypsum (calcium sulfate) stone, usually white to pink and slightly translucent. Alabaster stone can be carved in fine detail for ornamental objects and hardened by intense heat. Italian alabaster is also called Florentine marble. Ivory alabaster is composed of alabaster but is non-translucent and acquires a patina with age like that of old ivory.

Allotment. A number of plates, all alike and usually at issue, allocated by a maker to a distributor or dealer. See *Lot*.

Alloy. Two or more metals combined while molten. Alloying is done to achieve hardness, toughness, or luster. See *Pewter*.

Annual. A plate issued once each year as part of a series. The term is most often used when a plate does not commemorate a specific holiday.

Annular kiln. A round oven made from brick used to fire ceramic plates.

Art Deco, Art Décoratif. A style of decoration popular in Europe and America from 1920 to 1945. The Art Deco movement sought to glorify progress and the future by using as motifs such shapes as the cylinder, circle, rectangle, and cone.

Art Nouveau. A style of decoration in Europe and America from 1890 to 1920. The Art Nouveau movement used twining floral patterns as its primary decorative motifs.

Asked Price, Ask. The offering price posted for a plate by a seller on the Exchange.

At Issue. A plate being offered for sale at the time of its manufacture and at the original price set by the maker.

B

Back Issue. See *Issue*.

Backstamp. The information on the back of a plate, usually including the maker's signature, name, or trademark (logo-type). It may also record serial number, title, artist's signature, edition limit, explanation of the plate, sponsor, production techniques, awards, or release initials. It may be hand-applied, stamped, incised (cut or pressed), or applied as a decalcomania.

Banding. A method for hand-application of precious metals, such as gold, silver, or platinum, to the edge or other parts of a glazed plate. The decorator uses a camel's hair brush to apply a liquid metal suspended in special oils. The plate is then fired to adhere the metal to the glaze.

Baroque. An elaborate style of decoration developed in Europe in the seventeenth and eighteenth centuries and noted for exaggerated gesture and line. Example: Dresden **(22-D68-0.0)**.

Bas-relief. See *Relief Sculpture*.

Bavaria (Bayern). A province in the southwest corner of Germany long known as a center for porcelain factories. The region contains large deposits of kaolin, the key porcelain component.

Bearish. Marked by declining prices, either actual or expected. A bear market is one of declining prices.

Bedroom Dealer. A trade term for a small dealer who usually operates from his home, buys discounted plates, and resells them for a small profit.

Bid Price, Bid. The amount a prospective buyer offers to pay for a plate on the Exchange.

Bisque, Biscuit. A plate that has been fired but not glazed, leaving it with a matte texture. So called because of the biscuit-like appearance. Example: Lladró **(72-L41-0.0)**.

Blue Chip. An established series by a well-known maker in which nearly every issue shows a steady sequence of price rises above issue price, usually over an extended period of time.

Body. 1. The formula or combination of substances that make up potter's clay, generally referring to stoneware and earthenware. **2.** The basic plate form to which ornamentation is applied.

Bone Ash. Calcium phosphate, a component of bone china, added to give whiteness and translucency. It is obtained by calcinating (reducing to powder by heat) animal bones, usually those of oxen.

Bone China (Bone Porcelain). A type of china developed by Josiah Spode in England in the 1790s. By replacing part of the kaolin in the china formula with bone ash, greater translucency and whiteness is obtained at lower firing temperatures. The finest bone china contains up to 50% bone ash. It is the most commonly made china in England. Example: Royal Doulton **(26-R62-0.0).**

Bradex. Common term for the *Bradford Exchange Current Quotations*, a periodic listing of the current market prices of collector's plates now listed on the Exchange. See *Listed Plate, Exchange.*

Broker. A representative of the Bradford Exchange Trading Floor who enters bids and asks of all traders and confirms all transactions.

Bullish. Marked by rising prices, either actual or expected, and optimistic atmosphere. A bull market is one of rising prices.

Buy Order. An offer by an individual or dealer to purchase one or more plates on the secondary market. See *Bid Price, Exchange.*

C

Cameo Effect. Ornamentations in relief on a background of contrasting color to resemble a cameo. Examples: Wedgwood Jasper ware **(26-W90-0.0)** and Incolay Studios **(84-I31-0.0).**

Carnelian. A hard translucent quartz that has a reddish color.

Celsius, Centigrade. The thermometric scale in which 0° represents the freezing point of water and 100° the boiling point. Celsius temperature is denoted by "C" after the number.

Ceramic. A general term applying to all of the various plates made from clay and hardened by firing.

Certificate. An attestation of authenticity which may accompany each plate in an edition. A certificate authenticates a plate as being part of an issue and usually confirms the plate's individual number within the edition.

China, Chinaware. A hard, vitreous ceramic whose main components are kaolin and china stone fired at high temperature. Originally the term was used for those ceramics

which only came from China. Later it was applied to all "hard" and "soft" porcelain. China is often used as a generic term which includes porcelain, but is properly distinguished from it by a high bisque firing temperature and a lower glaze firing temperature. The main firing (bisque) of china is approximately 7% lower than the main firing (glaze) of porcelain. In china production, the glaze is applied after the main firing and fixed with a second lower-temperature firing. A typical china formula is 40% kaolin, 10% ball clay, and varying proportions of china stone, feldspar, and flint. See *Porcelain.*

China Clay. See *Kaolin.*

China Stone, Petuntse. A feldspathic material in china formulas. China stone acts as a flux which helps dissolve and fuse the other components into a vitreous mass.

Christmas Plates, Christmas Series. Annual plates issued to commemorate Christmas, usually as part of a series. Plate names for Christmas include Noël (French), Weihnachten (German), Jul (Danish), Navidad (Spanish and Portuguese), and Natale (Italian). The oldest Christmas series is that of Bing & Grøndahl, produced continuously since 1895 **(14-B36-1.0).**

Clay. Any of various plastic, viscous earths used to make plates. It is formed by the decomposition, due to weathering, of igneous rocks such as granite, feldspar, and pegmatite.

Close. Last traded price on the Exchange.

Closed-End Series. A series of plates with a predetermined number of issues. Example: D'Arceau-Limoges *Douze Sites Parisiens de Louis Dali (Twelve Parisian Places)* **(18-D15-6.0).**

Cobalt Blue. Cobalt oxide in the form of a dark black powder which, when fired, turns a deep blue. It was the first known and is still the most commonly used ceramic under-glaze color because of its ability to withstand high firing temperatures. It can produce a variety of shades. Examples: Kaiser cobalt blue **(22-K4-0.0)**, Bing & Grøndahl Copenhagen blue **(14-B36-0.0)**, Royal Copenhagen Danish blue **(14-R59-0.0)**, and Rörstrand Scandia blue **(76-R54-0.0).**

Collector's Plate. A decorative plate produced in a limited edition for the purpose of being collected. Although the earliest plates were not produced with this objective, they have since acquired the name by virtue of being collected and are now produced for this purpose.

Commemorative Plate. A plate produced in remembrance of an event. Example: Wedgwood *Bicentennial of American Independence.* **(26-W90-3.0).**

Coterie Plate. A collector's plate with a limited following which is traded too infrequently to be listed on the Exchange.

Crystal. See *Lead Crystal.*

Cut Glass. Glass decorated by the cutting of grooves and facets, usually done with a copper engraver's wheel.

D

Damascene. An electroplating effect, created and patented by Reed & Barton **(84-R18-0.0)**, of etching and then depositing layers of gold, copper, and silver on bronze. Originally the term referred to the art, developed in Damascus, of ornamenting iron or steel with inlaid precious metals.

Dealer. A marketer of plates who buys primarily from makers or distributors and sells primarily to the public.

Dealer-Broker. A dealer who acts as an agent of the Bradford Exchange to transact secondary market purchases and sales for his customers via the Instaquote Trading System. See *Broker, Instaquote Trading System, Market.*

Decalcomania. The printed reproduction of original artwork which is produced by individual color separations, either in offset lithography, silk-screen printing, or a combination of both.

Delftware. Earthenware covered with an opaque white glaze made of stannic oxide, and oxide of tin. Originally developed in Delft, Holland, in the sixteenth century, Delftware has the appearance of being covered with a thick white paint. Similar ware is the majolica of Italy and faience of France and Germany. See *Faience, Majolica, Tin Glaze.*

Dilute Colors. Solutions of metallic salts which are absorbed by the bisque body of a plate when it is glazed and fired, producing soft, impressionistic tones. Perfected in Copenhagen in about 1883. Examples: Royal Copenhagen **(14-R59-0.0)**, Bing & Grøndahl **(14-B36-0.0)**, and Grande Copenhagen **(14-G65-0.0)**.

Distributor. A marketer of plates who buys from manufacturers and sells to dealers. Some distributors also act as makers and as dealers.

Dresden, Meissen. Neighboring cities now in East Germany where the first hard-paste porcelain outside of China was produced by Johann Friedrich Böttger in 1708.

Dresden China. Term used in England beginning in the eighteenth century to describe true hard-paste porcelain. See *Dresden, Porcelain*.

E

Earthenware. A term for any ceramics which are not vitrified. Typical components of earthenware are 43% ball clay, 24% kaolin, 23% flint, and 10% pegmatite. Fired earthenware is normally covered with either a transparent or opaque glaze. High-fired earthenware is fired at a higher temperature to produce a harder ware. Example: Royal Doulton *Beswick Christmas* series **(26-R62-1.0)**.

Edition. The total number of plates, all with the same decoration, produced by a maker. Editions of collector's plates are normally limited to a fixed number and are not repeated. To do so would constitute a violation of the edition limit.

Electroplating. A process by which metal plates are coated with another metal by electrical charges.

Embossed Design. Raised ornamentation produced by the plate mold or by stamping a design into the body of the plate. Example: Belleek **(26-B18-0.0)**.

Enamel. A glaze material colored with suspended mineral oxides for decorating plates.

Engraved Design. Decoration produced by cutting into the surface of metal, glass, or china plates with either a tool or acid, as in etching. See *Intaglio*.

Etched Design. Decoration produced by cutting into the surface of a plate with acid. The plate is first covered with an acid-resistant paint or wax, and the design is carved through this coating. When the plate is immersed in acid, the acid "bites" into the plate surface in the shape of the design. Example: Franklin Mint silver plates **(84-F64-0.0)**. See *Intaglio*.

Exchange. A place where plates are traded, most commonly the Bradford Exchange, the world's largest trading center in limited-edition collector's plates. Incorporated in 1962, it was formerly known as Bradford Galleries Exchange. See *Trading Floor*.

F

Faience. Tin-enameled earthenware from France, Germany, or Spain developed in the seventeenth century and named for the Italian town of Faenza, a center for majolica, another name for this ware. See *Delftware*.

Feldspar. A mineral composed of aluminum silicates with either potassium, sodium, calcium, or barium. Feldspar decomposes to form kaolin, the key ingredient of china and porcelain. The addition of undecomposed feldspar to china formulas gives the ware greater hardness.

Fine China. A designation of quality which is made after firing; those plates which do not merit the designation are simply called "china."

Fire. The heating process which hardens ceramic plates in a kiln. Ceramic clay begins to undergo chemical change at 500° C and vitrifies at around 1300° C.

First Edition. The first, and presumably the only, edition of a collector's plate. The term (or its abbreviation, "FE") is sometimes used for the edition which is the first issue in a series of collector's plates. However, since no edition is normally ever reopened and therefore no "second edition" is possible, all issues of collector's plates are properly termed first editions.

First Issue. Chronologically, the first plate in a series, i.e., the plates issued in the first year of an annual series.

Flint Glass. See *Lead Crystal*.

Flux. Finely ground material added to porcelain formulas which lowers the vitrification temperature and helps fuse the components. See *Feldspar*.

Foot Rim. A slightly projected ring on the convex side of a plate. The foot rim raises the plate in the kiln during firing.

G

Glaze. Glassy, hard surface coating on plates made of silicates (glass-forming compounds) and mineral oxides. Glaze is put on ceramic ware to make it wear-resistant, waterproof, decorative, and to seal the pores. Glaze material suspended in water is applied after the first firing and is heated to the glaze's vitrification point when it fuses to the plate body. Glaze is applied by dipping, spraying, or painting. Decorating is added under, over, or with the glaze layer. See *Underglaze Decoration, Overglaze Decoration*.

I

Incised Design. Ornamentation cut into the body of the plate. Example: Veneto Flair **(38-V22-0.0)**.

Incolay Stone. The material from which the cameo-like plates produced by Incolay Studios are made. Incolay stone may contain, among other minerals, semi-precious carnelian and crystal or topaz quartz. Example: Incolay Studios **(84-I31-0.0)**.

Inlaid. Decoration on a plate created by etching, incising, or engraving a design on the surface and filling with another material.

Instaquote Trading System.™ The computerized auction market for collector's plates that is an exclusive service of The Bradford Exchange Trading Floor. Both individual collectors and dealers may trade on the system.

Intaglio. Decoration created by cutting beneath the surface of the plate. Example: Morgantown Crystal **(84-M58-0.0)**. See *Engraved Design, Etched Design*.

Iridescence. A rainbow effect on a plate's surface caused by the diffraction of light. True iridescent color

effects are readily distinguished from a plate's inherent color because the pattern will change as the plate is moved. Example: Belleek (26-B18-0.0).

Issue. 1. The release for sale of an edition of plates by a maker. **2.** A plate in an edition. **3.** An edition within a series. A new issue is the release of the most recent plate in a continuing series. A back issue is a plate other than the most recently-issued plate in a series. Back issue usually denotes a plate that has sold out at issue price and is available only on the secondary market. See *Market.*

Issue Price. Original or first price of the plate established by the maker at the time the plate is released for sale.

J

Jasper Ware. Hard, fine-grained, unglazed stoneware made by adding barium sulfate to clay, developed by Josiah Wedgwood in the 1770s. The term "jasper" does not indicate the presence of jasper stone but most likely denotes the variety of colors in which Jasper ware can be produced. Though white in its original form, Jasper ware can be stained in blue, green, lilac, yellow, maroon, pink, taupe, or black to serve as a background for embossments of white Jasper relief for a cameo effect. When stained throughout, the body of it is called solid Jasper ware. Example: Wedgwood (26-W90-0.0).

Jigger. A machine with a revolving mold on which plates are formed. Semi-malleable clay is thrown on the revolving mold forming the top of the plate. The bottom of the plate is formed by a metal blade which is fastened to a pivotal arm.

K

Kaolin. The only clay which yields a white material when fired and the indispensable element of porcelain and china plates. Also called true clay or china clay, it is formed by the complete decomposition by weathering of feldspar. Kaolin is a refractory clay which can be fired at high temperatures without deforming. It produces a vitreous, translucent ceramic when fired with fluxes (fusible rocks) such as feldspar. The

components of kaolin clay are 50% silica, 33% alumina, 2% oxides, 1% magnesia, 2% alkali, and 12% water.

KPM. The trademark on plates from Königliche Porzellan-Manufaktur, Berlin, Germany. Plates made by this manufacturer date from as early as 1763.

L

Lead Crystal. Extremely transparent fine quality glass, also called flint glass and lead glass, which contains a high proportion of lead oxide to give extra weight, better refractiveness and a clear ringing tone when tapped. Full lead crystal is the term used to identify glass with a 24% or greater lead content. Example: Lalique (18-L3-0.0).

Lead Glass. See *Lead Crystal.*

Limited-Edition Plates. Plates produced in a fixed quantity, either predetermined by number or determined by a specific period of issue or by a period of production. All true collector's plates are limited-editions.

Limoges. A town in south central France famous for its porcelain production since the discovery of kaolin deposits nearby in 1768. Limoges porcelain manufacturers have joined together to enforce quality standards. Examples: D'Arceau-Limoges (18-D15-0.0), Haviland (18-H6-0.0), Haviland & Parlon (18-H8-0.0), and Limoges-Turgot (18-L52-0.0).

Listed Plate. A plate listed and regularly quoted on the *Bradford Exchange Current Quotations.* Such a plate is often referred to as being "Bradex-listed." See *Bradex, Exchange, Over-The-Counter Plate.*

Lot. A number of plates, all in the same edition and represented by a sell order on the Exchange, usually on the secondary market and not at issue. See *Allotment.*

Luster. Decoration applied to a plate surface by application of metallic oxides such as gold, silver, platinum, or copper over the glaze. When gently fired, this leaves a thin metallic film.

M

Majolica, Maiolica. Earthenware finished with opaque white enamel, similar to faience and Delftware, but first made in the Spanish island of Majorca. See *Delftware.*

Maker. The name by which a plate is known or under which it is issued, e.g., manufacturer, distributor, or sponsor. In most cases the "maker" is the actual manufacturer, e.g., Bing & Grøndahl (14-B36-0.0). However, it can also be a commissioner or distributor, e.g., Schmid (22-S12-0.0), using a trade name, while the physical production is in fact done by a sub-contractor.

Market. The structure within which plates are bought and sold. The primary market consists of new issues which are sold by the makers or their sales representatives to dealers and distributors. Dealers and distributors in turn normally sell the new issues to the public at issue price. Secondary market or aftermarket refers to the buying and selling of plates previously sold, and usually sold out, on the primary market. In many cases secondary market prices are higher than those of the primary market.

Market Bradex. A kind of "Dow Jones" index of the overall collector's plate market expressed as a percentage, based on the current price/issue price ratio of twelve key indicator series.

Market Price. The price at which a plate is currently traded, regardless of its issue price. See *Issue Price.*

Market Price Order. An open bid posted on the Exchange to purchase an issue at the price the market demands. Only over-the-counter plates are currently traded in this way on the Exchange. See *Over-The-Counter Plate.*

Meissen. See *Dresden.*

Mint Condition. A plate in new or like-new condition (free of manufacturer defects and damage) accompanied by any original certificates and packing materials included at issue.

Modeling. The process of making the original pattern from which the master mold is made for a sculptured plate.

Mold. A general term for the form which gives a plate its shape. Clay,

metal or glass is pressed into a mold to form a blank (without ornamentation). Intaglio decoration or raised ornamentation may also be formed in the mold. China or porcelain slip-casting is done in plaster-of-paris molds. Slip (diluted clay formula) is poured into the mold, and the excess water is absorbed into the plaster-of-paris. When the plate is jiggered, the mold forms the back and a tool forms the front using a moist clay mixture. See *Slip*.

N

New Issue. See *Issue*.

O

Open-End Series. A continuing series of annual plates with no established termination. Example: Royal Copenhagen *Christmas* series **(14-R59-1.0).**

Open Stock. Plates available in or produced in unlimited numbers or for an unlimited time period (and therefore not considered collector's plates).

Overglaze Decoration. A decoration consisting of precious metals such as gold, platinum, or silver and/or lithographic patterns in up to twenty-five colors, applied by hand to a porcelain piece after it has been glazed and fired a second time (glost fired). Hand-applied lithographic decoration—the most widely used form of overglaze decoration—can also be used underglaze. See *Glaze, Underglaze Decoration*.

Over-The-Counter Plate. A collector's plate not traded in sufficient volume to be *listed* on the Exchange. The majority of such plates, however, are *traded* on the Exchange and can be obtained, when available, at the prevailing market prices. See *Listed Plate*.

P

Parian China. A highly vitrified, translucent china characterized by an iridescent luster and rich, creamy tint much like that of parian marble, for which it is named. The process for making parian ware was invented by the Copeland and Garrett firm in

England in the mid-nineteenth century. Example: Belleek **(26-B18-0.0).**

Paste. The combination of substances that make up potter's clay, generally that for porcelain or china.

Pewter. An alloy of tin with copper and antimony as hardeners. The greater the amount of copper and antimony, the harder the ware. Fine pewter is composed of 80% tin and 20% antimony and brass or copper. See *Alloy*.

Point, Bradex Point. One percentage point of the Market Bradex.

Porcelain. The hardest vitreous ceramic fired at the highest temperatures. Although the term porcelain is often interchanged with china, true porcelain, as the term is used in the field, is distinguished from china by its very high glaze firing and low bisque firing temperature compared with the high bisque firing and lower glaze firing of china. The main firing (glaze) of porcelain is approximately 7% higher than the main firing (bisque) of china. The glaze fuses with the porcelain plate body and produces an extremely hard surface. Hard-paste or true porcelain is made from a formula whose primary components are kaolin and china stone (petuntse). When fired, the china stone vitrifies, producing a hard, glassy ceramic. True porcelain is translucent when thin, white unless colored, impervious to scratching, and transmits a ringing tone when struck. A typical porcelain formula is 50% kaolin, 25% quartz and 25% feldspar. Soft-paste porcelain was developed in Renaissance Europe in an attempt to imitate the true porcelain of China. Soft-paste porcelain was a mixture of white sand, gypsum, soda, alum, salt, and niter, fired until it vitrified. It had a soft texture, great sensitivity to sudden temperature changes, was warmer to the touch than true porcelain, and could be scratched with a file. The terms "hard" and "soft" porcelain refer to the "hard" firing temperature (around 1450°C) required for true porcelain and the "soft" firing temperature (around 1150°C) used for soft-paste porcelain. See *China*.

Pottery. 1. A general term used for all ceramic ware, but in fact properly applied only to earthenware and non-vitrified ceramics. 2. The place

where ceramic objects are made and fired.

Primary Market. See *Market*.

Q

Queen's Ware. An earthenware of ivory or cream color developed by Josiah Wedgwood. The name "Queen's Ware" was adopted by other potters for similar stoneware; also often referred to as "white ware."

Quote. The Exchange's best estimate of market price at the close of the current bi-monthly trading period.

R

Relief Sculpture. Sculpture in which the design or figure is not freestanding but is raised from a background. There are three degrees of relief sculpture: Alto-relievo or high relief, where the design is almost detached from the background; Basso-relievo or bas-relief, where the design is raised somewhat; and Relievostiacciato, where the design is scarcely more than scratched. Relief designs on plates may be formed in the plate mold or formed separately and applied to the plate body. Examples: Davenport Pottery *Toby Plate Collection* **(26-D8-1.0)** and Edwin M. Knowles *Biblical Mothers Collection* **(84-K41-6.0).**

S

Saggers. Boxes of fire-clay into which objects to be glost fired are put for protection against direct contact with the flames.

Second, Second Sorting. A plate judged to be a grade below first quality; usually indicated by a scratch or gouge through the glaze over the backstamp on the back.

Secondary Market. See *Market*.

Sell Order. An offer at an asked price given by an individual or dealer to sell one or more plates on the secondary market. See *Asked Price, Exchange*.

Slip. Ceramic paste or body diluted with water to a smooth, creamy consistency used for slip-casting. See *Mold*.

Sponsor. Authoritative body (prestigious organization, museum, or person) which attests to the authenticity of the artwork depicted on a plate.

Steatite, Soapstone. A natural rock whose primary component is talc. Steatite is used in porcelain formulas as a flux.

Sterling Silver. An alloy which, by United States law, must have the minimum fineness of 92.5% by weight of pure silver and a maximum of 7.5% by weight of a base metal, usually copper. Example: Franklin Mint *Christmas* **(84-F64-1.0).**

Stoneware. A hard ceramic fired to vitrification but not to translucency. Typical components of stoneware are 30% ball clay, 32% kaolin, 15% flint, and 23% cornish stone. Example: Wedgwood's Jasper Ware **(26-W90-0.0).**

Supermarket Plate. Common term for a plate edition of dubious limitations, cheaply produced and not considered a true collector's plate.

Swap 'n' Sell Event. An open buy and sell auction for the trading of plates from one collector to another. Swap 'n' Sell events have been organized at major plate conventions, traveling shopping mall shows, and between collector's clubs. A registration fee is normally charged for those plates offered by sellers.

T

Terra Cotta. A general term for any kind of fired clay. Strictly speaking, terra cotta is an earthenware produced from a clay which fires to a dull ochre or red color. The ware, left unglazed is coarse and porous. Example: Veneto Flair **(38-V22-0.0).**

Tin Glaze. A glaze, colored white by oxide of tin, which produces a heavy opaque surface when fired. See *Delftware.*

Toriart. The process by which wood shavings and resin are combined to form a wood material which is then molded and carved into three-dimensional forms. Example: Anri **(38-A54-0.0).**

Trader. An individual or a dealer who buys, sells, or bids on plates through the Exchange. See *Trading Floor, Exchange.*

Trading Floor. The physical area of The Bradford Exchange where the trading of plates takes place. All secondary market trading on the Exchange originates here, and it is the daily market activity on the Trading Floor that determines the prices quoted on the Exchange. See *Broker, Bradex, Quote.*

Transfer-Printing. Method by which an engraved design may be transferred from an engraver's plate or lithographer's block to the surface of a plate. Originally, thin papers were inked with a mixture of metallic oxide in an oily medium, or sometimes used with a greasy substance onto which metallic oxide could be dusted. Transfer-printing may be overglaze or underglaze.

Translucency. The quality of transmitting light without transparence. In a plate, translucency depends on the quality of the china or porcelain, thickness of the plate, and firing temperature. Underfired porcelain is not translucent.

Triptych. A set of three panels hinged side by side, bearing paintings or carvings, usually on a religious theme and originally used as a portable altarpiece. Example: Anna-Perenna **(22-A3-3.0).**

True Clay. See *Kaolin.*

U

Underglaze Decoration. Decoration applied after a plate has been fired once (bisque fired) but before it is glazed and fired a second time. Underglaze painting is most commonly done in cobalt blue pigment (although other colors can be used) because this is the most stable color and can withstand high firing temperatures. True underglaze technique indicates that such painting was done by hand. See *Glaze, Overglaze Decoration.*

V

Vitrification. A fusion of potters clay at temperatures between 1250°C and 1450°C to form a glassy, non-porous substance. With continued heating, the substance will become translucent.